UNIVERSITY OF NOTRE DAME
WARD-PHILLIPS LECTURES IN
ENGLISH LANGUAGE AND LITERATURE
VOLUME 3

The Wit of Love

Frontispiece. Gerhard Seghers (1591–1651): "St. Teresa in Ecstasy." (*Antwerp: Koninklijk Museum voor Schone Kunsten.*)

The Wit

of

Love

Donne   Carew
Crashaw   Marvell

LOUIS L. MARTZ

THE UNIVERSITY OF NOTRE DAME PRESS
NOTRE DAME   LONDON

To My Sister Lucille

Preface

The essays that follow have been considerably revised and extended since the occasion of their original delivery as lectures in March, 1968. In reworking them I have kept many traces of oral presentation, since these qualities seemed essential to the basic composition of each piece. I am glad to remember them as lectures, since they remind me of the gracious hospitality of the University of Notre Dame, and of the generous, receptive audiences that helped me to understand my own thoughts. I wish to express my gratitude to everyone concerned with the thoughtful arrangements for the Ward-Phillips Lectures during my week at Notre Dame, with many friendly, stimulating conversations and informal gatherings. I am especially grateful to Professor Ernest Sandeen for many favors, including his help in choosing a title for this book; and to Professors Rufus Rauch and Walter Davis for hospitality and for illuminating discussion of many seventeenth-century matters. I am grateful to Miss Emily Schossberger, Director of the University of Notre Dame Press, for her interest in the design of this book, and to Dean Porter, Curator of the University of Notre Dame Art Gallery, for arranging to take photographs of the altarpiece in the University Church.

I owe my thanks to many people for special aspects of this book. Mr. Thomas Wragg, Librarian and Keeper of the Devonshire Collection at Chatsworth, made it possible for me to spend rewarding hours with the Inigo Jones drawings at Chatsworth, and also arranged to send me photographs of certain drawings, along with the permission to reproduce them here. The Courtauld Institute of Art has provided excellent photographs of the Inigo Jones drawings and of the statue of John Donne in St. Paul's. The Very Reverend Martin Sullivan, Dean of St. Paul's, kindly allowed me to view the portrait of Donne that hangs in the Deanery, and has also given his permission to reproduce it here. Mr. D. M. Davin, of the Clarendon Press, has helped me in gaining a photograph of the Deanery portrait of Donne. Miss A. H. Scott-Elliot, Keeper of Prints and Drawings in the Royal Library, Windsor Castle, has generously assisted me in gaining photographs of the miniatures of John Donne and Queen Henrietta Maria. Mrs. Margaret Cousland, of the Lord Chamberlain's Office, has provided me with the photographs of the Van Dyck portraits here reproduced.

The Marquess of Lothian has given his kind permission to reproduce the portrait of Donne in his possession. Miss Caroline Brown, of the National Portrait Gallery, has provided me with a photograph of the Lothian portrait of Donne, along with a photograph of the portrait of Andrew Marvell. Sir Geoffrey Keynes has generously allowed me to examine the Leconfield Manuscript of Donne's poetry in his possession. Mr. A. R. B. Fuller, Librarian of St. Paul's Cathedral Library, has allowed me to examine the St. Paul's Manuscript of Donne's poetry and has helped me to acquire a photograph of the Deanery portrait of Donne. Mr. E. T. Floyd Ewin, Registrar of St. Paul's, has assisted me in gaining a photograph of the statue of Donne, along with permission to reproduce it here. Mr. Herbert F. Potter, Secretary-Treasurer of the Church of All Hallows Barking, has kindly provided me with a photograph of the font-cover ascribed to Grinling Gibbons, along with permission to reproduce it here. Dr. A. Monballieu, of the Koninklijk Museum, Antwerp, has provided me with valuable advice concerning the provenance of the Seghers painting of St. Teresa, and has assisted me in gaining a photograph of this picture, along with permission to reproduce it here. The Fondation Cultura in Brussels has been of great help in providing a photograph of, and information concerning, the version of the Seghers painting that exists in the English Convent at Bruges. I am grateful to the Bodleian Library, the Cambridge University Library, and the British Museum, for allowing me to examine various manuscripts of Donne in their possession. My wife, Edwine Montague, has lent her scholarly assistance in the verification of my manuscript. Mrs. Fannie Gillette has typed and retyped, with scrupulous accuracy, several versions of this book. To all of the above I express my deep appreciation.

Finally, I would like to mention a debt to the exhibition of Van Dyck's paintings presented in the Queen's Gallery, Buckingham Palace, during the summer of 1968. This beautiful exhibition of newly cleaned paintings, along with its excellent catalogue, created a vivid sense of the "Cavalier World" at a time when I was engaged in revising and selecting illustrations for the lectures. This exhibition also contained a number of the finest miniatures of the era, including the Oliver portrait of Donne and, as an item acquired too late for inclusion in the catalogue, the Hoskins miniature of Henrietta Maria, purchased by the Queen in June, 1968. A special notice at the exhibition identified the costume in the miniature as that worn by Henrietta Maria in the production of *Tempe Restord* (see the *Times* [London], May 28, 1968, pp. 12, 14; June 5, 1968, p. 1).

Louis L. Martz

Saybrook College
Yale University
March 25, 1969

Contents

Illustrations

I

John Donne

Love's Philosophy

I

John Donne

Love's Philosophy

One way of grasping the variety of John Donne's career and personality is to ponder the various portraits of Donne that have come down to us from different stages of his life, from the age of eighteen until his death-bed. We have no such variety of portraits for any other poet of this era; and this variety may be taken to indicate some essential qualities of Donne, including his well-known admiration for the art of painting, which led him to fill his house in London with pictures. The last point we know from the touching way in which he distributes various paintings to his friends in his will.

To Doctor King my executor I give that medal of gold of the synod of Dort which the estates presented me withal at the Hague as also the two pictures of Padre Paolo and Fulgentio which hang in the parlour at my house at Paul's and to Doctor Montford my other executor I give forty ounces of white plate and the two pictures that hang on the same side of the parlour.

Item I give to the right honourable the Earl of Carlisle the picture of the blessed Virgin Mary which hangs in the little dining-chamber. And to the right honourable the Earl of Dorset the picture of Adam and Eve which hangs in the great chamber.

Item I give to Doctor Winniff Dean of Gloucester and residentiary of St. Paul's the picture called the Skeleton which hangs in the Hall and to my kind friend Mr. George Garrard the picture of Mary Magdalene in my chamber and to my ancient friend Doctor Brook, Master of Trinity College in Cambridge the picture of the blessed Virgin and Joseph which hangs in my study and to Mr. Tourvall a French Minister (but by the ordination of the English Church) I give any picture which he will choose of those which hang in the little dining-room and are not formerly bequeathed.

* * * * *

Item I give to my honourable and faithful friend Mr. Robert Carr of his Majesty's bed-chamber that picture of mine which is taken in shadows and was made very many years before I was of this profession. And to my honourable friend Sir John Danvers I give what picture he shall accept of those that remain unbequeathed.[1]

The earliest of the portraits of Donne that have come down to us is the one that appears as the frontispiece for the 1635 edition of his poetry, a portrait based, it seems, upon a lost original by Nicholas Hilliard. It is dated in 1591 at the age of eighteen, and it shows the picture of a young cavalier, with long curled locks, a large earring, and a sword firmly grasped by the hilt. Above is a motto in Spanish which reads in translation "Sooner dead than changed," a motto taken from a song in a popular pastoral romance, the *Diana* of Montemayor.

TWENTY

ANNO DNI. 1591.
ÆTATIS SVÆ·18

ANTES MVDADO
MVERTO QVE

This was for youth, Strength, Mirth, and wit that Time
Most count their golden Age; but t'was not thine.
Thine was thy later yeares, so much refind
From youths Drosse, Mirth, & wit; as thy pure mind
Thought (like the Angels) nothing but the Praise
Of thy Creator, in those last, best Dayes.
    Witnes this Booke, (thy Embleme) which begins
  With Love; but endes, with Sighes, & Teares for sins.

Will: Marshall .sculpsit.   IZ:WA:

Figure 1. John Donne at the age of 18. Frontispiece to the
second edition of Donne's *Poems*, 1635.

Figure 2. John Donne: the Lothian Portrait.
(*Reproduced by kind permission of the Marquess of Lothian.*)

The next portrait is the one referred to in Donne's will as "that picture of mine which is taken in shadows"; it was rediscovered by John Bryson ten years ago in the possession of the Marquess of Lothian.[2] This is an even more striking picture, presenting Donne in the costume and the manner of a melancholy lover,[3] with a large dark hat, a fine lace collar, carelessly thrown open at the neck, thin tapering fingers, and in the background the motto "Illumina tenebr[as] nostras Domina" ("Enlighten our darkness, Lady"). This is a witty adaptation of a prayer from the service of Compline in the Sarum *Breviarium*: "Illumina quesumus domine deus tenebras nostras"—words that have passed into the *Book of Common Prayer* for the service of Evensong: "Lighten our darkness, we beseech thee, O Lord."[4]

The next is a superb miniature now in the Library of Windsor Castle, signed with the monogram of Isaac Oliver, and dated 1616, when Donne was about forty-four years old:

Figure 3. John Donne at the age of 44. Miniature by Isaac Oliver, 1616. (*Royal Library, Windsor Castle; reproduced by gracious permission of Her Majesty Queen Elizabeth II.*)

a year after he had entered the priesthood of the English Church. It presents Donne in the mode of a newly ordained preacher, with pointed beard, high collar of pleated ruff, deep circles under the eyes, and a sober, almost ascetic expression.

Fourthly, there is a portrait that hangs in the Deanery at St. Paul's, inscribed "*Aetatis Suae* 49 1620"—the year before Donne was made the Dean of St. Paul's. He is dressed here in what looks like a scholar's lounging-robe; the expression shows the beginning of a pleasant smile, with an effect of ease and happiness that we do not often associate with Donne. The whole figure presents an image of secure achievement and profound wisdom, an impression reinforced by the fact that the painting is conceived in that favorite form of the High Renaissance, the circular or *tondo* form.

Finally, we have that strange and wonderful effigy carved in marble and still visible in St. Paul's, said to be the only piece of the Cathedral's statuary saved from the great fire of 1666. The occasion of the statue is described by Izaak Walton in his *Life of Donne*, where he tells us that a few weeks before Donne's death, in the full knowledge that he was dying, Donne was persuaded by his physician to have a monument made of himself, and this Donne proceeded to do in the following fashion:

> A Monument being resolved upon, Dr. *Donne* sent for a Carver to make for him in wood the figure of an *Urn*, giving him directions for the compass and height of it; and to bring with it a board of the just height of his body. 'These being got: then without delay a choice Painter was got to be in a readiness to draw his Picture, which was taken as followeth.— Several Charcole-fires being first made in his large Study, he

Figure 4. John Donne at the age of 49. (*The Deanery of St. Paul's Cathedral; reproduced by kind permission of the Very Reverend the Dean of St. Paul's. Photo: Fleming.*)

brought with him into that place his winding-sheet in his hand, and, having put off all his cloaths, had this sheet put on him, and so tyed with knots at his head and feet, and his hands so placed, as dead bodies are usually fitted to be shrowded and put into their Coffin, or grave. Upon this *Urn* he thus stood with his eyes shut, and with so much of the sheet turned aside as might shew his lean, pale, and death-like face, which was purposely turned toward the East, from whence he expected the second coming of his and our Saviour Jesus.' In this posture he was drawn at his just height; and when the Picture was fully finished, he caused it to be set by his bed-side, where it continued, and became his hourly object till his death: and, was then given to his dearest friend and Executor Doctor *Henry King*, . . . who caused him to be thus carved in one entire piece of white Marble, as it now stands in that Church . . .[5]

I mention all these portraits to suggest, first of all, Donne's lifelong practice of adopting dramatic postures, in many different attitudes, his way of constantly creating fictional roles out of aspects of his personality. As in his portraits, so in his poetry the complex personality that we call "Donne" is created by means of a continually shifting series of dramatic moments, spoken in a voice that we recognize, even while the voice presents an astonishing variety of roles. Whether Donne appears as the cavalier, the lover, the priest, the scholar, or the dying man, all of these were part of John Donne's awareness of himself at all stages of his career,[6] some aspects emerging into dominance while other aspects remained recessive for a time, to emerge as dominant at other times—sometimes, it almost seems, on the next day, or in the next hour.

Donne's own deep knowledge of himself, gained by relent-

Figure 5. John Donne in his shroud. Marble statue by Nicholas Stone, c. 1631. (*St. Paul's Cathedral; reproduced by kind permission of the Dean and Chapter of St. Paul's.*)

Corporis hæc Animæ fit Syndon Syndon Jesu
Amen.

Martin D. fcun. And are to be fould by R R and Ben: ffifhe:

Figure 6. John Donne in his shroud. Frontispiece to Donne's last sermon, *Deaths Duell,* published 1632. Engraved either from the statue by Stone or perhaps from the painting made as a design for this statue.

less self-scrutiny, is revealed by the analysis of his varied moods that he gives in that famous sonnet, so personal and private that it exists in only one manuscript and remained unpublished until the year 1899:

> Oh, to vex me, contraryes meete in one:
> Inconstancy unnaturally hath begott
> A constant habit; that when I would not
> I change in vowes, and in devotione.
> As humorous is my contritione
> As my prophane love, and as soone forgott:

—"humorous," that is, capricious, changeable, unsteady; "ridlingly distemperd," as he goes on to say, that is, disordered, in a state of puzzling instability:

> As ridlingly distemperd, cold and hott,
> As praying, as mute; as infinite, as none.
> I durst not view heaven yesterday; and to day
> In prayers, and flattering speaches I court God:
> To morrow I quake with true feare of his rod.
> So my devout fitts come and go away
> Like a fantastique Ague: save that here
> Those are my best dayes, when I shake with feare.[7]

Here, in his religious mood, Donne says, those are his best days when he shakes with the fear of God, but as a worldly lover his worst days were those when he feared his Lady did not love him.

What we see in this sonnet, as in the whole great series of portraits, is the image of a man who is attempting to hold within his consciousness an almost unbearable range of interests. In fact, Donne, both in his life and in his literary works, represents every aspect of the European Renaissance. His first portrait is that of a military man, and indeed, he sailed with the Earl of Essex on two arduous military voyages, for a complex of reasons that he himself sums up in his poem "The Calme":

> Whether a rotten state, and hope of gaine,
> Or to disuse mee from the queasie paine
> Of being belov'd, and loving, or the thirst
> Of honour, or faire death, out pusht mee first . . .

The reference to his love affairs speaks for itself, while his rash and secret marriage to the sixteen-year-old girl shows the passionate and impulsive nature of his affections. Meanwhile he had been preparing himself by the study of Law for a political career, and indeed, he appears to have served in Parliament. At the depth of his misfortunes he appears even to have considered emigrating to Virginia. At the same time his famous reference to his "hydroptique immoderate desire of humane learning and languages"[8] shows his full participation in the Renaissance love of letters. He travelled in France, Italy and Spain, and had some command of the languages of those three countries, along with his powerful command of Latin. The high quality of the portraits that he commissioned and the number of paintings contained in his house (including, it seems, a Madonna by Titian)[9] show his deep participation in the visual arts. And finally, more than any other writer of his time, Donne lived at the intense center of controversy between the Catholic and the Protestant currents of religion. Bred as a Roman Catholic in a family noted for its sufferings under persecution, Donne studied the whole body of "controverted divinity," and ultimately became a priest and famous preacher in the Church of England. In this variety of his concerns, then, Donne stands forth as symbolizing all the rich and warring interests of the Renaissance man. And it is these interests that cause the anguish and the glory of his poetry, for in his poetry the skeptic and the believer exist side by side, the lover of women and the lover of God are not separable, suicidal despair and transcendent faith are racking the speaker in opposite directions at the same time, ambition and asceticism are struggling for dominion in the same hour.

Thus, at the time when Donne was writing his indecent and outrageous love-elegies (those poems where the world of Ovid is pillaged and transformed into a much more ruthless and raging world of passion than the bland and sophisticated Ovid could ever represent), in those years when Donne was a young law student, and just before he departed (in 1596 and 1597) to participate in those two military voyages, just then in his famous Satire III Donne is found denouncing all these ventures, and demanding that his soul and ours must seek true religion: "O where?" Others, he says, speaking in a double voice both to himself and to his listeners—others may accept religion on easy terms:

> but unmoved thou
> Of force must one, and forc'd but one allow;
> And the right;

"Of force" because it is in his nature to demand one answer; he moves under an inner compulsion, "unmoved" by outward considerations and persuasions. And if "forc'd" in another

sense by those who attempt to draw him from the right by
threats of persecution or by loss of worldly power, he must
still pursue "but one" and "the right."

> To'adore, or scorne an image, or protest,
> May all be bad; doubt wisely; in strange way
> To stand inquiring right, is not to stray;
> To sleepe, or runne wrong, is. On a huge hill,
> Cragged, and steep, Truth stands, and hee that will
> Reach her, about must, and about must goe;
> And what th'hills suddennes resists, winne so;

In this famous passage, indispensable to an understanding
of Donne, one feels the strain of thought bending the lines
out of the couplet form, as though the rhymes were obstacles
to overcome. The whole of the Renaissance, the Reformation,
and the Counter-Reformation are pressing in upon that poem,
demanding one answer to their manifold problems. That God
exists, that Truth exists, Donne never doubts; but where these
absolutes are to be found on earth, Donne does not know.

This traditional image of the soul's journey up the mountain of Truth, beautifully illustrated in a Florentine painting
of the early Renaissance, represents perfectly the agonized
effort of Donne's mind to rise above the world of flux represented, from beginning to end, in his poetry—that world of
change, corruption, decay, self-seeking, betrayal, disease, and
death, which forms the somber ground from which his questing mind seeks to arise. As explained by Roberto Weiss,[10] the
hill of Knowledge in this Florentine miniature shows in all
its "cragged" or "ragged"[11] stages the process upward from

Figure 7 (opposite). "Turris Sapientiae." Florentine, 15th
century (?). (*Chantilly, Musée Condé. Photo: Giraudon.*)

grammar to theology. The aspirant toward Truth is met at the Renaissance doorway by the allegorical figure of Grammar (with the Roman grammarian Donatus writing in the foreground). Beyond the archway sits Pythagoras, the founder of Arithmetic, represented allegorically by the young lady behind him. As we move upward, each female figure, representing one of the seven liberal arts, has seated beneath her the figure of some ancient sage. Thus, we move in the following order: Zeno, with the figure of Logic above him; Tubal Cain, perhaps here fused with Jubal, "Father of all such as handle the harp and organ" (Genesis 4:21), with the figure of Music above him; on the same level the astronomer Ptolemy, with the figure of Astronomy above, holding in her hand an image of the universe; to the left of her the sage Euclid with Geometry above him. Next comes Cicero, with the figure of Rhetoric above. Then, second from the top, appropriately seated in the center, comes the figure of St. Augustine, who christianized the liberal arts and moved them upward toward Theology, who sits at the top with one hand holding the symbol of the Trinity, and the other hand pointing upward to the figure of God. I have explained the image in detail, because it shows so well how Donne's quest for Truth included this whole immense inheritance from the Middle Ages and moved it onward through the portal of the Renaissance into a new aesthetic dimension.

That new dimension I should like to explore within the body of Donne's "Songs and Sonets," where Donne's winding quest toward Truth is displayed in the unstable, constantly shifting movement that one feels within many of the best poems, and also in the oscillation that we feel as we move from poem to poem in their traditional order—or disorder.

Donne's love-poems take for their basic theme the problem of the place of human love in a physical world dominated by change and death. The problem is broached in dozens of different ways, sometimes implicitly, sometimes explicitly, sometimes by asserting the immortality of love, sometimes by declaring the futility of love. Thus the "Songs and Sonets" hold within themselves every conceivable attitude toward love threatened by change. At the one extreme lie the cynical, cavalier songs, the famous "Goe, and catche a falling starre," or "The Indifferent," spoken by one who can "love any, so she be not true." Even beyond this, we have the extreme of bitter disillusionment in that somber poem "Farewell to Love," where the poet asks whether love is no more than a gingerbread King discarded after a fair:

> But, from late faire
> His highnesse sitting in a golden Chaire,
>   Is not lesse cared for after three dayes
> By children, then the thing which lovers so
> Blindly admire, and with such worship wooe;
>   Being had, enjoying it decayes·
>   And thence,
> What before pleas'd them all, takes but one sense,
> And that so lamely, as it leaves behinde
> A kinde of sorrowing dulnesse to the minde.

At the other extreme, perhaps only a poem or two after some poem of cynicism, we will find such a poem as "The Undertaking," where Donne moves to the opposite extreme of pure platonic love, challenging the reader with these words:

But he who lovelinesse within
 Hath found, all outward loathes,
For he who colour loves, and skinne,
 Loves but their oldest clothes.

If, as I have, you also doe
 Vertue'attir'd in woman see,
And dare love that, and say so too,
 And forget the Hee and Shee;

And if this love, though placed so,
 From prophane men you hide,
Which will no faith on this bestow,
 Or, if they doe, deride:

Then you'have done a braver thing
 Then all the *Worthies* did,
And a braver thence will spring,
 Which is, to keepe that hid.

It is clear that the libertine poems are the obverse, the counterpart, the necessary context, for the poems on constancy. The libertine poems express the fatigue, the cynicism, the flippancy, and the bitterness of the disappointed seeker after the One and True, as Donne very clearly says in his poem "Loves Alchymie," which appropriately comes quite precisely in the middle of the "Songs and Sonets," just after the great poem of true love "A Valediction: of Weeping":

Some that have deeper digg'd loves Myne then I,
Say, where his centrique happiness doth lie:
 I have lov'd, and got, and told,

("told" in the sense of "have counted up the results")

> But should I love, get, tell, till I were old,
> I should not finde that hidden mysterie;
>> Oh, 'tis imposture all:

Clearly the "centrique happiness" that is here renounced represents an abstraction that lies beyond the physical. Such a poem as this represents a violent revulsion against the lover who has in such a poem as "Aire and Angels" sought for an ideal beauty and loved an ideal beauty in his imagination:

> Twice or thrice had I lov'd thee,
>> Before I knew thy face or name;
> So in a voice, so in a shapelesse flame,
> *Angells* affect us oft, and worship'd bee;
>> Still when, to where thou wert, I came,
> Some lovely glorious nothing I did see.
>> But since my soule, whose child love is,
> Takes limmes of flesh, and else could nothing doe,
>> More subtile then the parent is,
> Love must not be, but take a body too,
>> And therefore what thou wert, and who,
>> I bid Love aske, and now
> That it assume thy body, I allow,
> And fixe it selfe in thy lip, eye, and brow.

But he discovers that her physical beauty is too dazzling for love to work upon and that some other abode for his love must be sought, and so he concludes, referring to the medieval doctrine that angels appeared to men in forms of mist or vapor:

> Then as an Angell, face, and wings
> Of aire, not pure as it, yet pure doth weare,
>> So thy love may be my loves spheare;

> Just such disparitie
> As is twixt Aire and Angells puritie,
> 'Twixt womens love, and mens will ever bee.

It may seem at first that the last two lines, with this emphasis upon the superior "purity" of men's love to women's love, are not exactly complimentary to a being of such angelic nature; and yet, when we think of it closely, it is in fact a version of an old Petrarchan compliment. What he is saying is this: if she will extend her love toward him, if she will come down from her angelic status and deign to love a man, then his love for her may move like a planet within her love for him. But why is her love for him less pure than his love for her? Is it not because of the *direction* of their two loves: hers downward toward him, and his upward toward a creature of angelic purity? Donne appears to be combining here the Platonizing love philosophy of the Renaissance[12] with an older tradition, the tradition of the courtly lover inherited by Petrarch, in which the lady is a superior being of angelic purity and beauty, as is the lady of Spenser's sonnets. Donne is here, surprisingly enough, standing by the old Petrarchan tradition in his own winding way.

So it is with Donne's pursuit of love. It has many temporary conclusions, some cynical, some ennobling, but all only "for a moment final," as Wallace Stevens might say. Behind all these varied posturings lies the overwhelming question: what is the nature of love, what is the ultimate ground of love's being? His best poems are not those which move toward either extreme in his answer, but they are rather those in which the physical and the spiritual are made to work together, through the curiously shifting and winding manner that marks Donne's

movements toward Truth. One can sense that movement at
its best in the poem known as "Loves Growth" (though
entitled "Spring" in many of the manuscripts). It opens with
the characteristic brooding over the problem of change:

> I scarce beleeve my love to be so pure
>   As I had thought it was,
>   Because it doth endure
> Vicissitude, and season, as the grasse;

With such an opening one might expect that the lover is about
to lament the fact that his love has decayed; but, on the contrary, what worries him, what proves the instability of his
love, is the fact that it seems to be increasing:

> Me thinkes I lyed all winter, when I swore,
> My love was infinite, if spring make'it more.

What then is the nature of love, he asks?

> But if this medicine, love, which cures all sorrow
>   With more, not onely bee no quintessence,
>   But mixt of all stuffes, paining soule, or sense,
> And of the Sunne his working vigour borrow,
> Love's not so pure, and abstract, as they use
> To say, which have no Mistresse but their Muse,
> But as all else, being elemented too,
> Love sometimes would contemplate, sometimes do.

Having decided then that the nature of love involves the total
physical and spiritual being of man, Donne seems to drop the
problem entirely in the second half of the poem, shifts his

stance completely, and decides that in fact the problem of
vicissitude and season does not really exist for this particular
love of his:

> And yet not greater, but more eminent,
>   Love by the spring is growne;
>   As, in the firmament,
> Starres by the Sunne are not inlarg'd, but showne.

The scientific sound of the image has a satisfying effect, until
one tries to decide exactly what it means, and then, as so often
with Donne's conceits, the apparent assurance becomes considerably less sure. "Eminent" is certainly used in the sense of
"prominent" but from here on the best commentators dis-
agree. Grierson interprets the lines as meaning "The stars at
sunrise are not really made larger, but they are made to seem
larger." Miss Gardner, however, takes "by the Sunne" to mean
"near the sun," thus: "Love has risen higher in the heavens
by spring and shines the more brilliantly as do stars when near
to the sun."[13] The latter meaning is almost certainly right,
since Donne is not talking about sunrise, but about the rising
of the spring. But we are not to examine the image closely;
we are simply to gain its positive effect of security in love, as
the remaining images continue to assure us with their varied
action:

> Gentle love deeds, as blossomes on a bough,
> From loves awaken'd root do bud out now.
> If, as in water stir'd more circles bee
>   Produc'd by one, love such additions take,
>   Those like so many spheares, but one heaven make,
> For, they are all concentrique unto thee;

> And though each spring doe adde to love new heate,
> As princes doe in times of action get
> New taxes, and remit them not in peace,
> No winter shall abate the springs encrease.

But the last word "encrease" would appear to contradict the beginning of this stanza. If there has been "encrease" then love must have grown greater and love must not then be so pure as he had thought it was. And indeed, if we look closely at the last stanza we see that it does not basically deal with the assurance affirmed in the first four lines of that stanza, but rather carries on from the last line of the first stanza, "Love sometimes would contemplate, sometimes do." It soon appears that the speaker is talking about "love-deeds" and that it is love in action that he wishes to see develop: these are the additions that love will take, like circles stirred in water, or like "spheares" about one center. New heat is not a quality of a pure substance, in the scientific sense that Donne is broaching in the poem's first line. Love deeds, the buds of spring, circles in the water, the new heat of the season—all these are part of a transient and fluctuating physical universe. And indeed the surprising image

> As princes doe in times of action get
> New taxes, and remit them not in peace,

brings us vividly into the realistic world. Thus the assertion at the end, "No winter shall abate the springs encrease" stands as a defiance against all the imagery of vicissitude that dominates the poem. We may believe the assertion, or we may believe the whole poem. In the end, I think, the poem is bound to win.

One can never be sure, then, where Donne's probing of the problem of mutability will lead. This is especially clear in the two poems where Donne uses, in different ways, his image "A bracelet of bright haire about the bone." In "The Funerall" the poem begins by creating a symbol of constancy and immortality out of the "wreath of haire," as the speaker imagines himself dead:

> Who ever comes to shroud me, do not harme
> Nor question much
> That subtile wreath of haire, which crowns mine arme;
> The mystery, the signe you must not touch,
> For 'tis my outward Soule,
> Viceroy to that, which then to heaven being gone,
> Will leave this to controule,
> And keepe these limbes, her Provinces, from dissolution.

But, as with many of Donne's most resounding affirmations, the more the speaker broods about this and attempts to prove its truth, the more it tends to disintegrate. Here, in paralleling the mistress's hair with the nerves that run throughout his body, he is led toward a glimpse of his Lady herself:

> These haires which upward grew, and strength and art
> Have from a better braine . . .

This memory of the Lady in her actual life suggests to him another and more cruel possibility in keeping with her nature:

> Except she meant that I
> By this should know my pain,
> As prisoners then are manacled, when they'are condemn'd
> to die.

He does not know what she could mean by such a gift and in despair he swaggers with his "bravery," uttering at the end what amounts to a rude innuendo:

> What ere shee meant by'it, bury it with me,
>   For since I am
> Loves martyr, it might breed idolatrie,
> If into others hands these Reliques came;
>   As 'twas humility
> To'afford to it all that a Soule can doe,
>   So, 'tis some bravery,
> That since you would save none of mee, I bury some of
>   you.

In "The Relique" the direction of thought is reversed. Whereas "The Funerall" had moved from thoughts of fidelity to cynicism, "The Relique" moves from cynical thoughts about love to an affirmation of a miraculous purity in human love. Thus the poem opens with some of Donne's most satirical innuendoes:

> When my grave is broke up againe
> Some second ghest to entertaine,
> (For graves have learn'd that woman-head
> To be to more then one a Bed)
>   And he that digs it, spies
> A bracelet of bright haire about the bone,
>   Will he not let'us alone,
> And thinke that there a loving couple lies,
> Who thought that this device might be some way
> To make their soules, at the last busie day,
> Meet at this grave, and make a little stay?

Donne accepts the fact that even graves are not sacred, and suggests in the last few lines above that perhaps someone would think that this erotic symbol would indicate that some "loving couple" have arranged for a last carnal assignation even while the Judge is busy with his work of salvation and damnation. But, as it turns out, this is not at all what these two lovers had in mind. She is not a Mary Magdalene, that is to say, a reformed prostitute, and he is nothing of the kind either. It is only the continuous misunderstanding of man, whether in the field of religion or in the field of love, that makes it certain that people will misinterpret the nature of this symbol.

> If this fall in a time, or land,
> Where mis-devotion doth command,
> Then, he that digges us up, will bring
> Us, to the Bishop, and the King,
>   To make us Reliques; then
> Thou shalt be'a Mary Magdalen, and I
>   A something else thereby;
> All women shall adore us, and some men;
> And since at such times, miracles are sought,
> I would that age were by this paper taught
> What miracles wee harmlesse lovers wrought.

> First, we lov'd well and faithfully,
> Yet knew not what wee lov'd, nor why,
> Difference of sex no more wee knew,
> Then our Guardian Angells doe;
>   Comming and going, wee
> Perchance might kisse, but not between those meales;
>   Our hands ne'r toucht the seales,
> Which nature, injur'd by late law, sets free:

> These miracles wee did; but now alas,
> All measure, and all language, I should passe,
> Should I tell what a miracle shee was.

It is, no doubt, a pure love, as the speaker declares. And yet there is something in the last six lines which doth protest too much. Why should he regard their rare kisses as "meales"? Why should he regard the seals of chastity as a restriction placed upon nature by "late law" which thus injures the freedom of nature itself? And why should, at the end, his feelings falter ("alas") into such a desperate compliment? Perhaps the symbol of eroticism is not so wide of the mark as the speaker declares. In both poems the meaning of that macabre symbol appears to be essentially the same: it suggests the agonized reluctance of Donne to allow any severance between the physical and the spiritual.

In a more obvious way, this reluctance to sever physical and spiritual is shown in the short poem entitled "The Anniversarie," which opens with Donne's most splendid affirmation of the immortality of true love:

> All Kings, and all their favorites,
> All glory'of honors, beauties, wits,
> The Sun it selfe, which makes times, as they passe,
> Is elder by a yeare, now, then it was
> When thou and I first one another saw:
> All other things, to their destruction draw,
> Only our love hath no decay;
> This, no to morrow hath, nor yesterday,
> Running it never runs from us away,
> But truly keepes his first, last, everlasting day.

The plurality of the word *times* sums up the evanescence of worldly glories, and stresses, by contrast with the great doxology of the last line, the eternity of this true love. But then in the second stanza he remembers that in fact they must part, in some measure:

> Two graves must hide thine and my coarse,
> If one might, death were no divorce.
> Alas, as well as other Princes, wee,
> (Who Prince enough in one another bee,)
> Must leave at last in death, these eyes, and eares,
> Oft fed with true oathes, and with sweet salt teares;
> But soules where nothing dwells but love
> (All other thoughts being inmates) then shall prove
> This, or a love increased there above,
> When bodies to their graves, soules from their graves
> remove.

We feel the strong clinging to the physical; but of course it is a consolation to remember that the souls will be united in heaven—and yet another thought comes upon the speaker as he remembers that in heaven they will lose the unique, distinctive nature of their love because there everyone will be thoroughly blessed—"but wee no more, then all the rest." His mind turns back to earth where their monarchy is unique:

> Here upon earth, we'are Kings, and none but wee
> Can be such Kings, nor of such subjects bee;
> Who is so safe as wee? where none can doe
> Treason to us, except one of us two.
> True and false feares let us refraine,
> Let us love nobly', and live, and adde againe

> Yeares and yeares unto yeares, till we attaine
> To write threescore: this is the second of our raigne.

We notice how in the last four lines the poet tacitly concedes
that this perfect love is not immortal, but is subject to the rule
of times. They will celebrate the beginning of the second year
of their reign, which will last until they are threescore. He
speaks of holding back "True and false feares." The false
fear is fear that they will ever be untrue to one another, but
the true fear is that their mortal love is indeed subject to
mortality.

The same problem gives its deep poignancy to the famous
"Valediction: forbidding Mourning," where the affirmation
of a spiritual love, presumably between man and wife,[14] has
the effect of emphasizing the anguish of being forced to a
temporary physical separation. Everyone has admired the deli
cate opening of the poem in which the separation of lovers
is represented as a kind of death-bed scene:

> As virtuous men passe mildly' away,
>   And whisper to their soules, to goe,
> Whilst some of their sad friends doe say,
>   The breath goes now, and some say, no:
>
> So let us melt, and make no noise,
>   No teare-floods, nor sigh-tempests move,
> 'Twere prophanation of our joyes
>   To tell the layetie our love.

What Donne is representing here is the essence of many an
airport, or station, or dock-side scene, where true lovers may

attempt to repress their tears, not wishing to show the laity their love. And then the poem goes on to say

> Dull sublunary lovers love
>> (Whose soule is sense) cannot admit
> Absense, because it doth remove
>> Those things which elemented it.

> But we by' a love, so much refin'd,
>> That our selves know not what it is,
> Inter-assured of the mind,
>> Care lesse, eyes, lips, and hands to misse.

"Care lesse," but is it so? The very rigor and intricacy of the famous image of the compass at the end may be taken to suggest a rather desperate dialectical effort to control by logic and reason a situation almost beyond rational control.

The whole problem of the relationship between the soul and body in love is brought to a crisis of ambiguity in the frequently-discussed poem, "The Exstasie." This contains a curious and enigmatic combination of traditions in Renaissance poetry and thought. First of all, it grows from the poetical tradition represented by Sidney's Eighth Song in *Astrophil and Stella*,[15] a song in which the lover attempts to persuade the lady in a pastoral setting to give way to the lover's wishes. Donne's prologue in his poem is exactly the same length as Sidney's prologue: seven quatrains. But Donne's interest in nature is so little that it appears as though the flower-bed consists of just a single violet: Donne is not interested in pastoral but in other implications.

> Where, like a pillow on a bed,
>> A Pregnant banke swel'd up, to rest

> The violets reclining head,
>   Sat we two, one anothers best;
>
> Our hands were firmely cimented
>   With a fast balme, which thence did spring,
> Our eye-beames twisted, and did thred
>   Our eyes, upon one double string;
>
> So to'entergraft our hands, as yet
>   Was all our meanes to make us one,
> And pictures on our eyes to get
>   Was all our propagation.

The physical suggestions of the poem here have led some readers to feel that the following philosophical discourse is simply a smoke-screen, as in "The Flea," for a libertine design. On the other hand, a very strong tradition in Renaissance thought that lies behind the discussion in the rest of the poem has suggested to other readers that it really does present a true debate over love's philosophy.[16] From this standpoint the poem may be seen as an assertion of the purity of human love in all its aspects. The title then is quite ironical. We are not going to witness here an ecstasy of physical passion (as in Carew's "A Rapture"). On the other hand, although we do hear the souls of the lovers speak in a Neoplatonic state of ecstasis, in which the souls go forth from the body to discover the True and the One—nevertheless the Truth that they discover is in fact the Truth of Aristotle and the synthesis of St. Thomas Aquinas: that the soul must work through the body; such is the natural state of man. The last lines prove the purity of their love. If there is small change when the souls are to bodies gone, then spiritual love has succeeded in controlling passion. From this standpoint Donne is misleading us with false expectations by the physical imagery of the opening part. These lovers will probably go off and get properly married in good Spenserian fashion. And indeed the deep self-control of these lovers is perhaps implied by the strictness of the three-part structure that the poem displays, being (more precisely than usual with Donne) divided into setting, analysis, and resolution. The total effect of the poem suggests a philosophical mode of rational control superimposed upon a libertine situation. The libertine suggestions are finally dominated and transcended by a richer, more inclusive, more spiritual view of love.

And yet each poem within the "Songs and Sonets" can be no more than a temporary house of harmony, where Creative Mind, in Yeats's phrase, brings peace out of rage and creates the lovers' stasis and order, for a moment only. Thus, in the traditional order, the affirmation of the perfect "patterne" of love in "The Canonization" is followed at once by the semi-recantation, "The Triple Foole."

> I am two fooles, I know,
> For loving, and for saying so
> In whining Poëtry;
> But where's that wiseman, that would not be I,
> If she would not deny?

And then this half-despairing, half-cynical poem is followed at once by the slow, sad, quiet measures of the beautiful poem entitled "Loves [or "Lovers"] Infiniteness" where the word "all" rings throughout as the dirge of an unattainable Ideal:

> If yet I have not all thy love,
> Deare, I shall never have it all;

> I cannot breath one other sigh, to move,
> > Nor can intreat one other teare to fall.
> All my treasure, which should purchase thee,
> > Sighs, teares, and oathes, and letters I have spent,
> Yet no more can be due to mee,
> > Then at the bargaine made was ment.
> If then thy gift of love were partiall,
> That some to mee, some should to others fall,
> > Deare, I shall never have Thee All.

In the fifth line above we should note the excellent reading
of Miss Gardner's text, taken from the manuscripts: "All my
treasure," in place of the weaker traditional reading "And all
my treasure"; for this manuscript reading throws a proper
emphasis upon the thematic word "all," binding it with the
last word of the stanza and with the end rhymes that rein-
force the dirge-like repetitions. But then, in Donne's characteristically winding way, the poem shifts its posture and runs
over the same ground from a different point of view, ponder-
ing a new possibility which at the close is discarded for yet
another point of view:

> Or if then thou gav'st mee all,
> > All was but All, which thou hadst then,
> But if in thy heart, since, there be or shall,
> > New love created bee, by other men,
> Which have their stocks intire, and can in teares,
> > In sighs, in oathes, and letters outbid mee,
> This new love may beget new feares,
> > For, this love was not vowed by thee.
> And yet it was, thy gift being generall,
> The ground, thy heart is mine, what ever shall
> > Grow there, deare, I should have it all.

But as the third and final stanza opens we find the speaker discarding all these previous possibilities and turning toward a point of view which reaches a temporary conclusion in the powerful echo of one of the most famous of religious paradoxes (Mark 8:35):

> Yet I would not have all yet,
>   Hee that hath all can have no more,
> And since my love doth every day admit
>   New growth, thou shouldst have new rewards in store;
> Thou canst not every day give me thy heart,
>   If thou canst give it, then thou never gav'st it:
> Loves riddles are, that though thy heart depart,
>   It stayes at home, and thou with losing sav'st it:

But these lovers move beyond the Gospel paradox and have, this lover hopes, an even richer future:

> But wee will have a way more liberall,
> Then changing hearts, to joyne them, so wee shall
>   Be one, and one anothers All.

Despite that splendid final affirmation of Oneness, the whole poem creates, through its shifts and oscillations, a sense of the painful unlikelihood that this All will ever really be found. This great poem represents in itself the effect that one feels throughout the "Songs and Sonets"—the poignant fragility of human love. It is the state of lovers summed up for us in "A Lecture upon the Shadow." Here the lover and his Lady have been walking about in the morning, for three hours, in a situation representing the restless, yearning state of lovers seeking what T. S. Eliot calls the "still moment, repose of noon." Now the moment of declaration has come, the moment of "brave clearenesse"—"brave" in the old Elizabethan sense of "splendid," "superb," as well as "brave" in our modern sense. They must now declare their loves and try to maintain them against the world of time. Appropriately, the poem opens by creating the impression that the speaker is attempting, by a deliberate act of will, to force a pause in the flow of time.

> Stand still, and I will read to thee
> A Lecture, Love, in loves philosophy.
> These three houres that we have spent,
> Walking here, two shadowes went
> Along with us, which we our selves produc'd;
> But, now the Sunne is just above our head,
> We doe those shadowes tread;
> And to brave clearenesse all things are reduc'd.
> So whilst our infant loves did grow,
> Disguises did, and shadowes, flow
> From us, and our care; but, now 'tis not so.
>
> That love hath not attain'd the high'st degree,
> Which is still diligent lest others see.

Up to this point in time the lovers have been disguising the growth of their love from other people: thus their love has been accompanied by shadows in two senses, by disguises and by the worries that come from fear of revealing their love to other people. But now another danger arises, as the rest of the poem explains. Unless they can maintain their love at this high point they will begin to deceive each other and thus new shadows of a sadder kind will fall upon their love.

> Except our loves at this noone stay,
> We shall new shadowes make the other way.
>   As the first were made to blinde
>   Others; these which come behinde
> Will worke upon our selves, and blind our eyes.
> If our loves faint, and westwardly decline;
>   To me thou, falsly, thine,
> And I to thee mine actions shall disguise.
>   The morning shadowes weare away,
>   But these grow longer all the day,
> But oh, loves day is short, if love decay.
>
> Love is a growing, or full constant light;
> And his first minute, after noone, is night.

There is no comfort in this poem, only the presentation of a precarious dilemma. Love's philosophy, it seems, begins with the recognition of the shadow of decay.

We have seen in many of the preceding quotations the constant pressure of Donne's awareness of the shadow of time and death. It is indeed the point from which his poetical "lectures" all arise. Realizing this, one may see a certain propriety in two apparently anomalous poems that appear among the love-songs in the "Group I" manuscripts.[17] Almost exactly in the middle of the forty-seven poems contained in this collection of the love-poems, we find, as the twenty-fifth poem, the elegy entitled "Autumnall" (Grierson's Elegy IX), and two poems later, the curious two-part poem with the general title "Epitaph" and the sub-title "Omnibus." It is natural, of course, to remove the "Autumnall" to a place with the other elegies, since it is clearly entitled "Elegie" and it cannot be called a song or a "sonet" of the kind represented by nearly all the other poems here. And yet, as everyone has noticed, the

"Autumnall" is a poem of quite a different nature from that of the youthful poems that may have composed Donne's "Book of Elegies."[18] It is written in a style unusual for Donne: in a series of end-stopped, frequently-balanced pentameter couplets, a style quite in contrast with the headlong rushing movement of, say, the famous elegy "By our first strange and fatall interview." But this poised and balanced style is appropriate to the poem's theme, which celebrates the beauty of a Lady in her autumnal season:

> Here, where still Evening is; not noone, nor night;
> Where no voluptuousnesse, yet all delight.

This quiet, "tolerable" style helps to create the sense of a beauty delicately poised between passion and death, as Donne indicates by the act of denying the presence of the grave in her brow:

> Call not these wrinkles, graves; If graves they were,
> They were Loves graves; for else he is no where.
> Yet lies not Love dead here, but here doth sit
> Vow'd to this trench, like an Anachorit.
> And here, till hers, which must be his death, come,
> He doth not digge a Grave, but build a Tombe.

She is indeed lovely in her season, and yet the season stands at the far edge of beauty, as Donne realizes near the end of the poem when, with a certain horror, he moves back from the thought of the fate which certainly awaits such beauty:

> If we love things long sought, Age is a thing
> Which we are fifty yeares in compassing.

If transitory things, which soone decay,
Age must be lovelyest at the latest day.
But name not Winter-faces, whose skin's slacke;
Lanke, as an unthrifts purse; but a soules sacke;
Whose Eyes seeke light within, for all here's shade;
Whose mouthes are holes, rather worne out, then made;
Whose every tooth to a'severall place is gone,
To vexe their soules at Resurrection;
Name not these living Deaths-heads unto mee,
For these, not Ancient, but Antiques be.

They are "Antiques," as Miss Gardner explains,[19] in the sense of "antics"—grotesques—fantastic corruptions of humanity. Nevertheless Donne accepts this fate gently at the close of the poem. It is, he says, "loves naturall lation," using an old astrological term that indicates "the action of moving, or the motion of a body from one place to another" (*OED*). It is a phrase worth remembering, for it might be said that Donne's greatest love-poetry represents an effort to create a counteraction to "loves naturall lation."

One may find a similar propriety in the even more anomalous "Epitaph" which appears among the love-songs in three of the "Group I" manuscripts.[20] This neglected poem has had perhaps the most curious history of printing of all Donne's poems: at one time or another, in whole or in part, it has appeared among his funeral elegies, his Divine Poems, his verse letters, or in Grierson's edition, in a section created wholly for itself. The "Epitaph" proper is prefaced by a verse epistle to a Lady:

Madame,
That I might make your Cabinet my tombe,
And for my fame, which I love next my soule,

Next to my soule provide the happiest roome,
Admit to that place this last funerall Scrowle.
Others by Testament give Legacies, but I
Dying, of you doe beg a Legacie.

The speaker, in the person of his poem, asks his Lady to take this piece of writing into her "Cabinet," that is, into her boudoir, so that his reputation may reside next to his soul, which already lives in his Lady's intimate presence. Then follows the epitaph addressed to all, including the Lady herself. It is a death's head, warning the reader to realize that he is himself clay, as the speaker is now within his grave. And so the epitaph concludes:

Whilst in our soules sinne bred and pamper'd is,
Our soules become wormeaten carkases;
So we our selves miraculously destroy.
Here bodies with lesse miracle enjoy
Such priviledges, enabled here to scale
Heaven, when the Trumpets ayre shall them exhale.
Heare this, and mend thy selfe, and thou mendst me,
By making me being dead, doe good to thee,
And thinke me well compos'd, that I could now
A last-sicke houre to syllables allow.

It is a strange, and yet, with Donne, a characteristic gesture: that he should send his Lady this *memento mori* by which he wishes to be remembered (with a witty turn) as a man "well compos'd," well prepared for death—and still a good poet! It is a gesture quite in line with the passage that I have quoted from Izaak Walton's account of Donne's last illness: that scene where Donne arises from his death-bed to stand upon an urn and strike one final posture in marble. In both actions we may feel, while Donne makes his gesture of renunciation, that there remains a deep longing to maintain an involvement with the physical world, whether that involvement takes the form of a poem kept in his Lady's boudoir or the form of a marble statue preserved in a great Cathedral. In these and many other ways, throughout his poetry, Donne's questing mind reveals and controls the contraries that meet within his being.

II

Thomas Carew

The Cavalier World

Figure 8. "The Emperor Albanactus." Design by Inigo Jones for the role played by Charles I in the masque by Aurelian Town-shend, *Albions Triumph,* 1632. (*Devonshire Collection, Chatsworth; reproduced by kind permission of the Trustees of the Chatsworth Settlement. Simpson and Bell,* Designs, No. 124.)

II

Thomas Carew

The Cavalier World

In the cold spring of 1639, Thomas Carew, the favorite poet of the Court of Charles I, joined his King's army in an ill-conceived and ill-prepared expedition against the Scots. It was the same expedition for which Carew's friend and fellow poet, Sir John Suckling, had beggared himself in order to provide a beautifully clothed and plumed troop of cavalry-men –but whether they could fight was another matter. The King's hope was to quell the rebellious Scots, who had refused to abide by the rules of the Church of England; but he found the Scottish army much too strong for his own forces, stronger in motivation, bound together by religious zeal, and therefore stronger in military capacity. Charles did not dare to invade Scotland, and indeed hardly a shot was fired. Instead Charles made a humiliating, temporary peace, and planned to bide his time until, as he hoped, his power would grow stronger. Instead he grew steadily weaker. The Scottish expedition was the beginning of the end of Charles I's regime, an open revelation of the weaknesses that beset his state both in England and in Scotland; thus began a swift decay of royal power that reached its end when, in 1649, the Parliamentary army beheaded the King and abolished his monarchy.

Thomas Carew did not live to see the death of this "brave Prince of Cavaliers," as Robert Herrick called him, for Carew died in March, 1640—a symbolic date, for that was the very spring when Charles was forced to reconvene Parliament after his eleven years of personal rule. Thus began in November, 1640, the Long Parliament which utterly destroyed the King's power.

In the year 1640, shortly before Thomas Carew's death, it seems, he composed a poem in which memories of the Scottish campaign form a dark opening that fades away before an overwhelming appreciation of a way of life that represents the best of the Cavalier ideal: "To my friend G. N. from Wrest"—a country estate in Bedfordshire.

> I Breathe (sweet *Ghib:*) the temperate ayre of *Wrest*
> Where I no more with raging stormes opprest,
> Weare the cold nights out by the bankes of Tweed,
> On the bleake Mountains, where fierce tempests breed,
> And everlasting Winter dwells; where milde
> *Favonius,* and the Vernall windes exilde,
> Did never spread their wings: but the wilde North
> Brings sterill Fearne, Thistles, and Brambles forth.
> Here steep'd in balmie dew, the pregnant Earth
> Sends from her teeming wombe a flowrie birth,
> And cherisht with the warme Suns quickning heate,
> Her porous bosome doth rich odours sweate;[1]

We should note how, unlike Donne, Carew has a warm appreciation of the natural vigor of the earth. He goes on to admire the simple mansion, not erected "with curious skill" or with "carved Marble, Touch, or Porpherie." This is a house built for hospitality, without Doric or Corinthian pillars; it is designed for service, not for show. In the center of the poem he draws an active picture of the Lord and Lady at the head of "their merry Hall" filled with people of all ranks, servants, tenants, women, steward, chaplain, all eating at various tables in appropriate but flexible hierarchy. Meanwhile "others of better note"

> freely sit
> At the Lords Table, whose spread sides admit
> A large accesse of friends to fill those seates
> Of his capacious circle, fill'd with meates
> Of choycest rellish, till his Oaken back
> Under the load of pil'd-up dishes crack.

Although he praises the house for not being showy with statuary and extravagant artifice, the whole estate nevertheless reveals itself to be a work of art on the outside where nature and art have combined to direct the waters flowing from the local spring. Art, says Carew,

> entertaines the flowing streames in deepe
> And spacious channells, where they slowly creepe
> In snakie windings, as the shelving ground
> Leades them in circles, till they twice surround
> This Island Mansion, which i' th' center plac'd,
> Is with a double Crystall heaven embrac'd . . .

The whole view of the estate, then, is one in which simple dignity and generous hospitality combine with art to create an atmosphere of natural fertility and bounty. This theme reaches a climax in the finale as Carew sees the landscape and the fountain of waters mingled with pastoral and mythological figures out of Ovid's *Metamorphoses* and Vergil's *Georgics:*

> With variou. Trees we fringe the waters brinke,
> Whose thirstie rootes the soaking moysture drinke,
> And whose extended boughes in equall rankes
> Yeeld fruit, and shade, and beautie to the bankes.
> On this side young *Vertumnus* sits, and courts
> His ruddie-cheek'd *Pomona, Zephyre* sports
> On th'other, with lov'd *Flora,* yeelding there
> Sweetes for the smell, sweetes for the palate here.
> But did you taste the high & mighty drinke
> Which from that Fountaine flowes, you'ld cleerly think
> The God of Wine did his plumpe clusters bring,
> And crush the Falerne grape into our spring;
>
> . . . . .
>
> Thus I enjoy my selfe, and taste the fruit
> Of this blest Peace, whilst toyl'd in the pursuit
> Of Bucks, and Stags, th'embleme of warre, you strive
> To keepe the memory of our Armes alive.

Thus the poem is framed by memories of the war, as though the threat of destruction had led Carew to appreciate the values of this ancient, traditional way of noble country life—a way of life celebrated long before by Carew's poetical master and father, Ben Jonson, in his similar poem "Penshurst," and by Jonson's own masters, Vergil, Horace, and Martial.

And indeed had such a way of life really been honored and followed by King Charles and his Court, the monarchy would never have come to its disaster. But by the year 1640 Charles and his Court had lost touch with the common people, unlike the Lord and Lady in their crowded hall at Wrest. Charles and his Court lived more and more a life apart, charmed by art and music, led by a King of impeccable artistic taste, whose collection of works of art, gathered in his palaces, represented one of the greatest art collections in all of Europe. Inigo Jones, that architect of rare ability, was in charge of all the King's buildings; Jones's new banqueting house at

Figure 9. Van Dyck: "Charles I in Three Positions." Painted c. 1635–6 as a basis for the marble bust of Charles made by Bernini in Rome. (*Windsor Castle; reproduced by gracious permission of Her Majesty Queen Elizabeth II.*)

Whitehall, built in the latter years of King James's reign, had its ceiling painted by Rubens during Charles's reign; and Van Dyck came from Antwerp to live as the resident painter of King Charles and his Court. But by the year 1640 this era of courtly elegance and art was near its end.

That end may be seen as symbolized in two more events of this climacteric year: by the publication, in May or June, 1640, a few months after Thomas Carew's death, of his volume of collected poems, containing a world of Cavalier ideals; and secondly, by the presentation, in January, 1640, of the last of the great Court masques, *Salmacida Spolia*, composed jointly by Inigo Jones and by Carew's good friend and fellow poet, Sir William Davenant. The masque was based upon a curious allegorical interpretation of the myth of Salmacis, which is here interpreted as representing "Salmacian spoils," that is to say, rewards gained by peace and not by destructive war. It is the climax and epitome of the great series of Court masques that had flourished during the reign of James I on a relatively simpler scale, and then gradually rose to a scale of greater and greater extravagance after the reign of Charles I began in 1625. The masques of the Caroline era were glorious, expensive spectacles that called upon all the Court's immense artistic resources, for scene designing, for costume, for music, for dancing, and for poetry. All these resources were brought together for the last time in *Salmacida Spolia*, to give a moral allegory of the times, as the published version of the entertainment describes it:[2]

Figure 10. Van Dyck: Charles I, 1636. (*Windsor Castle; reproduced by gracious permission of Her Majesty Queen Elizabeth II.*)

The Subject of the Masque

Discord, a malicious Fury, appears in a storm and by the invocation of malignant spirits, proper to her evil use, having already put most of the world into disorder [a reference to the Thirty Years' War then raging on the Continent], endeavours to disturb these parts, envying the blessings and tranquillity we have long enjoyed.

These incantations are expressed by those spirits in an Antimasque; who on a sudden are surprised and stopped in their motion by a secret power, whose wisdom they tremble at; and depart as foreknowing that wisdom will change all their malicious hope of these disorders into a sudden calm, which after their departure is prepared by a dispersed harmony of music.

This secret wisdom, in the person of the King attended by his Nobles and under the name of Philogenes or Lover of his People, hath his appearance prepared by a Chorus, representing the beloved people, and is instantly discovered environed with those Nobles in the Throne of Honour.

Then the Queen personating the chief heroine, with her martial ladies, is sent down from Heaven by Pallas as a reward of his prudence for reducing the threatening storm into the following calm.

Thus, after a series of fantastic scenes representing various aspects of discord and disorder, the King makes his appearance in great magnificence:

Figure 11. A Masquer. Design by Inigo Jones for *Salmacida Spolia*, 1640; a similar costume was worn by the King in his role as Philogenes. (*Devonshire Collection, Chatsworth; reproduced by kind permission of the Trustees of the Chatsworth Settlement. Simpson and Bell*, Designs, No. 345.)

Then the further part of the scene disappeared, and the King's Majesty and the rest of the masquers were discovered sitting in the Throne of Honour, his Majesty highest in a seat of gold and the rest of the Lords about him. This throne was adorned with palm trees, between which stood statues of the ancient heroes. In the under parts on each side lay captives bound, in several postures, lying on trophies of armours, shields, and antique weapons, all his throne being feigned of goldsmith's work. The habit of his Majesty and the masquers was of watchet, richly embroidered with silver; long stockings set up of white; their caps silver with scrolls of gold and plumes of white feathers.

Then, after a song in praise of the King's virtues, particularly his patience and mercy in view of "those storms the people's giddy fury raise," the Queen descends in an even more magnificent scene.

Whilst the Chorus sung this song, there came softly from the upper part of the heavens a huge cloud of various colours, but pleasant to the sight; which, descending to the midst of the scene, opened, and within it was a transparent brightness of thin exhalations, such as the Gods are feigned to descend in; in the most eminent place of which her Majesty sat, representing the chief heroine, environed with her martial ladies; and from over her head were darted lightsome rays that illuminated her seat; and all the ladies about her participated more or less of that light, as they sat near or further off. This brightness with many streaks of thin vapours about it, such as are seen in a fair evening sky, softly descended; and as it came

Figure 12. Van Dyck: Queen Henrietta Maria, probably 1632. (*Windsor Castle; reproduced by gracious permission of Her Majesty Queen Elizabeth II.*)

near to the earth the seat of Honour by little and little vanished, as if it gave way to these heavenly graces. The Queen's
Majesty and her ladies were in Amazonian habits of carnation,
embroidered with silver, with plumed helms, baldrics with
antique swords hanging by their sides—all as rich as might be;
but the strangeness of the habits was most admired.

Thus with song and dance and extravagant splendor the King
and the Queen and the Court persuaded themselves that peace
was still at hand and that the Court would prevail.

One assumes that Thomas Carew must have been present
at this gorgeous spectacle, for he loved these masques and had
himself composed the libretto for a very expensive and elaborate show entitled *Coelum Britannicum*, presented at Court
in 1634. Of this splendid show, Sir Henry Herbert reports:
"It was the noblest masque of my time to this day, the best
poetrye, best scenes, and the best habitts. The kinge and
queene were very well pleasd with my service, and the Q. was
pleasd to tell mee before the king, 'Pour les habits, elle
n'avoit jamais rien vue de si brave.' "[3] The praise was well
deserved, for Carew's book for the masque is one of the most
thoroughly written that we have for any masque of the day.
Indeed the proportion of poetry to scenery appears to be
larger than that found in any other masque of the time except for Milton's Ludlow masque. It consists of an extravagant hymn of praise for the virtues of the royal pair whose
destiny it is to rout all the vices and disorders of the day and
to bring into the three kingdoms of England, Scotland, and
Ireland a perfect peace derived from perfect morality. Thus
after a long series of anti-masques have been performed,
representing the several disorders of existence, the Genius of
the three kingdoms appears and foresees the future:

Raise from these rockie cliffs, your heads,
Brave Sonnes, and see where Glory spreads
Her glittering wings, where Majesty
Crown'd with sweet smiles, shoots from her eye
Diffusive joy, where Good and Faire,
United sit in Honours chayre.
Call forth your aged Priests, and chrystall streames,
To warme their hearts, and waves in these bright beames.[4]

Then after a series of such songs of praise, the noblemen appear, gorgeously arrayed, to begin the defeat of evil:

At this the under-part of the Rocke opens, and out of a Cave are seene to come the Masquers, richly attired like ancient Heroes, the Colours yellow, embroydered with silver, their antique Helmes curiously wrought, and great plumes on the top; before them a troope of young Lords and Noblemens sonnes bearing Torches of Virgin wax, these were apparelled after the old British fashion in white Coats, embroydered with silver, girt, and full gathered, cut square coller'd, and round caps on their heads, with a white feather wreathen about them; first these dance with their lights in their hands: After which, the Masquers descend into the roome, and dance their entry.[5]

And then after several harmonious songs, the masque concludes by the appearance of seven magnificent allegorical figures: Religion, Truth, Wisdom, Concord, Government, Reputation, and lastly, Eternity, all joining in praise of the glorious virtues of Britain's King and Queen.

The fatal separation of this gorgeous world of art from the world of political actuality is clearly evidenced in a superb poem that Carew had written, probably in January of 1633, to his friend and fellow poet of the Cavaliers, Aurelian

Townshend. Townshend had written a poem to Carew, urging him to write a poetical tribute in honor of Gustavus Adolphus, who had been killed at the battle of Lützen, November 6, 1632. Thus Carew writes "In answer of an Elegiacall Letter upon the death of the King of Sweden from Aurelian Townsend, inviting me to write on that subject":[6]

> Why dost thou sound, my deare *Aurelian*,
> In so shrill accents, from thy *Barbican*,
> A loude allarum to my drowsie eyes,
> Bidding them wake in teares and Elegies
> For mightie *Swedens* fall? Alas! how may
> My Lyrique feet, that of the smooth soft way
> Of Love, and Beautie, onely know the tread,
> In dancing paces celebrate the dead
> Victorious King, or his Majesticke Hearse
> Prophane with th'humble touch of their low verse?
> *Virgil*, nor *Lucan*, no, nor *Tasso* more
> Then both, not *Donne*, worth all that went before,

(Notice his extraordinary admiration for the poetry of Donne.)

> With the united labour of their wit
> Could a just Poem to this subject fit,
> His actions were too mighty to be rais'd

Figure 13 (opposite). A Masquer. Design by Inigo Jones for Carew's *Coelum Britannicum*, 1634. (*Devonshire Collection, Chatsworth; reproduced by kind permission of the Trustees of the Chatsworth Settlement. Simpson and Bell*, Designs, No. 201.)

Figure 14. Head of a Masquer. Design by Inigo Jones for Carew's *Coelum Britannicum*, 1634. (*Devonshire Collection, Chatsworth; reproduced by kind permission of the Trustees of the Chatsworth Settlement. Simpson and Bell*, Designs, No. 207.)

Figure 15 (opposite). A Torch-bearer. Design by Inigo Jones for Carew's *Coelum Britannicum*, 1634. (*Devonshire Collection, Chatsworth; reproduced by kind permission of the Trustees of the Chatsworth Settlement. Simpson and Bell*, Designs, No. 206.)

Higher by Verse, let him in prose be prays'd,
In modest faithfull story, which his deedes
Shall turne to Poems:

It sounds like an honest tribute to a great military leader, and yet as the poem continues a certain ironic tone appears to arise in the following lines:

And (since 'twas but his Church-yard) let him have
For his owne ashes now no narrower Grave
Then the whole *German* Continents vast wombe,
Whilst all her Cities doe but make his Tombe.

That is to say, Gustavus has made all of Germany a grave-yard; therefore let him lie there. If we doubt the irony here the rest of the passage will bear it out:

Let us to supreame providence commit
The fate of Monarchs, which first thought it fit
To rend the Empire from the *Austrian* graspe,
And next from *Swedens*, even when he did claspe

Figure 16. "Fidamira." Design by Inigo Jones for Walter Montagu's play, *The Shepheards Paradise*, 1633. (*Devonshire Collection, Chatsworth; reproduced by kind permission of the Trustees of the Chatsworth Settlement. Simpson and Bell, Designs,* No. 176.)
    "Those fine, delicate, cool hands keep one away; they are part of the 'armour' behind which all feeling, directness, and intimacy are shut off. They are part and parcel of the 'accessories,' like the rich detail of the costumes, the carefully worked jewels and weapons, the architecture and sculpture, and the other things that prevent direct contact with the person portrayed." (Hauser, *Mannerism,* I, 200; referring to Bronzino.)

Fidamira.

> Within his dying armes the Soveraigntie
> Of all those Provinces, that men might see
> The Divine wisedome would not leave that Land
> Subject to any one Kings sole command.

It is clear that Carew is finding no great virtues in military conquest, and quickly he turns his mind to things upon which he places a much higher and indeed a supreme value:

> But let us that in myrtle bowers sit
> Under secure shades, use the benefit
> Of peace and plenty, which the blessed hand
> Of our good King gives this obdurate Land . . .

By the word "obdurate" Carew recognizes that the King is having some difficulty with his subjects, but the passage breathes not the slightest doubt that the King will prevail:

> Let us of Revels sing, and let thy breath
> (Which fill'd Fames trumpet with *Gustavus* death,
> Blowing his name to heaven) gently inspire
> Thy past'rall pipe, till all our swaines admire
> Thy song and subject, whilst they both comprise
> The beauties of the *SHEPHERDS PARADISE:*

Carew is referring here to a pastoral comedy written by his friend Walter Montagu, played (with splendid scenery and costumes) by Queen Henrietta Maria and her Ladies on January 9, 1633, and apparently repeated on February 2, 1633.[7] But the production that Carew now proceeds to describe in his poem is not *The Shepheards Paradise* as we know it from

Figure 17. "A Wood called Love's Cabinet." Design by Inigo Jones for Walter Montagu's play, *The Shepheards Paradise*, 1633; Act V: the setting for an important episode played by the Queen in her role as Bellesa. (*Devonshire Collection, Chatsworth; reproduced by kind permission of the Trustees of the Chatsworth Settlement. Simpson and Bell,* Designs, No. 167.)

the printed text of 1659; instead, as Dunlap has pointed out,[8] Carew's description suggests the masque *Tempe Restord*, which Aurelian Townshend and Inigo Jones had presented in February, 1632. Carew urges his friend to continue writing works in the pastoral genre, "For who like thee," Carew asks,

> In sweetly-flowing numbers may advance
> The glorious night? When, not to act foule rapes,
> Like birds, or beasts, but in their Angel-shapes
> A troope of Deities came downe to guide
> Our steerelesse barkes in passions swelling tide
> By vertues Carde, and brought us from above
> A patterne of their owne celestiall love.

With that echo of the concluding lines of Donne's "Canonization," Carew seems to be describing the elaborate descent of "Divine Beauty" and the "Stars," in *Tempe Restord*, as the Queen and her Ladies descended in one of Inigo Jones's miraculous machines and brought home to earth the meaning of true virtue as opposed to Circean corruption.[9] And this resemblance is borne out by Carew's reference to "the divine

Figure 18 (opposite). "Influences of the Stars." Design by Inigo Jones for *Tempe Restord*, 1632: "*Harmony* comes foorth attended by a *Chorus* of Musique, and under her conduct fourteene Influences of the stars, which are to come." Townshend, *Poems and Masks*, ed. Chambers, p. 88. (*Devonshire Collection, Chatsworth; reproduced by kind permission of the Trustees of the Chatsworth Settlement. Simpson and Bell*, Designs, No. 158.)
"... the ostentatious grace, the affectation and desire to please ... and the taste for the artificial and unspontaneous that here leads to characteristic mannerist dance poses, are pushed a stage further." (Hauser, *Mannerism*, I, 183; referring to Pontormo.)

Venus" and "her heavenly *Cupid*" in the following lines, for in *Tempe Restord* the appearance of the Queen and her Ladies is praised for creating an "Ayre" "Where faire and good, inseparably conioynd,/Create a *Cupid*, that is never blind."[10] Thus Carew continues:

> Nor lay it in darke sullen precepts drown'd
> But with rich fancie, and cleare Action crown'd
> Through a misterious fable (that was drawne
> Like a transparant veyle of purest Lawne
> Before their dazelling beauties) the divine
> *Venus*, did with her heavenly *Cupid* shine.
> The stories curious web, the Masculine stile,
> The subtile sence, did Time and sleepe beguile,
> Pinnion'd and charm'd they stood to gaze upon
> Th'Angellike formes, gestures, and motion,
> To heare those ravishing sounds that did dispence
> Knowledge and pleasure, to the soule, and sense.

So far the parallel may seem to fit; but the conclusion of Carew's account describes two events for which there is no real correspondence in *Tempe Restord*. At the close of this masque Cupid simply flies up into the air,[11] but Carew describes a much more elaborate action that suggests the Platonizing theme of Montagu's play:[12]

Figure 19 (opposite). "Divine Beauty" and "Stars." Design by Inigo Jones for roles played by the Queen and her Ladies in *Tempe Restord*, 1632: "in a garment of watchet Sattine with Stars of silver imbrodered and imbost from the ground, and on her head a Crowne of Stars mixt with some small falls of white Feathers." Townshend, *Poems and Masks*, ed. Chambers, pp. 91–2. (*Devonshire Collection, Chatsworth; reproduced by kind permission of the Trustees of the Chatsworth Settlement. Simpson and Bell*, Designs, No. 161.)

It fill'd us with amazement to behold
Love made all spirit, his corporeall mold
Dissected into Atomes melt away
To empty ayre, and from the grosse allay
Of mixtures, and compounding Accidents
Refin'd to immateriall Elements.

And finally, Carew makes the Queen's own singing the climax of his account, whereas in *Tempe Restord* the Queen does not sing:

But when the Queene of Beautie did inspire
The ayre with perfumes, and our hearts with fire,
Breathing from her celestiall Organ sweet
Harmonious notes, our soules fell at her feet,
And did with humble reverend dutie, more
Her rare perfections, then high state adore.

In the fifth Act of *The Shepheards Paradise*, however, a song of twenty lines is sung by the Queen in her role as Bellesa, chosen for her beauty as "Queen" of this pastoral retreat. Immediately after this she falls asleep, being alone, and Moramente enters, "sees her here lie sleeping and stands wondering," with the following speech:

Was it the rapture my soule was allwayes in, when she contemplates the divine *Bellesa*, that did present her voyce unto me here in heaven? Sure it was: her soul, uselesse now unto her body, is gon to visit heaven, and did salute the Angels with a song.[13]

Figure 20. Queen Henrietta Maria as "Divine Beauty" in *Tempe Restord,* 1632. Miniature by John Hoskins. (*Royal Library, Windsor Castle; reproduced by gracious permission of Her Majesty Queen Elizabeth II. Photo by courtesy of Messrs. Sotheby and Co.*)

These words of Moramente seem to "comprise" the subject for a song that appears in Townshend's collected works, with the title "On his Hearing her Majesty sing":

I have beene in Heav'n, I thinke,
For I heard an Angell sing,
Notes my thirsty ears did drinke.
Never any earthly thing
Sung so true, so sweet, so cleere;
I was then in Heav'n, not heere.

But the blessed feele no change,
So I may mistake the place,
But mine eyes would think it strange,
Should that be no Angels face;
Pow'rs above, it seems, designe
Me still Mortall, her Divine.

Till I tread the Milky way,
And I lose my sences quite,
All I wish is that I may
Hear that voice, and see that sight,
Then in types and outward show
I shall have a Heav'n below.[14]

It seems possible that this song may have formed a part of some adaptation of *The Shepheards Paradise*. And there is evidence that such an adaptation was made. A manuscript in the Folger Library represents an acting version of *The Shepheards Paradise*, with a prologue and certain songs between the acts which do not appear in the printed text of the play.[15] This prologue makes it plain that some kind of masque is being presented in coordination with Montagu's play, certainly at the beginning, and possibly between the acts as well. The prologue presents Apollo and Diana in conversation; Apollo tells Diana that the Gods have agreed to appear on this occasion in the form of stars:

> Soe now by this they all consented are,
> Each one to put himselfe into a starre:
> And thus in Gallantry each brings a light,
> And waites with it a servant to this night,
> They'le give the light & leave you to preside
> In vertue, but as you are Deifide;

Perhaps the Gods then, later in the evening, descended from their Heaven and appeared in the manner described in Carew's lines above:

> When, not to act foule rapes,
> Like birds, or beasts, but in their Angel-shapes
> A troope of Deities came downe to guide
> Our steerelesse barkes in passions swelling tide
> By vertues Carde

Certainly these lines accord much better with the Gods and stars of the prologue than they do with the descent of the Queen and her Ladies as stars in *Tempe Restord*. Has Townshend perhaps used some of the themes, along with the costumes, settings, and machinery, from his masque of the previous year, in order to enhance the beauties of *The Shepheards Paradise?*[16] It seems likely, all considered, and such a conclusion would resolve the puzzle of Carew's account, which seems to describe a production related to *The Shepheards Paradise*, and yet devised in some manner by Townshend as well. In any case, such are the "pastimes" that Carew asks his friend to celebrate, as he ends the poem to Townshend with these most significant and revealing lines:

These harmelesse pastimes let my *Townsend* sing
To rurall tunes; not that thy Muse wants wing
To soare a loftier pitch, for she hath made
A noble flight, and plac'd th'Heroique shade
Above the reach of our faint flagging ryme;
But these are subjects proper to our clyme.
Tourneyes, Masques, Theaters, better become
Our *Halcyon* dayes; what though the German Drum
Bellow for freedome and revenge, the noyse
Concernes not us, nor should divert our joyes;
Nor ought the thunder of their Carabins
Drowne the sweet Ayres of our tun'd Violins;
Beleeve me friend, if their prevailing powers
Gaine them a calme securitie like ours,
They'le hang their Armes up on the Olive bough,
And dance, and revell then, as we doe now.

The whole situation of the Cavalier world, as glimpsed in this poem, and indeed the full impact of Carew's poetry, may be seen as symbolized in a great Mannerist painting by Bronzino, of which I was reminded by reading *The Nice and the Good* by Iris Murdoch, who has given this painting a symbolic place in her book. It is Bronzino's allegory known as "Venus, Cupid, Folly, and Time," where the graceful, harmonious, beautifully posed figure of Venus forms the center of the picture, while her grace is threatened from all sides by corrupting forces. Her son, Cupid, kneels beside her on the left in a distorted posture, embracing her indecently. Old Father Time holds over the head of Venus a threatening muscular arm. On the right side dances the figure of Folly

Figure 21 (opposite). Bronzino: "Venus, Cupid, Folly, and Time." (*National Gallery, London; reproduced by kind permission of the Trustees of the National Gallery.*)

or Pleasure, a young boy with a glint of madness in his eyes. In the background, darkened in shadows, lurk three sinister figures: one in the upper left corner may represent the figure of Truth, who seems to be turning her face away in horror from the scene; down lower on the left one sees clearly the tormented face of a figure that must be Jealousy; and in the background on the right side lurks a strange composite monster who must be the figure of Deceit, for the bland, pretty face does not square with the animal lower parts that we can see in the corner of the painting; moreover, as critics point out, her left and right hands are misplaced.[17] Can the Queen of Love and Beauty survive these threats?

Thomas Carew is not wholly unaware of these dangers, for his poems deal incessantly with time, infidelity, and death. Many of his finest poems are funeral tributes or poems written to the King or to noble ladies when they are suffering illness. Here, for example, is a poem where the images of red and white common to love-poetry are turned gracefully to deal with the paleness of a young lady suffering from some anemic disease:

> Stay coward blood, and doe not yield
> To thy pale sister, beauties field,
> Who there displaying round her white
> Ensignes, hath usurp'd thy right;
> Invading thy peculiar throne,
> The lip, where thou shouldst rule alone;
> And on the cheeke, where natures care
> Allotted each an equall share,
> Her spreading Lilly only growes,
> Whose milky deluge drownes thy Rose.

> Quit not the field faint blood, nor rush
> In the short salley of a blush,
> Upon thy sister foe, but strive
> To keepe an endlesse warre alive;
> Though peace doe petty States maintaine,
> Here warre alone makes beauty raigne.

But sometimes Death will win, as Carew shows in a poem on the death of a young girl, Lady Mary Villers, where all the symbols of Love and Beauty are delicately brought together in balanced, measured form to pay a tribute to the death of youth:

> This little Vault, this narrow roome,
> Of Love, and Beautie is the tombe;
> The dawning beame that 'gan to cleare
> Our clouded skie, lyes darkned here,
> For ever set to us, by death
> Sent to enflame the world beneath;
> 'Twas but a bud, yet did containe
> More sweetnesse then shall spring againe,
> A budding starre that might have growne
> Into a Sun, when it had blowne.
> This hopefull beautie, did create
> New life in Loves declining state;
> But now his Empire ends, and we
> From fire, and wounding darts are free:
> His brand, his bow, let no man feare,
> The flames, the arrowes, all lye here.

It seems appropriate to call this poem a work of Mannerist art, if we do not use the term Mannerist in a derogatory sense. I will use it as many art historians do, when they seek to describe certain aspects of late Renaissance culture, during the last seventy years or so of the sixteenth century, the period after the death of the two great masters, Raphael and Leonardo. But we must define closely the term Mannerist, as John Shearman has tried to do in his recent book on this subject.[18] As he and many others have pointed out, "Mannerism" is derived from the Italian word *maniera*, meaning simply, *style*. A Mannerist painter is a painter with high style, with so strong an emphasis on style that it stands out as the figure of Venus stands out in Bronzino's painting among the threatening gestures of the other figures in the scene. A Mannerist painter has learned all that can be learned from the earlier great masters and he now proceeds to turn their art and craft toward other ends, creating a different kind of art in which the high style stands at the front, taking the eye with its elegance and its sophistication. Such art can, of course, be mere imitation in the bad sense of that word, but it may also be creative imitation—that is, imitation of the manner of the great masters which moves into a different era of sensibility and creates a new world of art. Now transferring cautiously this term into the poetic realm, perhaps we might say that Carew is a Mannerist because he imitates so skillfully the works of the great masters who preceded him and yet brings their art into a different dimension, celebrating values different from those presented by Donne and Jonson and other poets to whom Carew is obviously indebted. The short epitaph that I have just read inherits the Jonsonian form as displayed in many of Jonson's own epigrams and epitaphs, but carries beyond Jonson its elegance and perfection of form, its delicacy of sympathetic admiration for dead Beauty.

Carew's admiration for his master, Ben Jonson, is no empty adulation, as we may see from the remarkable poem that Carew wrote to Ben on the occasion of his poetical father's outrageous exhibition of bad temper when the public hissed his play, *The New Inn*, off the stage in 1629.[19] In 1631 Jonson published the play with a title-page in which he blames everybody but himself for the failure:

> A Comoedy. As it was never acted, but most
> negligently play'd, by some, the Kings Servants.
> And more squeamishly beheld, and censured by
> others, the Kings Subjects. 1629. Now, at last,
> set at liberty to the Readers, his Majesties
> Servants, and Subjects, to be judg'd.

He appends to the play a very bad-tempered poem in which he denounces the English audience in these words:

> Come leave the lothed stage,
>   And the more lothsome age:
> Where pride, and impudence (in faction knit)
>   Usurpe the chaire of wit!
> Indicting, and arraigning every day
>   Something they call a Play.
>   Let their fastidious, vaine
>   Commission of the braine
> Run on, and rage, sweat, censure, and condem'n:
> They were not made for thee, lesse, thou for them.

Carew pays his master Ben the ultimate tribute by judging this outburst of temper in strict accordance with the master's own principles. Carew's poem acts as a tacit reminder that Jonson has urged the use of reason and proportion, that he has represented the values of balance and self-control—the

virtues of Roman poetry and of Roman morality. The poem
is friendly, but judicious, gentle, but firm:

> Tis true (deare *Ben*:) thy just chastizing hand
> Hath fixt upon the sotted Age a brand
> To their swolne pride, and empty scribbling due,
> It can nor judge, nor write, and yet 'tis true
> Thy commique Muse from the exalted line
> Toucht by thy *Alchymist*, doth since decline
> From that her Zenith, and foretells a red
> And blushing evening, when she goes to bed,
> Yet such, as shall out-shine the glimmering light
> With which all stars shall guild the following night.

We should notice that Carew is paying a brilliant tribute
to his master here by writing his poem in the style of Jonson's
verse epistles, a style sufficiently end-stopped to keep the
couplet form alive, and observing the caesura frequently, in
good classical form with an effect of balance and proportion, and yet with a movement flexible enough to allow for
the colloquial idiom of a good verse-letter. At the same time
Carew reveals here his fine critical sense, recognizing that
Jonson had reached the peak of his power in the *Alchemist*,
produced nearly twenty years before. He chides his father
by saying that of course an author may very well bind "In
equall shares thy love on all thy race;" nevertheless it is the
reader's duty to "distinguish of their sexe, and place;"

> Though one hand form them, & though one brain strike
> Soules into all, they are not all alike.
> Why should the follies then of this dull age
> Draw from thy Pen such an immodest rage

> As seemes to blast thy (else-immortall) Bayes,
> When thine owne tongue proclaimes thy ytch of praise?

And he urges his master to continue his learned use of mate-
rials from ancient authors, and says that no one should

> thinke it theft, if the rich spoyles so torne
> From conquered Authors, be as Trophies worne -

thus defending Jonson against the charge of plagiarism from
ancient authors, a charge often leveled against him. In one
phrase he sums up the essence of Jonsonian technique.

> Repine not at the Tapers thriftie waste,
> That sleekes thy terser Poems . . .

Terser is the exact word to describe the essence of Jonsonian
art, for *terse* means not simply concise and compact, but it
means, in Elizabethan English, polished, brilliant, sleeked,
burnished by careful craftsmanship.

Such then is Carew's critical admiration for one of the old
masters, even in that master's declining years. But there were
other masters. One of them has inspired what is perhaps
Carew's greatest poem: "An Elegie upon the death of the
Deane of Pauls, Dr. John Donne." Here Carew sums up
Donne's achievement with a critical acumen never surpassed
in later critical writings: if we grasp the poem we grasp
Donne. Carew saw, as well as T. S. Eliot, Donne's power of
feeling his thought as immediately as the odor of a rose; he
saw as well as Grierson Donne's immense power of "passionate ratiocination" where image and argument are compressed
in one dramatic moment:

But the flame
Of thy brave Soule, (that shot such heat and light,
As burnt our earth, and made our darknesse bright,
Committed holy Rapes upon our Will,
Did through the eye the melting heart distill;
And the deepe knowledge of darke truths so teach,
As sense might judge, what phansie could not reach;)
Must be desir'd for ever.

And we note that Carew here surpasses all other critical essays on Donne by creating his essay in Donne's own style, with the enormous suspension of syntax over-riding the couplet form in the manner of Donne's long passionate utterances. He praises Donne for refusing to imitate ancient authors and for using the English language in a remarkably original fashion that enabled Donne to excel poets who were born to speak languages more musical than English—languages such as Latin or Italian, "whose tun'd chime/More charmes the outward sense."

Yet thou maist claime
From so great disadvantage greater fame,
Since to the awe of thy imperious wit
Our stubborne language bends, made only fit
With her tough-thick rib'd hoopes to gird about
Thy Giant phansie, which had prov'd too stout
For their soft melting Phrases.

Here the phrase "imperious wit" strikes to the very center of Donne's achievement, for Carew is using *wit* here in the broad seventeenth-century sense, meaning creative intellect, along with all the other associations that wit has in our own day.

Donne's *imperious* intellect, his indomitable reason, bends our stubborn language into forms unprecedented in earlier ages, creating those extraordinary stanza forms that Donne used for one poem and one poem only. We should note here that Carew is praising Donne in a way that seems to castigate himself, for Carew well knows that he himself is a writer of "soft melting Phrases" and that he himself has brought back into poetry the kind of mythological imagery which he praises Donne for having banished from English verse:

> But thou art gone, and thy strict lawes will be
> Too hard for Libertines in Poetrie.
> They will repeale the goodly exil'd traine
> Of gods and goddesses, which in thy just raigne
> Were banish'd nobler Poems, now, with these
> The silenc'd tales o'th' Metamorphoses
> Shall stuffe their lines, and swell the windy Page,
> Till Verse refin'd by thee, in this last Age
> Turne ballad rime, Or those old Idolls bee
> Ador'd againe, with new apostasie;

And Carew then concludes by lines that celebrate the end of an era, appropriately echoing both Shakespeare and Donne,[20] as his Elegy proclaims

> The death of all the Arts, whose influence
> Growne feeble, in these panting numbers lies
> Gasping short winded Accents, and so dies:
> So doth the swiftly turning wheele not stand
> In th'instant we withdraw the moving hand,
> But some small time maintaine a faint weake course
> By vertue of the first impulsive force:

Thus Carew, writing shortly after Donne's death in 1631, grasps both the style and the deep significance of Donne's poetical achievement. Carew is indeed one of the great critics of English literature; if he had been writing in our own day he would undoubtedly be known as one of the "new critics."

The extraordinary Mannerist quality that Carew has, in imitating to perfection the style of the great masters, is shown with equal strength in another "critical essay" that he wrote, "To my worthy friend Master Geo. Sands, on his translation of the Psalmes," as the title reads in Carew's collected poems. Here is another poem in pentameter couplets, but we notice that the style does not display either the moderate, flexibly end-stopped movement of Jonson's verse epistles, nor the passionate rush of Donne's over-riding Muse:

> I presse not to the Quire, nor dare I greet
> The holy place with my unhallowed feet;
> My unwasht Muse, polutes not things Divine,
> Nor mingles her prophaner notes with thine;
> Here, humbly at the porch she listning stayes,
> And with glad eares sucks in thy sacred layes.
> So, devout penitents of Old were wont,
> Some without dore, and some beneath the Font,
> To stand and heare the Churches Liturgies,
> Yet not assist the solemne exercise:
> Sufficeth her, that she a lay-place gaine,
> To trim thy Vestments, or but beare thy traine;
> Though nor in tune, nor wing, she reach thy Larke,
> Her Lyrick feet may dance before the Arke.

These couplets are completely end-stopped, each couplet standing as a perfect unit, somewhat anticipating the Augustan

manner in caesura, balance, and antithesis. Carew is presenting here a superb imitation of the couplet style that George
Sandys had achieved in his famous translation of Ovid's
Metamorphoses, published in 1626, and widely regarded by
modern scholars as a very important step in the creation of
the couplet form mastered by Dryden and Pope.[21] Equally
important, one should note that exactly this kind of closed
couplet also covers many pages in the volume, *A Paraphrase
Upon the Divine Poems*, by George Sandys, in which Carew's
poem first appeared, in 1638, headed simply "To my worthy
friend Mr. George Sandys." Carew is not thinking only of
the Psalms here, although Sandys did translate eighteen of the
Psalms in this volume into pentameter couplets; but the volume also contains enormous paraphrases of other books of
the Bible, such as the fifty-five-page paraphrase of the Book
of Job with which the volume opens, done in the closed
couplet form. As usual, Carew is fitting the style of his essay
to the form of the poetry that he is celebrating.

What we see then in these three poems to three early masters, Jonson, Donne, and Sandys, is Carew's critical ability to
enter into the very world created by other poets, to absorb
them, understand them, and recreate them in his own mind—
surely the basic quality that one expects in any good critic. But
Carew's critical sense is best shown by his realization of the
limitations of his own Muse, which, as he says, is made to sing
the cause of Love and Beauty, as indeed he has done for the
whole Cavalier Court. A great many of Carew's poems are
entitled "Song" and rightly so, for dozens of them were set
to music by the best musicians at the Court of Charles I. Some
sixty musical settings for his Songs have been discovered[22]—
most of them by Henry Lawes, the chief composer of the day

in England, the man who composed the music for Milton's masque in 1634, who in fact directed the masque and played the part of Thyrsis in it. In 1634, Carew and Milton were both participating in the Mannerist art of the Cavalier Court; and indeed the two Egerton boys, who played in Milton's masque, had played only a few months before in Carew's masque *Coelum Britannicum.* The great divisions that were soon to split all England had not yet appeared within the world of art.

In these love songs Carew is working in the great European tradition of the courtly love-lyric, inspired by all the Italian love-poets from Petrarch down to Carew's contemporary Marino, and also inspired by many French poets of the sixteenth century.[23] It is important to remember that Charles's Queen, Henrietta Maria, was a Frenchwoman, the daughter of a Medici, and that she brought with her into England an affection for the graceful beauty of French and Italian art-forms, from which the Court masque indeed derives. These European courtly analogues outweigh any echoes that may be assembled from Donne or even from Jonson. Certainly Carew owes something to Donne and distinct echoes of Donne's poems can easily be found, as in his poem, "Upon a Ribband," in which he echoes Donne's famous conceit, "A bracelet of bright haire about the bone," used by Donne in "The Funerall" and in "The Relique." But significantly, this macabre image, combining a symbol of physical love with a symbol of death, is turned by Carew into a graceful compliment. The bracelet here is no longer a "wreath of haire," but is simply a ribbon, a "silken wreath," tied gracefully about the poet's wrist. It is a symbol of what happened to Donne's inspiration when it entered into Carew's realm celebrating the Queen of Love and Beauty:

> This silken wreath, which circles in mine arme,
> Is but an Emblem of that mystique charme,
> Wherewith the magique of your beauties binds
> My captive soule, and round about it winds
> Fetters of lasting love; This hath entwind
> My flesh alone, That hath empalde my mind:
> Time may weare out These soft weak bands; but Those
> Strong chaines of brasse, Fate shall not discompose.
> This holy relique may preserve my wrist,
> But my whole frame doth by That power subsist:

Appropriately, the first five lines of the poem have something of the run-on movement of Donne's dynamic rhythms, but in the last five lines above, we notice that the verse-form gradually modulates into the courtly, Jonsonian mode of the pentameter couplet. The extravagant preoccupation with Donne's influence that marked literary criticism in the earlier years of the twentieth century has led to the listing of Carew in standard bibliographies and anthologies of "The Metaphysical Poets;" yet, as the above poem indicates, the word "metaphysical" will apply only to some of the surface aspects of Carew's work, and even then in only a few of his poems. Songs such as "Ingratefull beauty threatned" or "To my inconstant Mistris" clearly show the accent and the rigorous realism of Donne's dramatic addresses to his Lady:

> Know, *Celia*, (since thou art so proud,)
> 'Twas I that gave thee thy renowne:

Thou hadst, in the forgotten crowd
    Of common beauties, liv'd unknowne,
Had not my verse exhal'd thy name,
And with it, ympt the wings of fame.

           *   *   *   *   *

Tempt me with such affrights no more,
    Lest what I made, I uncreate;
Let fooles thy mystique formes adore,
    I'le know thee in thy mortall state:
Wise Poets that wrap't Truth in tales,
Knew her themselves, through all her vailes.

It has the ring of Donne about it, and yet the Lady's name, Celia, used in many of Carew's poems, links the poem also with the tradition of the Sons of Ben Jonson. The examples of both Donne and Jonson are present in this poem; both poets cooperated in giving Carew's lyrics this quality of terse, colloquial speech. But such a poem as this is quite unusual in Carew's work—there are only four or five other songs which might be found thus to combine the movement of Donne and Jonson. Most of Carew's lyrics are drawn from the courtly world of the whole European Renaissance. This is especially true of Carew's famous erotic poem, "A Rapture," where he urges his Celia in cadences that strongly echo Donne in many places, and yet the total effect of the poem does not at all create the world that we know from Donne's Elegies. Carew's poem achieves success and even a sense of purity, through Carew's delicate use of traditional pastoral images, all imbued with a sense of nature's deep vitality:

Meane while the bubbling streame shall court the shore,
Th'enamoured chirping Wood-quire shall adore
In varied tunes the Deitie of Love;

The gentle blasts of Westerne winds, shall move
The trembling leaves, & through their close bows breath
Still Musick, whilst we rest our selves beneath
Their dancing shade; till a soft murmure, sent
From soules entranc'd in amorous languishment
Rowze us, and shoot into our veines fresh fire,
Till we, in their sweet extasie expire.
    Then, as the empty Bee, that lately bore,
Into the common treasure, all her store,
Flyes 'bout the painted field with nimble wing,
Deflowring the fresh virgins of the Spring;
So will I rifle all the sweets, that dwell
In my delicious Paradise, and swell
My bagge with honey, drawne forth by the power
Of fervent kisses, from each spicie flower.

Thus it seems appropriate that the editor of Carew's volume of 1640 should have chosen as the first poem "The
Spring" (and we might remember and contrast it with Donne's
"Spring" poem "Loves Growth"). Here in Carew's poem
is none of Donne's passionate reasoning, none of Donne's
philosophical argumentation and racy wit. Carew's poem is
composed in courtly cadences with a perfection of Mannerist
elegance, in couplets marked with strong caesurae; indeed the
whole poem is poised upon a major caesura in the center, for
it is a poem of twenty-four lines which pauses and gracefully
turns in another direction exactly in the middle of its thir-
teenth line. In its Cavalier elegance, its Mannerist styling, with
all its subtle harmonies of sound, it draws together themes
celebrated in dozens of French, Italian, and English poems
of the earlier Renaissance, pastoral, and Petrarchan. But here
is the poem in all its perfection:

Now that the winter's gone, the earth hath lost
Her snow-white robes, and now no more the frost
Candies the grasse, or castes an ycie creame
Upon the silver Lake, or Chrystall streame:
But the warme Sunne thawes the benummed Earth,
And makes it tender, gives a sacred birth
To the dead Swallow; wakes in hollow tree
The drowzie Cuckow, and the Humble-Bee.
Now doe a quire of chirping Minstrels bring
In tryumph to the world, the youthfull Spring.
The Vallies, hills, and woods, in rich araye,
Welcome the comming of the long'd for May.
Now all things smile; onely my *Love* doth lowre:
Nor hath the scalding Noon-day-Sunne the power,
To melt that marble yce, which still doth hold
Her heart congeald, and makes her pittie cold.
The Oxe which lately did for shelter flie
Into the stall, doth now securely lie
In open fields; and love no more is made
By the fire side; but in the cooler shade
Amyntas now doth with his *Cloris* sleepe
Under a Sycamoure, and all things keepe
Time with the season, only shee doth carry
Iune in her eyes, in her heart *Ianuary*.

But whether the mistress represents June or January, it appears
that she is equally beautiful, since the beauty of the winter
is clearly being presented in a lovely manner in the first few
lines, and certainly the appreciation of nature suggests the
natural vitality that lurks within the Lady's eyes. And the
same is true of the entire poem: it is a graceful creation in
which a few touches of natural vigor suffice to prevent the
Mannerist perfection from falling into frigidity.

Finally, we may find all these forces, love-songs of the European Renaissance, the craftsmanship of Jonson, and something even perhaps of the metaphysical note of Donne, in Carew's most famous poem, properly entitled simply "A Song".

> Aske me no more where Iove bestowes,
> When Iune is past, the fading rose:
> For in your beauties orient deepe,
> These flowers as in their causes, sleepe.

As readers have often pointed out, the word *causes* adds to the poem a metaphysical note that carries the poem beyond the range of the usual Cavalier lyric, for it evokes Aristotle's doctrine of the four causes: formal, material, efficient, and final (purposive), all of which are contained in the Lady's beauty.

> Aske me no more whether doth stray,
> The golden Atomes of the day.
> For in pure love heaven did prepare
> Those powders to inrich your haire.

> Aske me no more whether doth hast,
> The Nightingale when May is past:
> For in your sweet dividing throat,
> She winters and keepes warme her note.

> Aske me no more where those starres light,
> That downewards fall in dead of night:
> For in your eyes they sit, and there,
> Fixed become as in their sphere.

ONE HUNDRED SEVEN

Aske me no more if East or West,
The Phenix builds her spicy nest:
For unto you at last shee flies,
And in your fragrant bosome dyes.

We notice how these stanzas move from the "golden Atomes" of daylight through the wintering song of the nightingale and into certain suggestions of death and falling in the third stanza—a movement from light to dark, from life to death, summed up in the final stanza where the Phoenix image provides a symbol of both death and resurrection. Thus the poem has, after all, something of the metaphysical movement from the Many toward the One. Here, of course, all is treated in a tone of courtly compliment, but nevertheless with something of Donne's manner of turning all transient images of the Many toward the Oneness that he seeks in his love. The sense of change and death is controlled by turning all things toward the *causes* of his love, and this in miniature is Donne's effect.

In miniature, Carew displays a perfection of form and manner that Donne and Jonson themselves never quite achieved with their more robust and wide-ranging powers; thus Carew's whole volume of 1640 may be said to represent the ideals of the Cavalier world in a series of poetical miniatures, graceful, elegant, perfectly crafted, perfectly absorbing

Figure 22 (opposite). A Masquer. Design by Inigo Jones for an unidentified masque. (*Devonshire Collection, Chatsworth; reproduced by kind permission of the Trustees of the Chatsworth Settlement. Simpson and Bell,* Designs, No. 420.)
"The picture shows . . . not only his elegant, highly-strung, highly-bred human type . . . his freely flowing line and effortless form, but also the subtlety with which he renders the provocative, erotic charm of his figures." (Hauser, *Mannerism,* I, 205; referring to Parmigianino.)

the lessons of the earlier masters. It is a world of art-forms, too fragile to sustain the violent pressures of the times. But in the paintings of Van Dyck, in the drawings of Inigo Jones, and in the poetry of Carew and his friends, those forms of art survive the ashes of political disaster.

III

Richard Crashaw

Love's Architecture

Figure 23. Bernini: *Baldacchino.* (*Photo: Giordani.*)

III

Richard Crashaw

Love's Architecture

During the course of the previous lectures we have moved from the time of that earliest portrait of John Donne, in 1591, down to the time of the death of Charles I, in 1649, the victory of the Cromwellian forces, and the establishment of the Puritan Commonwealth. This entire stretch of sixty years was a period of threatening conflict, both from within, and from foreign enemies, and the era ended in violent Civil War. And yet it was also, we must remember, the time that saw the publication of Spenser's *Faerie Queene*, the writing of all the plays of Shakespeare, and the writing of the earlier poems of John Milton, to say nothing of the works of Donne and Jonson and all the others. It was indeed a time of Renaissance, when London might be said without exaggeration to have rivalled Athens in the time of the great Greek dramatists, or Florence in the age of the Medici. It was a time when all the great currents of revival that had grown up gradually on the Continent over a period of more than two hundred years suddenly flowered in England, within this brief era. As a result, all the styles and stages of the European Renaissance were compressed and recapitulated in England during this brief time. Even more than on the Continent, the phases of style that we call Renaissance, Mannerist, or Baroque all flow together and in England become inseparably intermingled and simultaneous, because of the peculiar compression of the forces of the Renaissance during the first half of the seventeenth century.

I have suggested that Thomas Carew is an English Mannerist, a poet who brought to perfection a special emphasis on style, on the manner, the *maniera*, introduced by earlier masters, especially Donne and Jonson. And I suspect, picking up the suggestion of Roy Daniells,[1] that if John Milton had died in 1650 at the age of 42, with nothing written but those earlier poems published in one volume in 1645, Milton too might have been thought of as a fine Mannerist writer, experimenting in various styles: sonnets, the Court Masque, the Spenserian style (as in his Nativity Ode), the Jonsonian style (as in *L'Allegro* and *Il Penseroso*), a poet who was only beginning to show his greatness in one poem of that highly experimental volume: *Lycidas*, his first great venture in the Baroque idiom, and the poem in which he comes closest to Crashaw.

It is essential now to define what we mean by the term Baroque. I can do so only by beginning with some examples, great and small, from the seventeenth-century visual arts. First of all, let us consider the great *Baldacchino* of Bernini, which stands over the altar under the great dome of St. Peter's in Rome: a massive, elaborately decorated canopy, supported by huge bronze columns covered with gold. Viewed in and by itself, close-up, it may seem an awkward, unstable, and be-

Figure 24. Bernini: *Baldacchino.* (*Photo: Alinari.*)

wildering construction. Yet to see it thus is to mistake its function and effect, for it is not designed to be viewed in and by
itself. First of all, seen from the nave, it acts as a frame for
the "Cathedra" of St. Peter, as Wittkower has said.[2] Furthermore, these columns are twisted and spiralling upwards, carrying their intricate decorations toward the radiant Dove of God
that shines on the underside of the canopy. Beyond this, as
you look upward from the foot of the *Baldacchino*, the vision
moves into the perfect geometrical space of Michelangelo's
Renaissance dome, with its perfect circles and segments of
circles, while on all four sides of the cross-over the view opens
out into the semi-circular vaults of the great Church, built
of course on a basically Renaissance design, according to the
Renaissance ideal of perfect geometrical order, mirroring the
divine harmony of all being. Thus the Baroque *Baldacchino*
of Bernini must be considered within its total setting and not
simply by itself, for it acts within that setting as a symbol of
human aspiration, spiralling upward toward the domed and
vaulted harmonies of a perfect mathematical form. Thus
the Renaissance ideal of harmony controls and holds in place
the violent aspirations of the Baroque spirit.

Secondly, consider the painted ceiling of the Jesuit Church
in Rome, *Il Gesù*: again a basically Renaissance interior, with
strict geometrical arches and a dome. But on the ceiling of
the nave is a painting of the late seventeenth century which
bursts out of, literally breaks through, the frame, the panel,
of its Renaissance form and flows and radiates upward as
though the very ceiling were opening into the heavens to
reveal far off the radiant Name of Jesus. Here again, the
strict Renaissance form controls and makes possible this effect
of flowing Baroque aspiration.

Figure 25. Gaulli: Ceiling of *Il Gesù*, Rome. (*Photo: Alinari.*)

Figure 26. Seventeenth-century Altarpiece; Lady Chapel, Sacred
Heart Church, University of Notre Dame. (*Photo: University of
Notre Dame Art Gallery.*)

Figure 27. Seventeenth-century Altarpiece; Lady Chapel, Sacred Heart Church, University of Notre Dame: detail. (*Photo: University of Notre Dame Art Gallery.*)

Thirdly, rather unexpectedly, I would like you to think of the seventeenth-century altar-piece, said to be of the school of Bernini, that now stands at the end of the Lady Chapel at the University of Notre Dame. I have viewed it with admiration, and not only, I assure you, because it fits so well the points that I was planning to make about the Baroque. Its repeated theme of the heads and wings of cherubs, large and small, its intertwining theme of grape clusters and grape leaves, all circling richly about the center and then soaring upward in a graceful flame toward the curve of the Romanesque or Renaissance setting—all this demonstrates as well as Bernini's *Baldacchino* the way in which Baroque aspires toward and lives at its best within a geometrical harmony. But more important is the subtle firmness of the internal action: the bracing rays in the background that move out with geometrical precision from the center of that inner circle, lending a simple strength to the fragile, intricate details.

Fourthly, I would like to consider a very small, but exquisite, piece of Baroque, the wooden font-cover ascribed to Grinling Gibbons, dating from the latter part of the seventeenth century, and still in use over the font of the Church of All Hallows Barking in London. In many ways this small piece of carving illustrates perfectly the approach to the Baroque that I am trying to develop here: that the intricate repetitions and involutions and aspirations of the Baroque spirit must somehow be held under control by some kind of firm and formal setting. Thus the font-cover begins with a perfect circular block, upon which three cherubs seem to be constantly turning, moving, and aspiring upward, with the hop-plants of which the vegetative ornament is in part composed, all moving upward toward the Dove of God that forms

Figure 28. Grinling Gibbons (attrib.): limewood font-cover;
Church of All Hallows Barking, London. (*Reproduced by kind
permission of the Secretary-Treasurer, All Hallows Barking.*)

the peak of this triangular or conical creation. Indeed as we look closely at the sculpture we can see that it is all intricately carved within a cone. Thus Bernini's fountains live within the strict confinement of the Piazza Navona, and Juvarra's tall Church of the Superga crowns the top of its symmetrical hill outside of Turin.

Finally, inevitably, we must consider the famous sculpture of Bernini, representing the scene recorded in St. Teresa's autobiography (I quote from the translation known to Cra shaw and published in 1642 under the title *The Flaming Hart*):

> I saw an Angell very neer me, towards my left side, and he appeared to me, in a Corporeall forme . . . He was not great; but rather little; yet withall, he was of very much beautie. His face was so inflamed, that he appeared to be of those most Superiour Angells, who seem to be, all in a fire; and he well might be of them, whome we call *Seraphins;* but as for me, they never tell me their names, or rankes . . . I saw, that he had a long Dart of gold in his hand; and at the end of the iron below, me thought, there was a little fire; and I conceaved, that he thrust it, some severall times, through my verie Hart, after such a manner, as that it passed the verie inwards, of my Bowells; and when he drew it back, me thought, it carried away, as much, as it had touched within me; and left all that, which remained, wholy inflamed with a great love of Almightie God.[3]

In Bernini's statuary of this vision the stone is made to flow, the robes of the Saint and the Seraph ripple as though they were water or a soft fabric, and the two figures seem to be undulating in a way that has never been seen before or since

Figure 29. Bernini: "St. Teresa in Ecstasy." Cornaro Chapel, S. Maria della Vittoria, Rome. (*Photo: Anderson-Alinari*.)

in stone. Yet here again this dramatic image is not made to stand alone. The whole floating vision is held in focus within a highly symmetrical niche that has strict pillars on either side, while the niche itself is held in place within the whole of that enormous and dramatic composition known as the Cornaro Chapel.[4]

All this, then, by way of approach to the problem of reading Crashaw. I believe that many of the difficulties that face us in dealing with his extravagant use of Baroque techniques will disappear if we seek out and grasp the means by which these Baroque aspirations are brought into focus and under control. Let me begin with an example which has often been regarded as one of Crashaw's less successful poems: his poem entitled "The flaming Heart. Upon the booke and picture of *Teresa*. As she is usually expressed with a *Seraphim* beside her."[5] I have thought for many years that the key to this poem might well lie in discovering some particular painting of St. Teresa which Crashaw is using as the basis for this Baroque meditation. I think it may be found in a painting of St. Teresa by Crashaw's contemporary, the Antwerp artist Gerhard Seghers (see Frontispiece). This painting, now in the Museum of Fine Arts at Antwerp, was in Crashaw's day displayed in the Church of the Discalced Carmelites in Antwerp,[6] where Crashaw could have seen it during the 1640's when we know that he was living in the Low Countries. There is another copy of the painting in the English Convent at Bruges, there attributed to Velasquez, and apparently deriving from the seventeenth century.[7] The existence of this painting in two copies suggests that there may have been more copies and that perhaps this is why Crashaw thinks of the painting as representing the way in which "she is usually expressed," that is, portrayed or presented. In any case the coloration and the other characteristics of the painting fit exactly the qualities of the painting as humorously described in Crashaw's poem. With the painting before us the opening lines of the poem take on a triple reference, a characteristic flashing of Baroque wit:

> Well meaning Readers! you that come as Friends,
> And catch the pretious name this piece pretends,
> Make not so much hast to admire
> That faire cheek't fallacie of fire.

We are being addressed as readers of this particular poem, as readers, that is, interpreters, of this particular painting, and as readers of Saint Teresa's autobiography. The phrase, "the pretious name this piece pretends" (offers or sets forth), applies to all three works. Now in the opening "composition" based primarily upon the painting, the whole point lies in a witty paradox by which the poet argues that the Seraph and the Saint ought to be transposed, since the Saint is really the one who hurls the dart of Love through the means of her book. That is to say, as the Angel pierced Teresa with his dart of Love, so Teresa's book pierces us with her dart of Love. And so the poet cries with humorous exasperation:

> *Painter*, what did'st thou understand
> To put her dart into his *Hand*?
> See, even the yeares, and size of Him,
> Shew this the Mother *Seraphim*.

And, to be sure, the Seraph is a small and boyish figure compared to the larger and more mature figure of the Saint.

This is the Mistrisse *Flame*; and duteous *hee*
Her happier *fire-works*, here, comes down to see.
O most poore spirited of men!
Had thy cold Pencill kist her Pen
Thou could'st not so unkindly err
To shew us this faint shade for Her.

"Why man," the poet adds with a condescending archness:

Why man, this speakes pure mortall frame,
And mocks with Femall Frost Love's manly flame.
One would suspect thou mean'st to paint,
Some weake, inferior, *Woman Saint*.
But had thy pale-fac't purple tooke
Fire from the burning Cheekes of that *bright booke*,
Thou would'st on her have heap't up all
That could be form'd *Seraphicall*.

And it is true that the figure of Teresa in this painting has
none of the ecstatic intensity of Bernini's great statue; she is
a stiff and frosty figure, and the phrase "pale-fac't purple"
very well describes the coloration of her face. At the same
time the poet's reference to "that *bright booke*" seems to point
to something in the painting itself, and indeed in the lower
right-hand corner there is a bright book illuminated, as the
shadow from the Cross indicates, by light that comes from the
direction of the Saint's face. I suppose that the book which
thus extends out toward us in space is really a Bible, but there
is no lettering upon it and so the poet is free, if he wishes, to
interpret this as representing one of Saint Teresa's own books.
It may well be that this is why the title speaks so curiously of
"the booke and picture of *Teresa*" as though they somehow

occurred together in one scene. However this may be, the description of the Seraph fits exactly the quality and coloration that we see in the painting before us.

> What e're this youth of fire wore faire,
> *Rosie Fingers, Radiant Haire,*
> Glowing cheekes, and glistring wings,
> All those, faire and flagrant [i.e., burning] things,
> But before All, that fierie Dart,
> Had fill'd the *Hand* of this great *Heart.*
> Do then as equall Right requires,
> Since *his* the blushes be, and *hers* the fires,
> Resume and rectifie thy rude designe,
> Undresse thy *Seraphim* into *mine.*
> Redeeme this injury of thy art,
> Give *him* the *veyle*, give *her* the *Dart.*
> Give *him* the *veyle*, that he may cover,
> The red cheekes of a rivall'd Lover;
> Asham'd that our world now can show
> Nests of new *Seraphims* here below.
> Give *her* the *dart*, for it is *she*
> (Faire youth) shoot's both thy shafts and *thee.*

As the poet continues, line after line, to repeat this paradox in various guises, we have an elaborate example of the difference between a Baroque conceit and a metaphysical conceit. The metaphysical conceit is based upon the philosophical doctrine of correspondences[8] and it gives at its best the effect of truly exploring the nature of some metaphysical problem. But the Baroque conceit does not explore: it rather views the same paradox or symbol from various angles, reviewing and revising and restating and expanding the issue until some truth of emotion gradually grows out from all that glittering elaboration. Picking up the phrase *fire-works* from the above passage, one might say that the Baroque conceit develops like one of those seemingly unending sky-rockets which shoot out sparks of fire in a great shower, and then each spark blooms into a dozen further showers, and then all these bloom into further showers one after another after another until finally the whole display reaches its climax and the sparks fade away in the night sky. Thus at line 55 of "The flaming Heart," the first out-shooting of Love's fire reaches its climax in the rich pentameter lines that describe the effect of Teresa's book upon her readers:

> What *Magazins* of immortall armes there shine!
> Heav'ns great *Artillery* in each *Love-spun-line*.
> Give then the *Dart* to *Her*, who gives the *Flame*;
> Give *Him* the *veyle*, who kindly takes the shame.

With those lines the poem might well seem complete, as a long and witty Baroque epigram of commentary upon an interesting but imperfect painting. Crashaw has wittily taken advantage of some of the artistic techniques displayed here by this eclectic follower of Caravaggio and Rubens.[9] For Crashaw sees, no doubt, that the power of the painting resides in the Baroque quality of that Seraph who glides in with a diagonal shaft of light. The figure of the Seraph floats in mid-air, arrayed in those streaming robes of turquoise, light gold, and old rose, while the cheeks are flushed with red and the rosy fingers grip the Saint and dart. Crashaw conveniently ignores the rather effete Mannerist figure of the Angel on the other side of the picture, whose coyly posed leg reminds one of the youth similarly posed on the left-hand side of Parmigianino's "Madonna del collo lungo."

But one never knows when a Baroque work is likely to be finished. Crashaw looks again at the painting and decides to take it as it is and start a new movement of thought, a movement typographically indicated in the first (1648) printing of this poem, by having the following lines set off toward the middle of the page:

> But if it be the frequent *Fate*
> Of worst faults to be *Fortunate*;
> If all's *prescription*; and proud wrong,
> Hearkens not to an humble song;
> For all the *Gallantry* of *Him*,
> Give me the suff'ring *Seraphim*.
> His be the bravery of all those Bright things,
> The glowing cheekes, the glittering wings,
> The *Rosie* hand, the *Radiant Dart*,
> Leave her alone the *flaming-Heart*.

It is a characteristic technique of Baroque repetition, using the same images and phrases to begin a new approach to the central paradox of this painting. Thus he ends the second movement of the poem with lines that once again swell out from the tetrameter into long pentameter lines and conclude thus in the 1648 edition:

> *O Heart!* the equall *Poise*, of *Love's* both *Parts*,
> Big alike with *wounds* and *Darts*,
> Live in these conquering *leaves*; live all the same,
> And walke through all tongues one triumphant flame.
> Live here *great heart*; and Love, and dye, and kill,

And bleed, and wound, and yield, and conquer still.
Let this immortall Life, where e'er it comes,
Walke in a crowd of *Loves*, and *Martyrdomes*.
Let *Mystick Deaths* waite on't; and wise soules bee,
The *love-slaine-witnesses*, of this life of *Thee*.

It is a natural conclusion, returning to the book from which
the poem has drawn much of its inspiration, *The Flaming
Hart*, that is, the autobiography of Saint Teresa. And yet the
poem is not over, for when Crashaw's poems were republished
after his death, in 1652, we find a passage added, the richest
fiery shower of Baroque imagery to be found anywhere in
Crashaw's poetry, the famous lines:

O sweet incendiary! shew here thy art,
Upon this carcasse of a hard, cold, hart,
Let all thy scatter'd shafts of light, that play
Among the leaves of thy larg Books of day,
Combin'd against this *Brest* at once break in
And take away from me my self & sin,
This gratious Robbery shall thy bounty be;
And my best fortunes such fair spoiles of me.
O thou undanted daughter of desires!
By all thy dowr of *Lights* & *Fires*;
By all the eagle in thee, all the dove;
By all thy lives & deaths of love;
By thy larg draughts of intellectuall day,
And by thy thrists of love more large then they;
By all thy brim-fill'd Bowles of feirce desire
By thy last Morning's draught of liquid fire;
By the full kingdome of that finall kisse
That seiz'd thy parting Soul, & seal'd thee his;
By all the heav'ns thou hast in him
(Fair sister of the *Seraphim!*)

> By all of *Him* we have in *Thee*;
> Leave nothing of my *Self* in me.
> Let me so read thy life, that I
> Unto all life of mine may dy.

Thus the Baroque method of building, we might say, moves from the concrete to the abstract, moves from the picture before the poet's eyes to the "draughts of intellectuall day." The Baroque tries, by multiplication of sensory impressions, to exhaust the sensory and to suggest the presence of the spiritual. It does not analyze the image in Donne's manner, but rather it piles image upon image upon image, in a way that sometimes defies and destroys the basic principles of poetical architecture. Crashaw's poem "The Weeper," for example, lacks the focus of "The flaming Heart" and thus becomes only a necklace of epigrams "The flaming Heart," however, with its sharp focus on the book and picture, develops from its rather excessively clever opening, labors for a new start in the middle, and then at the end, in the passage added in 1652, flowers triumphantly into one of the greatest passages of poetry found anywhere in the seventeenth century. As this poem shows, the Baroque work tends to be an unstable and unsteady compound, requiring for its success, in some way, the sustaining or enclosing presence of an underlying control. Crashaw's "The flaming Heart" is, I think, a barely successful work, but with the painting before our eyes it has the necessary focus and control.

One of the ways in which such control may operate to produce a more successful poem we may find in Crashaw's (presumably) earlier poem on Saint Teresa, first published in his volume of 1646. We find that control established in the first two lines of the poem, with their firm statement of the theme:

> *Love thou art absolute sole Lord*
> *Of life and death,* ———

We can tell from the firmness of this opening that a mature, controlling, reasonable intelligence will be at work, dealing with the meaning of the Saint's life, as the narrator recalls it and recounts it for us. The poem begins with the story of the Saint's childhood, where, as she tells, she longed to run off to a martyrdom with the Moors:

> She never undertooke to know,
> What death with love should have to doe;
> Nor hath she e're yet understood
> Why to shew love, she should shed blood,
> Yet though she can not tell you why,
> She can *love*, and she can *dye*.

We have a tone here that resembles the smiling humor of an adult remarking on a child's activities, and gradually the speaker's manner becomes more and more familiar, more and more colloquial:

> Since 'tis not to be had at home,
> Shee'l travell for *A Martyrdome*.
> No *Home* for hers confesses she,
> But where she may a Martyr be.
> Shee'l to the *Moores* and trade with them,
> For this unvalued *Diadem*,
> Shee'l offer them her dearest Breath,
> With *Christ's* name in't, in change for death.
> Shee'l bargain with them, and will give
> Them God, and teach them how to live

In him; Or if they this deny,
For him, she'l teach them how to dye.
So shall she leave amongst them sown,
Her *Lords* Blood, or at least her *own.*

He has by now adopted something like the very tone and manner of a child, and in this tone the Prologue of the poem
concludes:

Farewell then all the world! Adiew,
Teresa is no more for you:
Farewell all pleasures, sports, and joys,
(Never till now esteemed *Toyes*)
Farewell what ever deare may bee,
Mother's armes or Father's Knee.
Farewell house and farewell home:
She's for the *Moores* and *Martyrdome.*

Then with a pause marked by an eloquent space in the edition
of 1648 the speaker continues, with the adult mind reasoning
in the presence of the young Saint, and foretelling her
future·

Sweet not so fast! Lo thy faire *Spouse,*
Whom thou seekst with so swift vowes
Calls thee back, and bidds thee come,
T'embrace a milder Martyrdome.

—that is, the mystic deaths of rapture and ecstacy:

Thou art *Loves* Victim; and must dye
A death more mysticall and *high.*

And after a series of rich images in which the dart of Cupid is converted into the dart of the heavenly Seraph, Crashaw moves into the erotic imagery by which the mystics of the Church traditionally attempted to express the inexpressible:

> O how oft shalt thou complaine
> Of a sweet and subtile *paine?*
> Of intollerable *joyes?*
> Of a *death*, in which who *dyes*
> Loves his *death*, and dyes againe,
> And would for ever so be slaine!
> And lives, and dyes; and knows not why
> To live; But that he thus may never leave to dye.

But the joys that await her above are inexpressible, as he finally concedes:

> and then,
> O what?—aske not the tongues of men.
> Angells cannot tell. Suffice,
> Thy self shall feele thine own full joyes,
> And hold them fast for ever.

Nevertheless he goes on to try to suggest those joys in heaven by imagining how the Saint will be received there by the Virgin Mary, the Angels, and the Lord. But in all these ecstatic visions and fiery, frequently extravagant images, the control of the reasonable speaker runs throughout, as, in the midst of this vision of heaven, we hear the simple language and the terse Jonsonian couplet constantly affirming the presence of the rational mind:

> Angells thy old friends, there shall greet thee,
> Glad at their owne home now to meet thee.
> All thy good works which went before,
> And waited for thee at the doore,
> Shall owne thee there; and all in one
> Weave a *Constellation*
> Of crownes with which the King thy spouse,
> Shall build up thy triumphant browes.
> All thy old woes shall now smile on thee,
> And thy Paines sit bright upon thee.
> All thy sorrows here shall shine,
> And thy suff'rings be divine.

And the poem concludes with the simple praise of "those waies of light,"

> Which who in death would live to see,
> Must learne in life to dye like Thee.

So in this poem the rational presence of the speaker, with his tone of familiar conversation, controls the Baroque extravaganza and makes one of Crashaw's perfect poems.

One should add, however, that these perfect poems are rather rare in the body of Crashaw's work, partly because of the very nature of the Baroque, which depends upon the daring cast of imagination for its most powerful effects, and also perhaps because Crashaw himself is living in a world of imagination that does not have its roots in England. The earlier poem on Saint Teresa achieves its success by a subtle blending of the art of Ben Jonson with the mystical fervor of Saint Teresa, but this kind of easy blending is almost unique in Crashaw's work. There is indeed very little in previous English poetry which could have prepared Crashaw to handle the Baroque mode. Robert Southwell, at the end of the sixteenth century, had made a valiant attempt to bring the Italian mode to England, in a rudimentary form. But his example was lost, as the poetical art of the Counter Reformation failed to achieve its aims in England, except as those aims were modified at the hands of Anglican poets such as George Herbert. And Herbert's modest, moderate wit creates his own version of the forms of the High Renaissance. He is not a Mannerist, he is not Baroque. Herbert in his poetry achieves the perfect harmony of a High Renaissance symbol. Yet Crashaw learned something from Herbert, the use of simple language and homely images in devotion. These he illustrates for us by an interesting poem with the following title, "On Mr. *George Herberts* booke intituled the Temple of Sacred Poems, sent to a Gentle-woman":

> Know you faire on what you looke;
> Divinest love lyes in this booke:
> Expecting fier from your eyes,
> To kindle this his sacrifice.
> When your hands untie these strings,
> Think yo'have an Angell by the wings.
> One that gladly will be nigh,
> To waite upon each morning sigh.
> To flutter in the balmy aire,
> Of your well-perfumed praier;
> These white plumes of his hee'l lend you,
> Which every day to heaven will send you:
> To take acquaintance of the *spheare*,
> And all the smooth-fac'd kindred there.

> And though *Herbert's* name doe owe
> These devotions, fairest, know
> That while I lay them on the shrine
> Of your white hand, they are mine.

Crashaw is paying tribute to Herbert in a poem composed in strict Jonsonian tetrameter couplets, while he transmutes Herbert's intimate manner of speech into another dimension, adding to it the tone of Petrarchan flattery, the tone by which the Cavalier poets conveyed their personal interest in a woman's beauty. That is, Crashaw shares these devotions with George Herbert, and yet obliquely manages to suggest that he is also devoted to this lady in a way that is somehow both religious and Cavalier. There is no poem in the works of George Herbert where he calls a woman *fairest*: he reserves that term for God.

The poem thus raises the central problem in Crashaw's aesthetic: his daring use of sensuous imagery, and especially the imagery of human love, in an effort to express his love of God, or of the Virgin Mary, or of Saint Teresa. We may see the problem clearly in a poem which Crashaw wrote in the form of an irregular Ode—a form not yet established in English literature. It is the poem entitled, "An ode which was prefixed to a Prayer booke given to a young Gentle-woman." Here Crashaw speaks to the young lady in extravagant and highly erotic images, drawing a contrast between the world of Cavalier lovers and the world of Christian lovers. The high art of prayer, he says, is not available to those who do not keep themselves pure to receive the spiritual embraces of the Virgin's Son; and so he warns her, beginning with imagery that echoes the parable of the wise and foolish Virgins (Matthew 25:1–13):

But if the noble *Bridegroome* when he come,
  Shall find the loyt'ring *Heart* from home,
    Leaving its chast aboad,
        To gad abroad,
Amongst the gay Mates of the God of flyes;
    To take her pleasure, and to play,
    And keep the devills Holy day;
To dance ith'sunne-shine of some smiling
                But beguiling
Spheare of sweet, and sugred lies,
    Some slippery paire,
    Of false perhaps as faire,
Flattering, but forswearing eyes;

Doubtlesse some other heart
    Will get the start,
    And stepping in before,
Will take possession of the sacred store
    Of hidden sweets, and holy joyes . . .

One should notice that Crashaw here is moving far outside the range of the parable in Matthew, by developing his poem through the imagery of the popular love-songs written by Cavaliers such as Carew. Indeed, A. F. Allison has shown[10] that some of the language that follows is directly imitative of Carew's most notorious poem, his erotic piece, "A Rapture" (see the passage quoted previously in the lecture on Carew, especially the line: "From soules entranc'd in amorous languishment"). Crashaw attempts to move this highly erotic imagery up into the realm of religious mysticism, speaking of

Amorous Languishments; Luminous Trances,
Sights which are not seen with *Eyes;*

Spirituall, and *Soule-piercing* glances,
Whose pure and subtile lightning *Flyes*,
Home to the Heart, and sets the house on fire,
And melts it downe in sweet desire:

* * * * *

Delicious deaths, soft *exhalations*
Of *Soule*; deare and Divine *annihilations*.
    A thousand unknowne *Rites*
    Of Ioyes and *rarefy'd Delights* . . .

At this point one may feel that Crashaw, with the help of St. Teresa, has transcended the physical successfully. But alas, the poem is not over. Some forty lines remain, in which Crashaw proceeds to produce a Baroque disaster, as the building collapses around a faulty metaphor:

    Of all this store
Of blessings, and ten thousand more;
        (If when he come
He find the Heart from home)
        Doubtlesse he will unload
Himselfe some other where,
        And powre abroad
        His precious sweets,
On the faire soule whom first he meets.

* * * * *

O let the blissefull *Heart* hold fast
Her *Heav'nly Arme-full*, she shall tast,
At once ten thousand Paradices;
      She shall have Power,
      To rifle and Deflower,
The rich and Roseall spring of those rare sweets,
Which with a swelling bosome there she meets.

It is not only that the imagery, so strongly reminiscent of Carew, leads to unfortunate associations; a more serious problem is that Crashaw is making a false effort to convey the struggle for a spiritual love in terms of the sort of rivalry that might occur between two females in their competition for an earthly lover, the sort of rivalry that Cleopatra expresses in Shakespeare's play when she sees that her handmaiden has died first, and says that she must kill herself quickly lest Iras get there first and steal the kiss from Antony:

> If she first meete the Curled *Anthony*,
> Hee'l make demand of her, and spend that kisse
> Which is my heaven to have.

But in Christian love this argument rings false because, although earthly lovers may be so exclusively attached to one woman that they have no time or love for anyone else, the love of God is boundless, and the matter of spending God's love can hardly arise. It seems a wholly unworthy argument, clever and courtly and flattering, but suggestive in a way that spoils the poem's central movement, which seems to lie in proving that heavenly joys are superior to earthly joys and not in suggesting that God may not have enough love to go round.

One may wonder what principle of art may have seemed to make it possible and acceptable to pour out such an extravaganza in honor of God. An answer may lie in a statement by Robert Southwell, who lived in Rome during the 1580's and experienced the beginnings of Baroque art as they poured forth in architecture, painting, music, and poetry. Southwell gives us, in a work published in 1591, a statement of the central principle at work in Crashaw. It occurs in a popular prose treatise that he wrote on that favorite Baroque theme: *Marie Magdalens Funeral Teares*, where he says:

> Passions I allow, and loves I approve, onely I would wishe that men would alter their object and better their intent. For passions being sequels of our nature, and allotted unto us as the handmaides of reason: there can be no doubt, but that as their author is good, and their end godly: so ther use tempered in the meane, implieth no offence.[11]

Thus the figure of the Magdalen, who washed Christ's feet with her tears and wiped them with her hair and kissed his feet and anointed them with ointment, provides a perfect symbol for the Baroque era. The goodness of the physical, "tempered in the meane," that is, reformed and rightly seen and used, constitutes the essence of the Baroque attitude, and it is this attitude that Crashaw puts to the ultimate test, sometimes failing, sometimes succeeding. Thus in his most notorious poem, "The Weeper," he piles up image upon image in honor of Mary Magdalen's penitent tears, every stanza providing its own Baroque celebration of each tear.[12] It is not so much a poem as a series of experimental epigrams, testing how far a Baroque conceit can be carried. Some stanzas succeed, some fail abominably. Thus in some Baroque churches the decoration cloys and the basic structure is lost to sight; and without a basic underlying design no work of art can hope to function. In estimating Crashaw's success, then, we must watch for the line of control. This may sometimes be found in his most extravagant odes, as, for example, in his long ode "On the name of Jesus," which, as I have shown elsewhere,[13] follows the divisions of an ancient scale of meditation, and thus proceeds by rational articulation of parts within the mind of the speaker who participates at every moment in the vision. Similarly, his other very long ode, that on the Epiphany, achieves an ultimate success by two means. First, the whole poem takes the form of an immense Baroque oratorio, sung by the Three Kings in the presence of the Christ-child and his Mother; and secondly, it derives its imagery from one basic paradox: day in night. The light shining here from the new-born Son of God is the true light, and the old Sun-god which the heathen Magi used to serve is now eclipsed. From that idea of the true light shining in darkness the whole poem develops. The sun's eclipse at the Crucifixion is taken as yet another example of the light shining in darkness. And at the close the paradox is summed up by reference to the mystical theology of the dark night of the soul, familiar to us today through its use by T. S. Eliot in his *Four Quartets*, and for Crashaw, set forth in its classic form by the writer known as Dionysius the Areopagite.

Finally, we may perhaps sum up this approach to the Baroque by looking in some detail at one of Crashaw's nearly perfect pieces: the poem "An Hymne of the Nativity, sung as by the Shepheards." It is a poem that includes the imagery of the Cavalier love song along with the tradition of the pastoral dialogue, so often sung in courtly airs and madrigals and masques. It is sung by the shepherds, sometimes singing as a choric group, and sometimes as individuals with Vergilian names, Tityrus and Thyrsis, who also sing as a duo in some stanzas. The emphasis is on the theme of love, and the basic motif is drawn from the ancient tradition of the lover's dawn-song, as represented in a poem by Carew's friend and fellow Cavalier, Sir William Davenant:

The Lark now leaves his watry Nest
    And climbing, shakes his dewy Wings;
He takes this Window for the East;
    And to implore your Light, he Sings,
Awake, awake, the Morn will never rise,
Till she can dress her Beauty at your Eies.

The Merchant bowes unto the Seamans Star,
    The Ploughman from the Sun his Season takes;
But still the Lover wonders what they are,
    Who look for day before his Mistress wakes.
Awake, awake, break through your Vailes of Lawne!
Then draw your Curtains, and begin the Dawne.

Thus in Crashaw's poem the Chorus opens by mocking the earthly sun which is now replaced by a greater light:

Come we shepheards whose blest sight
    Hath met Loves noone, in Natures night,
Come lift we up our loftier song,
    And wake the *Sun* that lyes too long.

The true light no longer comes from the earthly sun; the central image is the light that comes from the eyes of the Son of Mary; and these eyes are celebrated in the terms of the Cavalier lyric:

It was thy day, *Sweet!* and did rise,
Not from the *East*, but from thine eyes.

And the Chorus at once repeats these thematic lines. Then Thyrsis sings:

Winter chid aloud, and sent
   The angry North to wage his wars,
The North forgot his fierce intent,
   And left perfumes instead of scars,
By those sweet eyes perswasive powers,
Where he mean't frost, he scatter'd flowers.

And the Chorus repeats the last two lines. Then Tityrus and Thyrsis together sing:

We saw thee in thy Balmey Nest,
   Bright *dawn* of our eternall *day*!
We saw thine eyes break from their *East*,
   And chace the trembling shades away.
We saw thee, and we blest the sight,
We saw thee by thine owne sweet light.

And forty lines later this stanza is repeated by both shepherds word for word. In this pattern of intertwining repetitions, sometimes with a single voice, sometimes with a double voice, sometimes with a full Chorus, we have a clear example of the Baroque method of building, not by exploring images, not by analyzing them, but by piling them up one upon another until a unity, a oneness of impression is created. Here that oneness is represented in a stanza that comes near the middle of the poem:

Proud world (said I) cease your contest,
   And let the mighty *Babe* alone,
The Phaenix builds the Phaenix' nest.
   Love's Architecture is all one.

In the posthumous edition of Crashaw's works the last line here is changed to read: "Love's Architecture is his own," possibly a revision made by Crashaw himself, possibly not. Whichever reading we take, the line provides a summary of Crashaw's poetical aims. Love's Architecture is all one because all nature is God's own and thus all physical nature may be included properly within the poem's building. So now we see moving toward the manger scene the snowflakes,

> Offering their whitest sheets of snow,
> To furnish the faire *Infant's* Bed:

while the Seraphim

> Their Rosie *Fleece* of *Fire* bestow,
> For well they now can spare their wings
> Since Heaven it selfe lyes here below:

and we may watch the new-born Babe reposing "his new-bloom'd *cheeke*" between his Mother's breasts:

> Sweet choice (said I!) no way but so
> Not to lye cold, yet sleep in snow.

We may do all this because the Incarnation, in Crashaw's view, has sanctified the physical, and made "all one," as the full Chorus explains in the opening stanza of the grand finale:

> Welcome all *wonders* in one sight!
> Eternitie shut in a span,
> Summer in winter, day in night,

> Heaven in Earth, and God in man;
> Great little one! Whose all embracing birth
> Lift's earth to heav'n, stoops heav'n to earth.

But the exaltation of this concept leads Crashaw then into two daring stanzas that show what a dangerous and unstable mixture the height of the Baroque may become:

> Welcom though not to gold nor silke,
>   To more than *Caesars* birthright is;
> Two Sister Seas of Virgin *Milke*,
>   With many a rarely temper'd Kisse
> That breath's at once both *Maide* & *Mother*,
> Warmes in the one, cooles in the other.
>
> She sings thy Teares a sleep, and dips
>   Her Kisses in thy weeping eye,
> She spreads the red leaves of thy lips,
>   That in their buds yet blushing lye.
> She 'gainst those Mother-Diamonds tries
> The points of her young Eagles eyes.

Someone, perhaps Crashaw himself, found the last of these two stanzas too much, and omitted it in the posthumous edition of 1652. These two stanzas of excess are quickly brought under control in the remainder of the poem, where Crashaw gracefully concludes with stanzas that express the love of God with all the art of the Cavalier, mingling pastoral and Petrarchan themes with the imagery of divine love:

> Yet when young *Aprill's* husband showers,
>   Shall blesse the fruitfull *Maia's* bed,
> Wee'l bring the first borne of her flowers,

ONE HUNDRED FORTY-SIX

To kisse thy feet, and crowne thy head.
To thee dread *Lamb*! whose love must keepe
The shepheards more than they their sheepe.

To thee meeke *Majestie*! soft King
    Of simple *Graces* and sweet *Loves*;
Each of us his *Lamb* will bring,
    Each his paire of Silver Doves,
Till burnt at last in fire of thy faire eyes,
Our selves become our owne best sacrifice.

IV

Andrew Marvell

The Mind's Happiness

Figure 30. Andrew Marvell: artist unknown. (*National Portrait Gallery, London; reproduced by kind permission of the Trustees of the National Portrait Gallery.*)

". . . he was also a typical and unmistakable mannerist by reason of what he betrays about himself and those whose portraits he paints, as well as by what he holds back and conceals behind the cold and severe expressions, the self-discipline that his sitters preserve in relation to the outside world, the 'armour of cool bearing' with which he protects them against the importunity of the inquisitive." (Hauser, *Mannerism*, I, 199; referring to Bronzino.)

IV

Andrew Marvell

The Mind's Happiness

Thomas Carew and George Herbert were almost exact contemporaries, members of the generation immediately following the great masters, Donne and Jonson; and both Carew and Herbert were, in their own ways, courtly poets, gathering up in their collected poems all the grace and wit of the world of song that made this era of English culture the greatest era of English music. Both were, in their own ways, courtiers: one, the courtier of the Queen of Love and Beauty, the earthly Venus; and the other, the courtier of Heavenly Love, addressing to his Lord the art that the Cavalier world addressed to Mortal Love. Both sang their songs in what they felt to be a realm of true security: Carew within the elegant Court of Charles I, and Herbert within the "perfect lineaments" of "The British Church":

> A fine aspect in fit aray,
> Neither too mean, nor yet too gay,

> Shows who is best.
> Outlandish looks may not compare:
> For all they either painted are,
> > Or else undrest.
>
> . . . . .
>
> But, dearest Mother, what those misse,
> The mean, thy praise and glorie is,
> > And long may be.
> Blessed be God, whose love it was
> To double-moat thee with his grace,
> > And none but thee.

Richard Crashaw and Andrew Marvell, in the next generation, knew very little of such security, since both lived through the era of those Civil Wars which shattered the established institutions of Church and State. For a time, during the 1630's, they shared a brief security in place and thought, at Cambridge University, where Marvell was a student at Trinity, and Crashaw, older by about nine years, lived down the road a bit as a fellow of Peterhouse. In 1637 their poems (in Latin and Greek) appeared together in a volume published at Cambridge honoring the birth of the Princess Anne. At this time both poets seem to have shared High Church tendencies: Marvell seems for a short time to have been converted to the Roman Catholic faith, as Crashaw was to be a few years later. But during the Civil Wars their ways utterly diverged. Crashaw, ousted from his post at Peterhouse because of his loyalty to King and Church, went abroad, embraced the Roman faith, and died at the shrine of Loreto in the same year that saw his King's death, in 1649. Marvell, after a period of mixed loyalties, mirrored in the ambiguities of his famous

"Horatian Ode," at last gave his full support to the cause of the Commonwealth and, in particular, to Oliver Cromwell. Both the personal and the poetical careers of Crashaw and of Marvell may be taken to symbolize two utterly different ways of resolving the fierce dilemmas of the day.

In this hiatus, a period when a new world of religious and political thought was in the process of violent formation, Marvell looks back upon the remains of courtly culture with attraction and regret, as we may see from the poem that he wrote "To his Noble Friend Mr. Richard Lovelace, upon his Poems"—a poem prefaced to Lovelace's volume of Cavalier poetry published in 1649:

> Our times are much degenerate from those
> Which your sweet Muse which your fair Fortune chose,
> And as complexions alter with the Climes,
> Our wits have drawne th'infection of our times.
> That candid Age no other way could tell
> To be ingenious, but by speaking well.
> Who best could prayse, had then the greatest prayse,
> Twas more esteemd to give, then weare the Bayes:
> Modest ambition studi'd only then,
> To honour not her selfe, but worthy men.
> These vertues now are banisht out of Towne,
> Our Civill Wars have lost the Civicke crowne.
> He highest builds, who with most Art destroys,
> And against others Fame his owne employs.
> I see the envious Caterpillar sit
> On the faire blossome of each growing wit.[1]

It is appropriate that Marvell should thus pay tribute to this poet, whose songs to Lucasta and to Althea represent the very essence of the Cavalier devotion to the Lady and to the King, expressed with all the art of courtly elegance. I say it is appropriate, because Marvell's poetry in many ways derives from the Mannerist art that we have seen in Carew and his fellow Cavaliers. Marvell has a love song, "The Match," addressed to a girl named Celia, praising her as Nature's treasury of "*Orientest* Colours," "Essences most pure," and "sweetest Perfumes." He has another song addressed to a fair Lady singing—one of Carew's favorite themes. He has of course that famous poem "To his Coy Mistress," following in the tradition represented by Carew's poem in the same meter: "To A. L. Perswasions to love." And he has three graceful pastoral dialogues where nymph and shepherd converse in singing repartee, as in two elegant songs by Carew. In many ways Marvell and Carew show the same inheritance of the European love-lyric, modified by an infusion of Donne's argumentative wit, and by Jonson's art of terse craftsmanship.

Yet at the same time Marvell inherits the tradition of the religious love-lyric brought to perfection by Herbert, and in his poem "The Coronet" we find him "Dismantling all the fragrant Towers" which he has used to adorn his shepherdess's head, in an effort to recreate the flowers of secular poetry as a tribute to his Savior. But he finds the serpent old entwined within his garland of devotion, for motives of fame and self-interest have made the attempted tribute impure; and so he prays:

> But thou who only could'st the Serpent tame,
> Either his slipp'ry knots at once untie,
> And disintangle all his winding Snare:
> Or shatter too with him my curious frame:

> And let these wither, so that he may die,
> Though set with Skill and chosen out with Care.
> That they, while Thou on both their Spoils dost tread,
> May crown thy Feet, that could not crown thy Head

It is, for the most part, a powerful effort in the devotional mode of Herbert, and yet in the last few lines the gnarled and intricate evolution of thought, with a tortured vagueness in the pronouns, creates an effect quite different from the characteristic serenity of Herbert's endings. We need to remember such conclusions in Herbert as these:

> Love is that liquour sweet and most divine,
> Which my God feels as bloud; but I, as wine.

> * * * * *

> But while I bustled, I might heare a friend
> Whisper, *How wide is all this long pretence!*
> *There is in love a sweetnesse readie penn'd:*
> *Copie out onely that, and save expense.*

> * * * * *

> But grones are quick, and full of wings,
>   And all their motions upward be,
> And ever as they mount, like larks they sing;
> The note is sad, yet musick for a King.

> * * * * *

> But as I rav'd and grew more fierce and wilde
>   At every word,
>   Me thoughts I heard one calling, *Child*!
>   And I reply'd, *My Lord.*

> * * * * *

> You must sit down, sayes Love, and taste my meat:
>   So I did sit and eat.

ONE HUNDRED FIFTY-FIVE

Far from achieving the goal of humility that Herbert implies in those endings, Marvell ends with an intricate flourish of wit that shows the pride of an indomitable intellect, saying in effect, "I pray all this in order that my poems, while you, God, tread both on Satan and on my poetry, may crown your feet, since they could not succeed in crowning your head." It is all too clever, and yet the whole ending functions in the poem to show that Marvell's Mannerist pride in his exquisite contrivance, his "curious frame," is still a part of his being.

So in Marvell the art of the Cavalier and the religious problems of the time converge in an uneasy alliance: set with skill, and chosen out with care, his poems contemplate, from various angles, the deepest issues of the age. We can feel these issues breaking through the fragile Mannerist artifact in one of his pastoral dialogues, entitled "Clorinda and Damon," where the pagan world of "Gather ye rosebuds" meets with the Christian sense of mortality and sin.[2] Clorinda, the shepherdess, invites Damon to come to her grassy meadow "Where *Flora* blazons all her pride." "The Grass I aim to feast thy Sheep," she explains, "The Flow'rs I for thy Temples keep." But Damon refuses, saying "Grass withers; and the Flow'rs too fade." But Clorinda insists upon her *carpe diem* theme, and so their interplay continues:

> C. Seize the short Joyes then, ere they vade.
>   Seest thou that unfrequented Cave?
> D. That den? C. Loves Shrine. D. But Virtue's Grave.
> C. In whose cool bosome we may lye
>   Safe from the Sun. D. not Heaven's Eye.
> C. Near this, a Fountaines liquid Bell
>   Tinkles within the concave Shell.

> *D.* Might a Soul bath there and be clean,
>   Or slake its Drought?   *C.* What is't you mean?

Clearly Damon has at last shattered Clorinda's complacency and has indeed shattered the pastoral scene with the fearful religious question. And Damon then goes on to explain how all is now changed for him, alluding to Christ under the conventional name of Pan, as in Milton's "Nativity Ode":

> *D.* These once had been enticing things,
>   *Clorinda,* Pastures, Caves, and Springs.
> *C.* And what late change?   *D.* The other day
>   *Pan* met me.   *C.* What did great *Pan* say?
> *D.* Words that transcend poor Shepherds skill,
>   But He ere since my Songs does fill:
>   And his Name swells my slender Oate.
> *C.* Sweet must *Pan* sound in *Damons* Note.
> *D.* *Clorinda's* voice might make it sweet.
> *C.* Who would not in *Pan's* Praises meet?
>
> Chorus.
>   Of *Pan* the flowry Pastures sing,
>   Caves eccho, and the Fountains ring.
>   Sing then while he doth us inspire;
>   For all the World is our *Pan's* Quire.

It is a happy reconciliation, but does Clorinda know what Damon means by Pan? Or does Damon know what Clorinda means by Pan? Is not this happy Chorus perhaps a mixed marriage of voices singing different gods? They are too much in love, it seems, to inquire exactly what each of them means by Pan. Here, within the poem's fragile artifice, the clash between Christian and Pagan threatens for a moment the destruction of both the Mannerist and the pastoral world; but the conflict is gaily and humorously healed.

A more dangerous threat is perhaps suggested in the "Dialogue between Thyrsis and Dorinda," where the shepherd Thyrsis describes his pastoral Elizium in such attractive terms that the naive nymph Dorinda suddenly falls sick of longing for it and suggests that they commit suicide in order to achieve such beauty in the after-life:

Dorinda. Ah me, ah me. (*Thyrsis.*) *Dorinda*, why do'st Cry?

Dorinda. I'm sick, I'm sick, and fain would dye:
    Convince me now, that this is true;
    By bidding, with mee, all adieu.

Thyrsis. I cannot live, without thee, I
    Will for thee, much more with thee dye.

Chorus. Then let us give *Carillo* charge o'th Sheep,
    And thou and I'le pick poppies and them steep
    In wine, and drink on't even till we weep,
    So shall we smoothly pass away in sleep.

Is Marvell suggesting that there may be a certain danger in the tendency of some religious sects to emphasize the joys of the future life? It would be going too far to say this: one might better say only that Marvell's curiously detached mind is here using the pastoral artifice to contemplate, at a considerable distance, a possible religious issue. This indeed might be said of all five of the poems of conflict that Marvell has cast into the dialogue form, poems that range from the purely spiritual to the purely carnal: from the spiritual victory of the Resolved Soul to the physical victory of the girl Thestylis, as she entices Ametas into her hay-mow, with the words:

> What you cannot constant hope
> Must be taken as you may.

And Ametas answers:

> Then let's both lay by our Rope,
> And go kiss within the Hay.

Even when the pastoral guard is dropped and the religious issues are joined head-on, one senses the curious detachment of Marvell's wit—curious in our meaning of the word and also in Marvell's own meaning of "exquisite," "elegant." Consider the poem that opens Marvell's collected poems of 1681, "A Dialogue between the Resolved Soul, and Created Pleasure," where Marvell deals with a central topic of the age, "the spiritual combat." The poem opens traditionally enough, with a familiar self-address, echoing the words of St. Paul in the Epistle to the Ephesians:

> Courage my Soul, now learn to wield
> The weight of thine immortal Shield.
> Close on thy Head thy Helmet bright.
> Ballance thy Sword against the Fight.

But as we read on we may wonder exactly what is happening, for the temptations of Pleasure seem so absurdly over-drawn:

> On these downy Pillows lye,
> Whose soft Plumes will thither fly:
> On these Roses strow'd so plain
> Lest one Leaf thy Side should strain.

And the Soul's answers seem so clipped and pat and almost smug:

> My gentler Rest is on a Thought,
> Conscious of doing what I ought.

* * * * *

> A Soul that knowes not to presume
> Is Heaven's and its own perfume.

So the whole poem comes to suggest an undercurrent of playful wit, reinforced and brought into the open by the Soul's pun on the word *Chordage* in answer to the temptation by the pleasure of music:

> Cease Tempter. None can chain a mind
> Whom this sweet Chordage cannot bind.

Is the poem a serious exercise in self-analysis, or is it rather a graceful exercise of lyric wit in the Jonsonian mode of terse craftsmanship?

So it is too with "A Dialogue between the Soul and Body," where Marvell seems to enjoy developing the ingenious play of wit by which Soul and Body, each speaking in monologue rather than dialogue, blindly denounce each other for causing each other's torment. Then the poet at the close cleverly suggests a resolution to the dilemma by adding four lines to the Body's stanza:

> What but a Soul could have the wit
> To build me up for Sin so fit?
> So Architects do square and hew,
> Green Trees that in the Forest grew.

ONE HUNDRED SIXTY

So Marvell suggests to us, perhaps, that there is some purpose in this conflict that the two antagonists do not grasp—that there is a higher architecture in which both Soul and Body are made according to the Architect's design.

This range of subject is characteristic of Marvell's lyric poetry, which ranges from the total celebration of the Soul in "On a Drop of Dew," to the total celebration of the claims of physical passion in "To his Coy Mistress." I say *total*. And yet both poems are written with their own kind of curious detachment. The poem "On a Drop of Dew" is a perfectly executed spiritual exercise. It presents first a clear visual image or similitude (a composition of place): the drop of dew lying on the purple flower; then the understanding proceeds to apply this image to the plight of the human Soul; and finally the power of the will draws forth a firm spiritual meaning. Thus the middle of the poem develops an Augustinian theme:

> So the Soul, that Drop, that Ray
> Of the clear Fountain of Eternal Day,
> Could it within the humane flow'r be seen,
> Remembring still its former height,
> Shuns the sweat leaves and blossoms green;
> And, recollecting its own Light,
> Does, in its pure and circling thoughts, express
> The greater Heaven in an Heaven less.

The word *recollecting* means not only "remembering," and "collecting together," or "concentrating the attention," but it also suggests the spiritual state of "recollection," in which the Soul is absorbed in religious contemplation, leading to the state of "illumination." It would seem that Marvell is tending toward an intense insight, reminiscent of the poetry of Henry Vaughan. But then the poem breaks away into a strange and unexpected dance: a neat series of lines paced with a Cavalier elegance:

> In how coy a Figure wound,
> Every way it turns away:
> So the World excluding round,
> Yet receiving in the Day.
> Dark beneath, but bright above:
> Here disdaining, there in Love,
> How loose and easie hence to go:
> How girt and ready to ascend.
> Moving but on a point below,
> It all about does upwards bend.
> Such did the Manna's sacred Dew destil;
> White, and intire, though congeal'd and chill.
> Congeal'd on Earth: but does, dissolving, run
> Into the Glories of th' Almighty Sun.

It is a perfect spiritual exercise—yes—but may one say that it is almost too perfect, too coolly contrived to create a deep religious feeling? The fact that Marvell also wrote a companion poem to this in Latin, using the same themes and images, may suggest the highly tentative, detached, and experimental nature of the approach to religious experience that Marvell is dealing with here. The Latin poem and the English poem work together to create the impression that this poet is contemplating here the possibility of engaging in religious contemplation, but has not re-created the experience of contemplation itself.

This poem, in its ebbing and flowing lines, suggests a cool and miniature version of one of Crashaw's passionate Odes or abundant Hymns, and indeed in one phrase, "its own Tear," the poem echoes a phrase used in Crashaw's poem to Mary Magdalene entitled "The Teare." One may fairly grasp the curiously detached and guarded quality of Marvell's religious poems by contrasting the Baroque exuberance of Crashaw's poems on the tears of the Magdalene with the cool and logical precision of Marvell's contribution to this literature of penitence—his poem "Eyes and Tears." Two stanzas from Crashaw's "The Weeper" will serve to make the point, if set against the opening and closing stanzas of Marvell's poem:

> 15 O cheekes! Beds of chast loves,
> By your own showers seasonably dash't,
>   Eyes! nests of milkie Doves
>   In your owne wells decently washt.
> O wit of love that thus could place,
> Fountaine and Garden in one face!

> 18 'Twas his well pointed dart
> That dig'd these wells, and drest this Vine,
>   And taught that wounded heart,
>   The way into those weeping Eyne,
> Vaine loves avant! Bold hands forbeare,
> The Lamb hath dipt his white foote here.

Now contrast these exuberant stanzas by Crashaw with the lucid, logical couplets of Marvell:

I.

How wisely Nature did decree,
With the same Eyes to weep and see!
That, having view'd the object vain,
They might be ready to complain.

II.

And, since the Self-deluding Sight,
In a false Angle takes each hight;
These Tears which better measure all,
Like wat'ry Lines and Plummets fall.

XII.

Ope then mine Eyes your double Sluice,
And practise so your noblest Use.
For others too can see, or sleep;
But only humane Eyes can weep.

XIII.

Now like two Clouds dissolving, drop,
And at each Tear in distance stop:
Now like two Fountains trickle down:
Now like two floods o'return and drown.

XIIII.

Thus let your Streams o'reflow your Springs,
Till Eyes and Tears be the same things:
And each the other's difference bears;
These weeping Eyes, those seeing Tears.

One may wonder whether this is a religious poem, or whether it is better called a witty Mannerist exercise on a religious theme, mingling cleverly the argued wit of Donne, the Baroque paradoxes of Crashaw, and the neat trim craftsmanship of Jonson. However this may be, the strict rational discipline of the poem seems ill suited to the far-flung nature of the imagery here, with the result that the images have an effect of being coolly contrived, not growing out of some inevitable problem or passion, as in the better poems of Donne or Crashaw.

We can see somewhat the same effect in Marvell's poem "The Definition of Love," where Marvell seems determined to outdo Donne in the ingenuity of his metaphysical conceits. It is Marvell's most Donne-like poem, and yet the effect of these terse, clipped, neat stanzas is ultimately quite unlike Donne.

I.

My Love is of a birth as rare
As 'tis for object strange and high.
It was begotten by despair
Upon Impossibility.

II.

Magnanimous Despair alone
Could show me so divine a thing,
Where feeble Hope could ne'r have flown
But vainly flapt its Tinsel Wing.

III.

And yet I quickly might arrive
Where my extended Soul is fixt,
But Fate does Iron wedges drive,
And alwaies crouds it self betwixt.

IV.

For Fate with jealous Eye does see
Two perfect Loves; nor lets them close:

Their union would her ruine be,
And her Tyrannick pow'r depose.

V.

And therefore her Decrees of Steel
Us as the distant Poles have plac'd,
(Though Loves whole World on us doth wheel)
Not by themselves to be embrac'd.

It has surely a measure of Donne's passionate reasoning in his pursuit of Love's philosophy, but the reasoning here is so coolly and deliberately done that the passion is carefully tamped down, and never threatens to escape as it so often does in Donne's anguish. So Marvell's "Definition" firmly ends:

VII.

As Lines so Loves *oblique* may well
Themselves in every Angle greet:
But ours so truly *Paralel*,
Though infinite can never meet.

VIII.

Therefore the Love which us doth bind,
But Fate so enviously debarrs,
Is the Conjunction of the Mind,
And Opposition of the Stars.

We remember how in Donne's "Valediction: forbidding Mourning," the geometrical conceit at the close had served as an expression of the strain and anguish that besets the parting of two true lovers, to whom separation is as a death. But here, although one admires the geometrical neatness of this conclusion, there is little sense of an underlying passion. Here again Marvell seems to be contemplating the feeling of what it might be like to be in love instead of creating the dramatic state of Love's actuality.

Even the famous "To his Coy Mistress" has, in its own way, a quality of detachment about it, for all its apparent urgency. We may feel this quality with particular force if we compare the poem with Robert Herrick's "Corinna's Going A-Maying." In Herrick's poem human love is represented as a part of the fruitful process of nature: love blooms and dies as nature dies, and the emphasis falls upon the beauty of the natural process. Herrick's poem is in tune with nature, but Marvell's poem is at war with nature; the speaker's wit seems to resent the shortness of life, which Herrick's poem sadly accepts. The speaker's tone toward his reserved and respectable young Lady shifts within each of the poem's three sections, moving from sly, humorous banter, to sardonic threats, and finally to something like a fierce desperation. The poem opens with mock politeness:

> Had we but World enough, and Time,
> This coyness Lady were no crime.
> We would sit down, and think which way
> To walk, and pass our long Loves Day.
> Thou by the *Indian Ganges* side
> Should'st Rubies find: I by the Tide
> Of *Humber* would complain.

For, Lady, he says, "you deserve this State," this pomp, this ceremony, "Nor would I love at lower rate," that is, lower estimation. But, he continues, we have very little time:

> And yonder all before us lye
> Desarts of vast Eternity.

And after a gruesome reminder of what the worms will do to her he ends with a sardonic tone of excessive politeness:

> The Grave's a fine and private place,
> But none I think do there embrace.

And then he swings quickly into his conclusion with inevitable logic:

> Now therefore, while the youthful hew
> Sits on thy skin like morning glew, . . .

(I keep the reading of the first edition instead of using the common emendation "dew," because it seems likely that "glew" is simply a variant spelling of the word "glow," and that what the poet is saying here is that the youthful color sitting on her skin is like the morning-glow of sunrise.)[3]

> And while thy willing Soul transpires
> At every pore with instant Fires,
> Now let us sport us while we may;
> And now, like am'rous birds of prey,
> Rather at once our Time devour,
> Than languish in his slow-chapt pow'r.
> Let us roll all our Strength, and all
> Our sweetness, up into one Ball:
> And tear our Pleasures with rough strife,
> Thorough the Iron gates of Life.
> Thus, though we cannot make our Sun
> Stand still, yet we will make him run.

"We cannot make our Sun/Stand still," like Joshua or like Zeus when he seduced Alcmene and produced Heracles, but we can at least eat up our time with devouring strife. But what kind of pleasure is this? Marvell has consumed all the natural beauty out of the experience of human love. Is he suggesting that perhaps the rosebud-philosophy is self-destructive, corrosive, and ultimately empty? Is this a love poem at all? Is it not rather a poem about man's fear of Time?

I hope my emphasis on Marvell's detachment, his concern for style, his coolly crafted art, has not served to suggest that I think Marvell's poems are themselves rather empty. This is the problem that one often faces in dealing with Mannerist art. Is the manner mere imitation, lacking any depth or real significance, or is the manner a way of guarding the mind's uncertainty in its quest for ultimate values? Does the elegance of style stand as a mask before some inner tension? Or does it serve as a defense against the revelation of some intimate, impossible ideal? In asking this question I am moving away from the earlier and simpler account of Mannerism that I used in discussing the poetry of Carew. I am moving away from John Shearman's emphasis on *style* as the prime criterion, and moving on into the deeper and more inclusive account of Mannerism set forth in the splendid study of Arnold Hauser.[4] The greatness of Hauser's conception of Mannerism lies in the fact that he can include the spiritual, the intellectual, the playful, the poignant, and the elegant all within one compelling account of a great artistic movement, for which, I am convinced, Andrew Marvell stands as a prime English representative. For Marvell has the qualities that Hauser finds at the heart of Mannerism. "A certain piquancy, a predilection for the subtle, the strange, the over-strained, the abstruse and yet stimulating, the pungent, the bold, and the challenging, are characteristic of mannerist art in all its phases," says Hauser. And he adds, "It is often this piquancy —a playful or compulsive deviation from the normal, an affected, frisky quality, or a tormented grimace—that first betrays the mannerist nature of a work. The virtuosity that is always displayed contributes greatly to this piquancy."[5] But underneath this playfulness or piquancy Hauser finds a quality that seems to me to lie at the very center of Marvell's vision: an intellectualized view of existence that makes it possible to maintain all the conflicting elements of life within a flexible yet highly regulated vision:

> The conflict expresses the conflict of life itself and the ambivalence of all human attitudes; in short, it expresses the dialectical principle that underlies the whole of the mannerist outlook. This is based, not merely on the conflicting nature of occasional experience, but on the permanent ambiguity of all things, great and small, and on the impossibility of attaining certainty about anything. All the products of the mind must therefore show that we live in a world of irreducible tensions and mutually exclusive and yet inter-connected opposites. For nothing in this world exists absolutely, the opposite of every reality is also real and true. Everything is expressed in extremes opposed to other extremes, and it is only by this paradoxical pairing of opposites that meaningful statement is possible. This paradoxical approach does not signify, however, that each statement is the retraction of the last, but that truth inherently has two sides, that reality is Janus-faced, and that adherence to truth and reality involves the avoidance of all over-simplification and comprehending things in their complexity.[6]

ONE HUNDRED SEVENTY

Thus Marvell, in 1650, could write that great "Horatian Ode" in which he carefully weighs the virtues of the King and of Cromwell, seeing the poignancy of one and the power of the other, including both within an intellectual vision that is able to choose, at the end, the side of destiny, without ceasing to regret the necessity of the destruction of ancient institutions. And alongside the paradoxical vision of that Ode, Marvell could then place, perhaps only a few years later, his great poem "The Garden," in which the joys of intellectual peace are praised as the center of existence. Thus, in the famous central stanzas of "The Garden," the speaker finds his harmony, both physical and mental, in an easy relationship with the created universe:

> What wond'rous Life in this I lead!
> Ripe Apples drop about my head;
> The Luscious Clusters of the Vine
> Upon my Mouth do crush their Wine;
> The Nectaren, and curious Peach,
> Into my hands themselves do reach;
> Stumbling on Melons, as I pass,
> Insnar'd with Flow'rs, I fall on Grass.

And while the body enjoys that fortunate fall, the mind, withdrawing from these lesser (physical) pleasures, discovers and creates its own happiness:

> Mean while the Mind, from pleasure less,
> Withdraws into its happiness:
> The Mind, that Ocean where each kind
> Does streight its own resemblance find;

> Yet it creates, transcending these,
> Far other Worlds, and other Seas;
> Annihilating all that's made
> To a green Thought in a green Shade.

The mind, that is to say, contains within itself the images drawn from the outer world; yet it creates, transcending these, worlds of the human imagination, which arise from the creative and unifying power that Marvell suggests in the word *annihilating*. There is an allusion here to the mystical usage of the word, as Crashaw has used it when he speaks of "soft *exhalations*/Of *Soule;* deare and Divine *annihilations*."[7] But of course the word is used by Marvell in a characteristically playful sense, for in mystical annihilation all sensory images are destroyed and the soul ascends into the realm of pure spirit. In "The Garden" the process of annihilation blends the greenness of nature with the abstract purity of thought. And even as the soul ascends upward in Marvell's poem, thought remains still allied with sensory things, as we may see from the next stanza, where the soul does not leave the physical, but remains connected with the body through the tree:

> Here at the Fountains sliding foot,
> Or at some Fruit-trees mossy root,
> Casting the Bodies Vest aside,
> My Soul into the boughs does glide:
> There like a Bird it sits, and sings,
> Then whets, and combs its silver Wings;
> And, till prepar'd for longer flight,
> Waves in its Plumes the various Light.

Then in the next stanza Marvell's quiet humor reminds us that the mind is still within the world of man, as he humorously recalls Adam's happy state, before Eve, the cause of all his woes, was created as an help meet for him:

> Such was that happy Garden-state,
> While Man there walk'd without a Mate:
> After a Place so pure, and sweet,
> What other Help could yet be meet!
> But 'twas beyond a Mortal's share
> To wander solitary there:
> Two Paradises 'twere in one
> To live in Paradise alone.

And finally, in Stanza IX, perhaps a symbol of numerical perfection, Marvell returns gently and easily into the world of time as he presents his image of the floral sun-dial, and concludes:

> How could such sweet and wholsome Hours
> Be reckon'd but with herbs and flow'rs!

Less wholsome hours, no doubt, await the speaker in the outer world, but the mind's happiness remains within, a sure retreat that underlies the varied explorations conveyed in all his other poems.

As at the end of a long avenue, one catches a distant glimpse of this ideal in the poem that might be regarded as the most obviously Mannerist of all Marvell's works, the one entitled "The Gallery," which Jean Hagstrum has suggested[8] must be influenced by the famous volume of Marino's poetry entitled *La Galeria*, where Marino bases his poetry upon various paintings and sculptures, or gives in similar terms imaginary portraits of his own. Following this mode of action Marvell here presents to us the art gallery of his soul, hung, he says, with various portraits of his Lady:

> *Clora* come view my Soul, and tell
> Whether I have contriv'd it well.

It opens with the characteristic gesture of all Mannerist art: he urges the viewer to watch closely and to judge whether the work is well "contrived." Here in his Soul, he says, she is first painted in the dress "Of an Inhumane Murtheress," tormenting her lover with "Black Eyes, red Lips, and curled Hair." Then on the other side he says she is drawn as a great Renaissance nude:

> Like to *Aurora* in the Dawn;
> When in the East she slumb'ring lyes,
> And stretches out her milky Thighs;

In the next painting she is shown as an "Enchantress," and in the next she sits afloat "Like *Venus* in her pearly Boat," as in some painting by a Botticelli. "These Pictures and a thousand more," he says, form in his Soul "a Collection choicer far/Then or *White-hall's*, or *Mantua's* were." That is to say, choicer than King Charles's collection in his palace at Whitehall, or the collection of the Duke of Mantua which Charles had purchased. Then he concludes with a significant movement of the mind toward a scene that forms the deep and inner center of all Marvell's poetry, in the close revealing the ideal that underlies his art:

> But, of these Pictures and the rest,
> That at the Entrance likes me best:

> Where the same Posture, and the Look
> Remains, with which I first was took.
> A tender Shepherdess, whose Hair
> Hangs loosely playing in the Air,
> Transplanting Flow'rs from the green Hill,
> To crown her Head, and Bosome fill.

The memory of the green hill, the pastoral landscape, the effort to regain the vision of a lost garden—this is the deep theme of Marvell's poetry, the center of security which lies within his mannered, stylish surface, which is in fact guarded and treasured within that surface. Here Marvell joins the central quest of many of the most significant writers of this mid-century era of turmoil. On the one side he joins the pagan Paradise of Robert Herrick, with the many "fresh and fragrant" girls that live like flowers and live with flowers throughout the *Hesperides*. And on the other side he joins Henry Vaughan, Thomas Traherne, and John Milton in *Paradise Lost*—all in their own ways keeping a kindred image of a pastoral Paradise before their inner eyes.[9] And other writers too, notably Izaak Walton, in his *Compleat Angler*, where he gives us a georgic pastoral,[10] in which the art of fishing provides the setting for a truly religious retreat into an inner Paradise, where man is at one with Nature and with God.

The meaning of this central quest of the mid-century may be suggested in Marvell's small poem "Bermudas," where the longing for the earthly Paradise represents a search for peace amidst the cruel controversies of the age, the ravaging of England by the Civil Wars, the efforts at repressive persecution by whichever side was temporarily dominant in the religious conflicts of the day. Here we have the imagined song of the Puritan refugees from King Charles's High Church policy, refugees who found peace in the remote Bermudas, as others did in Massachusetts:

> What should we do but sing his Praise
> That led us through the watry Maze,
> Unto an Isle so long unknown,
> And yet far kinder than our own?
> Where he the huge Sea-Monsters wracks,
> That lift the Deep upon their Backs.
> He lands us on a grassy Stage;
> Safe from the Storms, and Prelat's rage.
> He gave us this eternal Spring,
> Which here enamells every thing;
> And sends the Fowl's to us in care,
> On daily Visits through the Air.
> He hangs in shades the Orange bright,
> Like golden Lamps in a green Night.
>
>   *   *   *   *   *
>
> And in these Rocks for us did frame
> A Temple, where to sound his Name.
> Oh let our Voice his Praise exalt,
> Till it arrive at Heavens Vault:

It is a Puritan Psalm of Thanksgiving in praise of the Creator's bounty and goodness, by which they have been enabled to reach a place amid these remote rocks to praise their Lord. One should note that, as in *Paradise Lost*, the meaning of Paradise lies in the human response to nature and not in the beauties of nature itself. The physical imagery of nature's beauty is meaningless unless man lives in a state of joyful harmony, with gratitude toward the Creator. Or rather one might say that outer nature has no beauty except as man receives it gratefully within the mind.

Such an attitude toward the meaning of Eden we may see developed in Marvell's symbol of the Mower, whose pastoral existence has been destroyed by love of his particular Eve, named Juliana. In "The Mower to the Glo-Worms" we see that these beneficent works of nature now shine in vain,

> Since *Juliana* here is come,
> For She my Mind hath so displac'd
> That I shall never find my home.

And he continues in "The Mower's Song":

> My Mind was once the true survey
> Of all these Medows fresh and gay:
> And in the greenness of the Grass
> Did see its Hopes as in a Glass;
> When *Juliana* came, and She
> What I do to the Grass, does to my Thoughts and Me.

But now he reproaches the meadows for growing in luxuriance when he is pining away with frustrated love. They ought, he feels, to be fading away like him, but they have instead disloyally forsaken him and have gone their own way. The pastoral condition, we see, depends upon man's state of mind:[11] it is by this that nature becomes either a Paradise or a ruin. Externally, the Mower as he mows is simply doing his usual job: to reap crops, to clear the land for further crops. This is his natural function. But now his function is perverted by sorrow and pain: and so in "Damon the Mower" he

sees nature falsely and recklessly seeks revenge upon it for a
state of mind which creates his own fall and ruin:

> While thus he threw his Elbow round,
> Depopulating all the Ground,
> And, with his whistling Sythe, does cut
> Each stroke between the Earth and Root,
> The edged Stele by careless chance
> Did into his own Ankle glance;
> And there among the Grass fell down,
> By his own Sythe, the Mower mown.

But his own self-destruction is only a symbol of man's
general corruption of these natural harmonies, as the Mower
declares in his tirade against artificial gardens:

> Luxurious Man, to bring his Vice in use,
>   Did after him the World seduce:
> And from the fields the Flow'rs and Plants allure,
>   Where Nature was most plain and pure.
> He first enclos'd within the Gardens square
>   A dead and standing pool of Air:
> And a more luscious Earth for them did knead,
>   Which stupifi'd them while it fed.
>
> *   *   *   *   *
>
> 'Tis all enforc'd; the Fountain and the Grot;
>   While the sweet Fields do lye forgot:
> Where willing Nature does to all dispence
>   A wild and fragrant Innocence:
> And *Fauns* and *Faryes* do the Meadows till,
>   More by their presence then their skill.
> Their Statues polish'd by some ancient hand,
>   May to adorn the Gardens stand:

> But howso'ere the Figures do excel,
> The *Gods* themselves with us do dwell.

Marvell has in his poetry many other symbols of this kind of "fragrant Innocence," always threatened or overcome by some corruption. Thus even the small girl whom he celebrates in "The Picture of little T. C. in a Prospect of Flowers" must grow up, damage mankind by her beauty, and then die, despite her Eden-like beginning:

> See with what simplicity
> This Nimph begins her golden daies!
> In the green Grass she loves to lie,
> And there with her fair Aspect tames
> The Wilder flow'rs, and gives them names:
> But only with the Roses playes;
> > And them does tell
> What Colour best becomes them, and what Smell.

Like Adam she names the other creatures, and as with Adam the world of mortality awaits her, as Marvell makes plain in the last stanza:

> But O young beauty of the Woods,
> Whom Nature courts with fruits and flow'rs,
> Gather the Flow'rs, but spare the Buds;
> Lest *Flora* angry at thy crime,
> To kill her Infants in their prime,
> Do quickly make th'Example Yours;
> > And, ere we see,
> Nip in the blossome all our hopes and Thee.

Thus in one way or another she is threatened with the fate that has overtaken the innocent Nymph who complains for the death of her fawn in the enigmatic, fascinating poem that has attracted so much attention by critics and scholars of this century, beginning with Eliot's remark in his fine essay on Marvell:

> Marvell takes a slight affair, the feeling of a girl for her pet, and gives it a connexion with that inexhaustible and terrible nebula of emotion which surrounds all our exact and practical passions and mingles with them.[12]

Everyone agrees that the poem must have some symbolic significance—but hardly anyone agrees on what this is.[13] It seems to have some local significance for the English Civil Wars in its opening lines:

> The wanton Troopers riding by
> Have shot my Faun and it will dye.

The Troopers are the marauding cavalrymen of the Civil Wars, on both sides, for the word "Troopers" was a general term: one could speak of Cromwell's Troopers or of Prince Rupert's Troopers.[14] In either case they are wanton in their unruly lack of discipline, in their carelessness of others' rights. But what does the fawn represent? Some have found in him the symbolism of Christ, since the Nymph says

> There is not such another in
> The World, to offer for their Sin.

And a little later she echoes the phrase of Jeremiah (2:2) when she says that the fawn "seem'd to bless/Its self in me." These religious implications are enforced by the garden imagery that follows a little later, imagery that clearly echoes the Song of Solomon, particularly the verses:

> My beloved is gone down into his garden,
> to the beds of spices, to feed in the gardens,
> and to gather lilies.
>
> I am my beloved's, and my beloved is mine:
> he feedeth among the lilies.   (6:2–3)

So we find the fawn in a garden of roses and lilies, and the Nymph says:

> Among the beds of Lillyes, I
> Have sought it oft, where it should lye;

and she finds the fawn feeding upon the roses. The purity of the fawn, and the fact that it dies "as calmely as a Saint," have led some to see in the poem profound Christian implications. But on the other hand the pagan and classical implications are equally strong: similar stories about the deaths of pet deer occur in Vergil and Ovid;[15] the Nymph's tears will be placed "in *Diana's* Shrine," and the fawn will go to a pagan Elizium. The Nymph imagines herself turned into a statue like that of Niobe, forever weeping. Furthermore, she is not weeping just for her pet deer, but also for the faithless man who gave him to her: "unconstant *Sylvio*," a seducer who talks the old Petrarchan sweet talk:

> Said He, look how your Huntsman here
> Hath taught a Faun to hunt his *Dear*.

The point is that the fawn and the Nymph are both destroyed by "false and cruel men," and the whole poem thus
becomes a lament for lost innocence, whether destroyed by
war or by human infidelity, whether it exists in pagan or in
Christian story. Wanton men kill the very innocence that
prays for their salvation.

The end of innocence, the destruction of the pastoral garden, and the search for their recovery in the mind—these are
Marvell's deepest themes. His abrasive political satires and his
great political poems on Cromwell have all been made possible
by the existence of the interior retreat which he describes in
the latter half of his long pastoral poem, "Upon Appleton
House." Here in the fourth section of that poem (which is
clearly divisible into six main parts: the House, the History,
the Garden, the Meadow, the Wood, and the Vision of Maria)
the speaker's mind plays over the meadow, inventing from its
images a fanciful entertainment, a theatrical presentation of
worldly scenes, a playful nightmare, where at first man seems
to drown in the abyss of greenness:

> To see Men through this Meadow Dive,
> We wonder how they rise alive.

It is a world of flux and change, mingling images of the ideal
and the actual, creating a "scene" that seems to change by
some mechanical devices such as were used by Inigo Jones in
the Court entertainments that we have discussed:

> No Scene that turns with Engines strange
> Does oftner then these Meadows change.
> For when the Sun the Grass hath vext,
> The tawny Mowers enter next;

Enter, that is, like theatrical performers. And as they mow the meadows we have suggestions of blood and death as the edge of the scythe cuts into the peaceful birds nesting on the ground. Then another change brings in a battle scene, intricately "wrought":

> The Mower now commands the Field;
> In whose new Traverse seemeth wrought
> A Camp of Battail newly fought:
> Where, as the Meads with Hay, the Plain
> Lyes quilted ore with Bodies slain:
> The Women that with forks it fling,
> Do represent the Pillaging.

The word "traverse" means literally the action of the mowers as they make their ways back and forth across the field; but "traverse" in the language of Marvell's time could also mean a curtain. It is upon this curtain, as though it were a tapestry, that the "Camp of Battail" is "wrought," "Camp" being used here in the old sense of *champ*, that is, a field of battle, as the word "Plain" in the next line makes clear. In this curiously inverted analogy, Marvell is saying that as on some great curtain, the Meads are quilted over with fallen hay just as on a battlefield the plain "Lyes quilted ore with Bodies slain"—the word "quilted," of course, carrying on the imagery of handicraft and artifact. At the same time it is relevant to feel something of the military sense of the word "traverse," which means, of course, a barrier in a fortification. Finally, the word "represent" in the last line carries on the imagery of theater or tapestry.

In spite of these threats, however, it is all only a harmless pastoral scene, as the next stanza tells us:

> And now the careless Victors play,
> Dancing the Triumphs of the Hay;

(With a pun on the word *hay*, meaning also a rustic dance)

> Where every Mowers wholesome Heat
> Smells like an *Alexanders sweat*.
> Their Females fragrant as the Mead
> Which they in *Fairy Circles* tread:
> When at their Dances End they kiss,
> Their new-made Hay not sweeter is.

Pastoral, yes, but as we continue reading we find that further hints of the world of time and death are brought in, as the hay suggests to the poet a resemblance to Pyramids on the "*Desert Memphis Sand*," and also to the Roman camps which rise "In Hills for Soldiers Obsequies." But again the scene changes as the next stanza shows:

> This *Scene* again withdrawing brings
> A new and empty Face of things;
> A levell'd space, as smooth and plain,
> As Clothes for *Lilly* strecht to stain.

The reference to the paintings of Sir Peter Lely maintains the vision seen through the world of art forms, but soon the actual world comes in upon this levelled space as the poet mentions the bull-ring at Madrid, or sees in the field a pattern for "the *Levellers*," that radical left-wing sect which threatened the hierarchies of society in Marvell's day.

Thus throughout the contemplation of the meadow a conflict is set up between the imagery of art forms and the actuality of war and death, as though the pastoral scene were living on the verge of destruction—and then suddenly it is destroyed, as a flood overtakes this "painted World":

> Then, to conclude these pleasant Acts,
> *Denton* sets ope its *Cataracts*;
> And makes the Meadow truly be
> (What it but seem'd before) a Sea.

In the midst of this comical catastrophe, while the whole world turns topsy-turvy, we discover that behind the Mannerist facade of art lies something deeper:

> But I, retiring from the Flood,
> Take Sanctuary in the Wood;
> And, while it lasts, my self imbark
> In this yet green, yet growing Ark;

It is the ark of the contemplative mind, where the poet (wittily, with a play on the word "imbark") finds his refuge; although even here nature is fallen, as the woodpecker knows, acting as moral judge of the world within the wood:

> He walks still upright from the Root,
> Meas'ring the Timber with his Foot;
> And all the way, to keep it clean,
> Doth from the Bark the Wood-moths glean.

He, with his Beak, examines well
Which fit to stand and which to fell.

The good he numbers up, and hacks;
As if he mark'd them with the Ax.
But where he, tinkling with his Beak,
Does find the hollow Oak to speak,
That for his building he designs,
And through the tainted Side he mines.
Who could have thought the *tallest Oak*
Should fall by such a *feeble Strok'*!

Nor would it, had the Tree not fed
A *Traitor-worm*, within it bred.
(As first our *Flesh* corrupt within
Tempts impotent and bashful *Sin*.)

The whole passage, particularly the witty inversion of the relationship between flesh and sin in the last two lines, gives a clear instance of Marvell's unique tone of serious wit, of playful morality, the tone that Eliot long ago gave its classic description, when he spoke of Marvell's wit as maintaining "this alliance of levity and seriousness (by which the seriousness is intensified)."[16] Then Marvell sums up this attitude in two lines:

Thus I, *easie Philosopher*,
Among the *Birds* and *Trees* confer:

Easie is the right word, meaning, at ease, detached from care, free from pain, annoyance, or burden, free from pressure or hurry. The poet's mind is wholly in harmony with nature, and as he reads thus "in *Natures mystick Book*" the artifice of the theater is turned into the robes of nature herself as the speaker is garbed with a costume that reminds one of some Court Masquer:

> And see how Chance's better Wit
> Could with a Mask my studies hit!
> The Oak-Leaves me embroyder all,
> Between which Caterpillars crawl:
> And Ivy, with familiar trails,
> Me licks, and clasps, and curles, and hales.
> Under this *antick Cope* I move
> Like some great *Prelate of the Grove,*

(*Antick:* meaning both "fantastic," as in a masque, and "antique.")

This then is the center of the mind's security, as the poet lives in physical and mental harmony:

> How safe, methinks, and strong, behind
> These Trees have I incamp'd my Mind;
> Where Beauty, aiming at the Heart,
> Bends in some Tree its useless Dart;
> And where the World no certain Shot
> Can make, or me it toucheth not.
> But I on it securely play,
> And gaul its Horsemen all the Day.

(A foreshadowing of the time when Marvell's satires will play their bitter wit against the leaders of Charles II's regime.) And finally, this natural harmony reaches its climax in a pastoral ecstasy, as the speaker implies his realization that he cannot stay forever in this sanctuary, through his hyperbolic imagery of joyous bondage and happy crucifixion:

ONE HUNDRED EIGHTY-SEVEN

Bind me ye *Woodbines* in your 'twines,
Curle me about ye gadding *Vines*,
And Oh so close your Circles lace,
That I may never leave this Place:
But, lest your Fetters prove too weak,
Ere I your Silken Bondage break,
Do you, *O Brambles*, chain me too,
And courteous *Briars* nail me through.

Now, gradually, we become aware that in the poet's vision
the outer world itself has undergone a magical transformation:

For now the Waves are fal'n and dry'd,
And now the Meadows fresher dy'd;
Whose Grass, with moister colour dasht,
Seems as green Silks but newly washt.

In this renewed world there comes to complete the scene the
perfection of human beauty and virtue in the figure of the
young Fairfax daughter, Marvell's student, who by a fortunate coincidence is named Mary. Calling her by the name
Maria, Marvell universalizes the young girl into a figure of the
highest humanity, and declares, through hyperbolic rhetoric,
that this virtuous human beauty is necessary to unify and
perfect the created world:

'Tis *She* that to these Gardens gave
That wondrous Beauty which they have;
She streightness on the Woods bestows;
To *Her* the Meadow sweetness owes;
Nothing could make the River be

> So Chrystal-pure but only *She*;
> *She* yet more Pure, Sweet, Streight, and Fair,
> Then Gardens, Woods, Meads, Rivers are.

But as he recapitulates the scenes of his poem he insists that human nature must rise above even these superb physical beauties, for the perfection of human nature lies in heavenly wisdom.

> For *She*, to higher Beauties rais'd,
> Disdains to be for lesser prais'd.
> *She* counts her Beauty to converse
> In all the Languages as *hers*;
> Nor yet in those *her self* imployes
> But for the *Wisdome*, not the *Noyse*;
> Nor yet that *Wisdome* would affect,
> But as 'tis *Heavens Dialect.*

Grasping thus in imagination the vision of an ideal harmony of the natural and the human, Marvell is able to see the whole estate as an image of interior restoration:

> 'Tis not, what once it was, the *World*;
> But a rude heap together hurl'd;
> All negligently overthrown,
> Gulfes, Deserts, Precipices, Stone.
> Your lesser *World* contains the same.
> But in more decent Order tame;
> *You Heaven's Center, Nature's Lap.*
> *And Paradice's only Map.*

The words apply to the estate, to Mary, and to the inner condition of the speaker himself. At the close of this long, pastoral-meditative work, Marvell has attained an ideal vision by creating, for a time, a vision of nature seen through the lens of art, with an effect of "dream-like sublimation or high-spirited play," in the words of Arnold Hauser.[17] Thus Marvell's "Upon Appleton House" may be said to represent, better than any other English poem, the "revolution in sensibility" which Hauser has found in Mannerism:

> The essential to be borne in mind is the heterogeneous and contradictory nature of reality as seen by mannerism in general. In mannerist art things are seen alternately in concrete and abstract form, now as substantial, now as insubstantial, and now one and now the other aspect is uppermost. Appearance and reality, truth and illusion are inextricably interwoven, and we live in a borderland of wakefulness and dream, knowledge and intuition, sensuous and ideal awareness; it is this that matters, not precise determination of the boundaries between the various provinces of being. The point is the difference between the two worlds we belong to, between which there is no making any final and exclusive choice . . .[18]

Notes

Notes

NOTES FOR JOHN DONNE

1. Edmund Gosse, *The Life and Letters of John Donne*, 2 vols. (London, Heinemann, 1899), II, 360–63.

2. See John Bryson, "Lost Portrait of Donne," *Times* (London), 13 Oct. 1959, pp. 13, 15. Also Helen Gardner, "The Marshall Engraving and the Lothian Portrait," in her edition of Donne's *Elegies and Songs and Sonnets* (Oxford, Clarendon Press, 1965), Appendix E. I am indebted to both of these essays for some of the details concerning Donne's portraits. See also the "Iconography" in Geoffrey Keynes, *A Bibliography of Dr. John Donne*, 3rd edn. (Cambridge University Press, 1958), pp. 265–68.

3. For evidence that the wide-brimmed hat and folded arms are signs of the melancholy lover see Bryson and Gardner (above, n.2); also Roy Strong, "The Elizabethan Malady: Melancholy in Elizabethan and Jacobean Portraiture," *Apollo*, 79 (April, 1964), pp. 264–69. One should add the striking analogy with Donne's posture and costume found in Inigo Jones's drawing of a melancholy lover for Ben Jonson's masque *Loves Triumph through Callipolis* (1631); see the description by Percy Simpson and C. F. Bell, *Designs by Inigo Jones for Masques & Plays at Court* (Oxford, 1924), Walpole Society, vol. 12, p. 55,

no. 77; this is reproduced in Enid Welsford, *The Court Masque* (Cambridge University Press, 1927), facing p. 216.

4. Bryson (above, n. 2) quotes the Latin passage from the *Breviary*, but locates it in the third Collect for Evening Prayer; this is correct for the English service, but the Latin source is in the service for Compline: see F. E. Brightman, *The English Rite*, 2nd edn., 2 vols. (London, 1921), I, 164; and *Portiforium seu Breviarium ad usum ecclesie Sarisburiensis . . . Pars Hyemalis* (Paris, Regnault, 1554), "Preces completorii," f. 69v. See also Ps. 17:29: "Quoniam tu illuminas lucernam meam, Domine: Deus meus, illumina tenebras meas;" and 2 Kings 22:29: "et tu, Domine, illuminabis tenebras meas."

5. Izaak Walton, *Lives*, World's Classics edn. (Oxford University Press, 1927), p. 78.

6. Bryson's remark concerning the Lothian portrait (above, n. 2) is most astute: "Nor is it without interest that he should to the end of his life have preserved this image of his youthful self. The picture with its inscription must have been hanging in a neighbouring room in the Deanery when that 'choice painter' was summoned to the death-bed to make the last terrible portrait of the poet in his shroud."

7. Quotations from Donne's poetry are given according to the text of the new Clarendon Press edition of Donne: *Divine Poems*, ed. Helen Gardner, 1952; *Elegies and Songs and Sonnets*, ed. Helen Gardner, 1965; *Satires, Epigrams, and Verse Letters*, ed. W. Milgate, 1967. I am throughout this lecture indebted to the admirable introductions and commentaries in these volumes.

8. Walton, *Lives*, p. 37.

9. See Abraham Van der Doort, *Catalogue of the Collections of Charles I*, ed. Oliver Millar (Glasgow, 1960), Walpole Society, vol. 37, p. 89, item 71: "And the other of your Majesty's pictures was done by Titian, being our Lady and Christ and St. John half figures as big as the life, which was placed in your Majesty's middle privy lodging room being in a carved gilded frame, and was given heretofore to your Majesty by my lord of Carlisle who had it of Doctor Donne; painted upon the right

light." (I have here modernized the text.) This may be the item mentioned in the second paragraph of my previous quotation from Donne's will: see W. Milgate, "Dr. Donne's Art Gallery," *Notes and Queries*, 194 (1949), pp. 318–19. Like Milgate, I have not been able to identify this painting.

10. See *The Age of the Renaissance*, ed. Denys Hay (New York, McGraw-Hill, 1967), p. 132; a superb color-reproduction of the painting is given here, along with the explanation, forming part of Roberto Weiss's chapter, "The New Learning." I have followed Weiss in most of the details.

11. Some good manuscripts of Donne read "Ragged" instead of "Cragged" in line 80 of Satire III. Milgate regards "Ragged" as an authentic reading of an earlier version of this line: see his edition of the *Satires*, p. 146.

12. See the interesting analysis of this poem by Helen Gardner, *The Business of Criticism* (Oxford, Clarendon Press, 1959), pp. 62–75.

13. *Poems of John Donne*, ed. Herbert J. C. Grierson, 2 vols. (Oxford, Clarendon Press, 1912), II, 31. *Elegies and Songs and Sonnets*, ed. Gardner, p. 207.

14. Izaak Walton says the poem was given by Donne to his wife when he went abroad with Sir Robert Drury, i.e., in 1611 (*Lives*, p. 42). The point is not essential, though the situation seems plausible to me. But see Miss Gardner's contrary arguments in her edition of the *Elegies and Songs and Sonnets*, p. xxix.

15. See George Williamson, "The Convention of *The Extasie*," in his *Seventeenth Century Contexts* (University of Chicago Press, 1961), pp. 63–77.

16. See the illuminating account of the poem's relation to the *Dialoghi* of Leone Ebreo by Helen Gardner, "The Argument about 'The Ecstasy,'" in *Elizabethan and Jacobean Studies Presented to Frank Percy Wilson* (Oxford, Clarendon Press, 1959), pp. 279–306; also the study of the poem in relation to a number of Renaissance philosophers of love in Italy, by A. J. Smith, "The Metaphysic of Love," *Review of English Studies*, n.s. 9 (1958), pp. 362–75.

17. See Miss Gardner's account of the five manuscripts that constitute "Group I" in her edition of Donne's *Divine Poems*, pp. lvii–lxvi. One of the most interesting aspects of Miss Gardner's analysis is her evidence that this group of manuscripts may derive from the collection of Donne's poems that we know Donne himself was making in 1614, just before he entered the priesthood. A study of these five manuscripts leaves me with the conviction that Miss Gardner's hypothesis is the only possible conclusion. The arrangement of the love-songs in "Group I" forms the core of the traditional order (or disorder) of the "Songs and Sonets," as they have come down to us through the editions of 1633, 1635, and Grierson (though the editor of 1635 removed "The Flea" from its manuscript position and placed it first in the section that he presented under the title "Songs and Sonets").

The contents and order of the section devoted to the love-songs in "Group I" have been very closely followed by John Shawcross in his recent edition of Donne's *Complete Poetry*, New York, Doubleday, Anchor Books, 1967. In Shawcross's numbering, poems 25 through 71 (beginning with "The Message" and ending with "The Dampe") follow almost exactly the order of the Dowden and St. Paul's mss. (for slight variations in the other three "Group I" mss. see Miss Gardner's account in *Divine Poems*, p. lix). But there are two exceptions: poem 26 in Shawcross, "Witchcraft by a Picture," is not a part of "Group I" (though it is added by a different hand on a blank page of the Leconfield ms.); and after poem 51, "Twicknam Garden," the two-part "Epitaph" is found in three of the "Group I" mss.

As Miss Gardner notes in her edition of the *Elegies and Songs and Sonnets* (p. lxv, n. 2), nine of Donne's love-songs are missing in "Group I": six of the lesser poems ("love-epigrams", as Miss Gardner calls them), and three of Donne's more important poems: "Farewell to Love," "A Nocturnal upon St. Lucy's Day," and "The Dissolution." The first of these, Donne's most bitter poem of sexual disillusionment, may well have been omitted for reasons of propriety; the other two, poems lamenting the death of the beloved lady, may both have been written after the death of Donne's wife in 1617.

18. See *Elegies and Songs and Sonnets,* ed Gardner, pp. xxxi–ii.

19. *Ibid.,* p. 150.

20. This two-part poem is omitted from the Cambridge University Library ms. (Add. Ms. 5778), and the Leconfield ms., belonging to Sir Geoffrey Keynes.

Among the vast number of books and articles on Donne, I wish to express a general appreciation of insights gained from the following: Pierre Legouis, *Donne the Craftsman*, Paris, Didier, 1928; C. S. Lewis, "Donne and Love Poetry in the Seventeenth Century," and Joan Bennett, "The Love Poetry of John Donne, A Reply to Mr. C. S. Lewis," in *Seventeenth-Century Studies Presented to Sir Herbert Grierson* (Oxford, Clarendon Press, 1938), pp. 64–104; Leonard Unger, *Donne's Poetry and Modern Criticism*, Chicago, Regnery, 1950; J. B. Leishman, *The Monarch of Wit*, London, Hutchinson, 1951; Clay Hunt, *Donne's Poetry*, New Haven, Yale University Press, 1954; *The Songs and Sonets of John Donne*, ed. Theodore Redpath, London, Methuen, 1956; Arnold Stein, *John Donne's Lyrics*, Minneapolis, University of Minnesota Press, 1962.

NOTES FOR THOMAS CAREW

1. Quotations from Carew's poetry are taken from *The Poems of Thomas Carew, with his Masque Coelum Britannicum*, ed. Rhodes Dunlap, Oxford, Clarendon Press, 1949; I am throughout this lecture indebted to Dunlap's introduction and commentary.

2. The text of *Salmacida Spolia* (ed. T. J. B. Spencer) is available in *A Book of Masques, in Honour of Allardyce Nicoll* (Cambridge University Press, 1967), pp. 337–70; for my quotations see pp. 347, 357–8. Many of Inigo Jones's drawings for *Salmacida Spolia* are handsomely reproduced in *Festival Designs by Inigo Jones: Drawings for Scenery & Costume from the Devonshire Collection, Chatsworth*, Introduction and Catalogue by Roy Strong, Foreword by Thomas S. Wragg (International Exhibitions Foundation, 1967), plates 90–103. See the full catalogue of the Jones drawings at Chatsworth: Percy Simpson and C. F. Bell, *Designs by Inigo Jones for Masques & Plays at Court* (Oxford, 1924), Walpole Society, vol. 12; with many illustrations. Also Allardyce Nicoll, *Stuart Masques and the Renaissance Stage*, New York, Harcourt, Brace and Co., 1938; with many illustrations.

3. *The Dramatic Records of Sir Henry Herbert*, ed. Joseph Quincy Adams (New Haven, Yale University Press, 1917), p. 55. For extracts from contemporary documents concerning the production of Carew's masque see Gerald Eades Bentley, *The Jacobean and Caroline Stage*, 7 vols. (Oxford, Clarendon Press, 1941–68), III, 106–10. For Inigo Jones's drawings for this masque see Simpson and Bell, *Designs*, Nos. 191–209.

4. *Poems of Carew*, ed. Dunlap, p. 177.

5. *Ibid.*, pp. 178–9.

6. Townshend's poem to Carew is printed in *Poems of Carew*, ed. Dunlap, pp. 207–8. My dating of Carew's poem depends upon the reference to Montagu's *Shepheards Paradise*, produced on January 9, 1633. Of course, the elaborate preparations for this play were discussed at Court throughout the preceding Fall: see Bentley, *op. cit.*, IV, 917–21; the Queen and her Ladies were reported as already "practising" their parts by September 20, 1632. Carew may well have seen rehearsals; but his poem seems to be describing a full-scale performance of some kind. Townshend's verse-letter speaks of how "the windes from every corner bring/ The too true nuse of the dead conquering king." Allowing several weeks for this "news" to reach England, one might

wish to date Carew's answer in late November or in December, 1632. On the other hand, if Townshend was writing around to his friends to collect a group of elegies, he might well have been doing this in January. A collection of ten elegies on Gustavus Adolphus was in fact published in *The Swedish Intelligencer*, Third Part, London, 1633; all of these are printed anonymously, except for one by Henry King.

7. See Bentley, *op. cit.*, IV, 918; Simpson and Bell, *Designs*, Nos. 163–79.

8. *Poems of Carew*, ed. Dunlap, p. 252.

9. See *Aurelian Townshend's Poems and Masks*, ed. E. K. Chambers (Oxford, Clarendon Press, 1912), pp. 90–91:

> In the midst of the ayre the eight *Spheares* in rich habites were seated on a Cloud, which in a circular forme was on each side continued unto the highest part of the Heaven, and seem'd to have let them downe as in a Chaine.
>
> To the Musicke of these Spheares there appear'd two other Clouds descending, & in them were discovered eight *Stars*; these being come to the middle Region of the skie, another greater Cloud came downe above them; Which by little and little descending, discovered other glistering Stars to the number of sixe: and above all in a Chariot of gold-smithes workes richly adorned with precious Iemmes, sat divine Beauty, over whose head, appear'd a brightnesse, full of small starres that inviron'd the top of the Chariot, striking a light round about it. . . .
>
> This sight altogether was for the difficulty of the Ingining and number of the persons the greatest that hath beene seene here in our time. For the apparitions of such as came downe in the ayre, and the *Choruses* standing beneath arrived to the number of fifty persons all richly attired, shewing the magnificence of the Court of *England*.

See Simpson and Bell, *Designs*, Nos. 139–62.

10. Townshend, *Poems and Masks*, ed. Chambers, p. 93.

11. *Ibid.*, p. 96: "the *Eagle* with *Iove* flew up, and *Cupid* tooke his flight through the Ayre, after which the Heavens close."

12. The whole fourth Act of *The Shepheards Paradise* is full of abstract conversation about the pure and spiritual nature of Love, and at the beginning of the fifth Act, Genorio exclaims:

Me-thinks I find my mind on wing, loose from my senses, which like limed twigs held it till now. It is so light, and so ascensive now, it meanes to work it selfe above *Martiroes*. I am already so farre towards it, as the beliefe that I did never love till now. O how I was deceived, while I conceived that Love was so Materiall it could be touched, and grasp't! I find it an undepending ayrinesse that both supports, and fills it selfe, and is to be felt by what it nourisheth, no more then aire, whose virtue onely we discerne.

Shepheards Paradise (1659), p. 110.

13. *Ibid.*, p. 112. Bentley (*op. cit.*, IV, 918) quotes a contemporary as reporting that the Queen, in her performance of *The Shepheards Paradise*, "is said to have herself excelled really all others both in acting *and singing*" (my italics).

14. Townshend, *Poems and Masks*, ed. Chambers, p. 13; taken from Henry Lawes, *The Second Book of Ayres and Dialogues*, 1655, where the song is attributed to Townshend.

15. Folger ms. 4462: see Bentley, *op. cit.*, IV, 920; and G. Thorn-Drury, *A Little Ark, Containing Sundry Pieces of Seventeenth-Century Verse* (London, Dobell, 1921), pp. 4–7, where Thorn-Drury prints the Prologue and four songs that occur between the acts; the Folger ms. was then in Thorn-Drury's possession.

16. Thus Townshend's work might be said to "comprise" (comprehend, contain, sum up) "the beauties of the *SHEP-HERDS PARADISE*." In this connection, Erica Veevers has called attention to the existence in the Huntington Library of a printed fragment or synopsis of a pastoral masque by Townshend that seems to bear a close relation to *The Shepheards Paradise*. She suggests that Townshend may have written this entertainment "to complement a performance of Montagu's play." See *Notes and Queries*, 210 (1965), pp. 343–5. (The fragment by Townshend is also described by Bentley, *op. cit.*, V, 1231.) See also the rejoinder by Paulina Palmer (*Notes and Queries*, 211 [1966], pp. 303–4), who calls attention to Townshend's poem in praise of the Queen's singing. Since there appear to have been at least two performances of *The Shepheards Paradise*, there

is room to conjecture several occasions on which Montagu's play may have been enhanced by Townshend's aid.

17. See the interpretation of this painting by Erwin Panofsky, *Studies in Iconology*, Harper Torchbooks (New York, Harper and Row, 1962), pp. 86–91 (originally pub. by Oxford University Press, 1939).

18. John Shearman, *Mannerism* (London, Penguin Books, 1967), pp. 15–30.

19. See the analysis of this poem by Edward I. Selig, *The Flourishing Wreath. A Study of Thomas Carew's Poetry* (New Haven, Yale University Press, 1958), pp. 150–60; this whole book has many fine insights into Carew's poetry. See also the excellent series of articles by Rufus Blanshard: "Carew and Jonson," *Studies in Philology*, 52 (1955), pp. 195–211; "Thomas Carew and the Cavalier Poets," *Transactions of the Wisconsin Academy*, 43 (1954), pp. 97–105; "Thomas Carew's Master Figures," *Boston University Studies in English*, 3 (1957), pp. 214–27. See also the chapter by George Williamson, "The Fringe of the Tradition," in *The Donne Tradition*, Cambridge, Harvard University Press, 1930; and the classic essay by F. R. Leavis, "The Line of Wit," in *Revaluation* (London, Chatto and Windus, 1936), esp. p. 38, with its witty summation of the eclectic effects of Carew's epitaph on Maria Wentworth: "It opens in the manner of Ben Jonson's Epitaphs. The conceit in the second stanza is both Jonson and Donne, and the third stanza is specifically Metaphysical. After the Augustan passage we come to the Caroline wit of the 'chaste Poligamie.' And we end with a line in Marvell's characteristic movement . . . ."

20. Dunlap (*Poems of Carew*, p. 251) notes the echo of the opening lines of *I Henry IV:* ". . . Finde we a time for frighted Peace to pant,/ And breath shortwinded accents of new broils . . ." One should note too the echo of Donne's *First Anniversary* (67–73), esp. of Donne's phrase "A faint weake love of vertue" (71). See also Donne's *Second Anniversary* (6–7): "But as a ship which hath strooke saile, doth runne/ By force of that force which before, it wonne."

21. See Ruth C. Wallerstein, "The Development of the Rhetoric and Metre of the Heroic Couplet, Especially in 1625–1645," *PMLA*, 50 (1935), pp. 166–209; esp. pp. 186–93 for the influence of Sandys's Ovid and paraphrase of Job.

22. See Dunlap's "Note on the Musical Settings of Carew's Poems," in his edition of Carew, pp. 289–93.

23. See Dunlap's many analogies in the notes to his edition of Carew.

NOTES FOR RICHARD CRASHAW

1. Roy Daniells, *Milton, Mannerism and Baroque*, University of Toronto Press, 1963.

2. See Rudolf Wittkower, *Gian Lorenzo Bernini*, 2nd edn. (London, Phaidon Press, 1966), p. 19.

3. *The Flaming Hart or the Life of the Glorious S. Teresa* (Antwerp, 1642), pp. 419–20; the translation is attributed to Sir Toby Matthew.

4. See the superb accounts by Rudolf Wittkower, *Art and Architecture in Italy: 1600 to 1750*, 2nd edn. (Penguin Books, 1965), pp. 103–5; and *Bernini*, pp. 25–6, with the painting of the entire chapel, facing p. 28.

5. Quotations from Crashaw are taken from the text in *The Anchor Anthology of Seventeenth Century Verse*, Vol. I, ed. Martz, New York, Doubleday, Anchor Books, 1969; this text is based on the second edition of Crashaw's *Steps to the Temple*, London, 1648, with certain readings and additional lines drawn from the posthumous edition of Crashaw's poems, *Carmen Deo Nostro*, edited by Thomas Car and published in Paris, 1652.

6. See Jacobus de Wit, *De Kerken Van Antwerpen*, ed. J. de Bosschere (Antwerp, 1910), p. 104; and J. B. Descamps, *Voyage Pittoresque de la Flandre et du Brabant* (Paris, 1769), p. 181. I am grateful to Dr. A. Monballieu, of the Antwerp Museum, for pointing out these references to me.

7. I know this version only from a monochrome photograph provided by the courtesy of Fondation Cultura, Brussels, and l'Institut Royal du Patrimoine Artistique, Brussels. A letter from the English Convent to Fondation Cultura gives the information that, in comparison with a photograph of the Antwerp painting, the Bruges version is darker in its colors and slightly larger, both in length and in breadth. One can see from the monochrome photograph that a much larger expanse of wing is shown for the angel at the left in the Bruges version, while the whole painting is slightly extended on the other three edges. The difference in size may be due to framing, now, or in the past. I have made an effort to see this version in Bruges, but was unable to do so, since the picture is placed in the nun's enclosure. A large reproduction of the Antwerp version in full color is available in the portfolio published by Cultura: *Rubens en de Barokschilderkunst* (*Kunst in België* VI), Plate 42.

8. See Joseph Anthony Mazzeo, "A Seventeenth-Century Theory of Metaphysical Poetry," and "Metaphysical Poetry and the Poetic of Correspondence," in his *Renaissance and Seventeenth-Century Studies* (New York, Columbia University Press, 1964), pp. 29–59.

9. For a careful account of Seghers, with numerous illustrations, see D. Roggen and H. Pauwels, "Het Caravaggistisch Oeuvre van Gerard Zegers," *Gentse Bijdragen Tot de Kunstgeschiedenis*, 16 (1955–56), pp. 255–301. The authors would date the St. Teresa painting in the years 1625–30, during Seghers' period of transition from *caravagisme* to *l'esprit rubénien*.

10. A. F. Allison, "Some Influences in Crashaw's Poem 'On a Prayer Booke Sent to Mrs. M. R.,'" *Review of English Studies*, 23 (1947), 34–42; see pp. 41–2 for parallels with Carew's "A Rapture."

11. Robert Southwell, *Marie Magdalens Funeral Teares* (London, 1591), Preface.

12. See the important essay by Mario Praz, "The Flaming Heart: Richard Crashaw and the Baroque," *The Flaming Heart* (New York: Doubleday, Anchor Books, 1958), pp. 204–63; see

pp. 218–26 for comments on "The Weeper."

13. See my study *The Poetry of Meditation,* 2nd edn. (New Haven, Yale University Press, 1962), pp. 331–52.

I wish to acknowledge a general debt to the classic study by Austin Warren, *Richard Crashaw: A Study in Baroque Sensibility,* Louisiana State University Press, 1939; and to the introduction and commentary in L. C. Martin's edition of Crashaw's *Poems,* 2nd edn., Oxford, Clarendon Press, 1957.

NOTES FOR ANDREW MARVELL

1. Quotations from Marvell's poetry are taken from *The Poems & Letters of Andrew Marvell,* ed. H. M. Margoliouth, 2nd edn., 2 vols., Oxford, Clarendon Press, 1952. I am indebted to the commentary in this edition.

2. See the interesting discussion of this and other pastoral poems of Marvell by Edward William Tayler in his chapter "Marvell's Garden of the Mind," *Nature and Art in Renaissance Literature,* New York, Columbia University Press, 1964.

3. For detailed discussion of this controversial point see my note in *The Anchor Anthology of Seventeenth-Century Verse,* I, 487; and the philological support for this argument given by George Lord in his admirable new edition, *Andrew Marvell: Complete Poetry* (New York, Modern Library, 1968), p. 24.

4. Arnold Hauser, *Mannerism: The Crisis of the Renaissance and the Origin of Modern Art,* 2 vols., London, Routledge and Kegan Paul, 1965.

5. *Ibid.,* I, 12–13.

6. *Ibid.,* I, 13.

7. See Crashaw's "Ode which was prefixed to a Prayer booke given to a young Gentlewoman," 77–8. Also the great passage at the close of Sir Thomas Browne's *Urne Buriall:* "And if any have been so happy as truly to understand Christian annihilation,

extasis, exolution, liquefaction, transformation, the kisse of the Spouse, gustation of God, and ingression into the divine shadow, they have already had an handsome anticipation of heaven; the glory of the world is surely over, and the earth in ashes unto them." (*Urne Buriall,* ed. John Carter, Cambridge University Press, 1958, p. 50.)

8. Jean H. Hagstrum, *The Sister Arts* (University of Chicago Press, 1958), pp. 114–17. See also the comment on "The Gallery" by Frank J. Warnke, "Play and Metamorphosis in Marvell's Poetry," *Studies in English Literature,* 5 (1965), pp. 23–30.

9. I have explored some aspects of this quest in *The Paradise Within: Studies in Vaughan, Traherne, and Milton,* New Haven, Yale University Press, 1964.

10. See the recent study by John R. Cooper, *The Art of The Compleat Angler,* Durham, N. C., Duke University Press, 1968.

11. Cf. Tayler, *op. cit.,* p. 159.

12. T. S. Eliot, *Selected Essays, 1917–1932* (New York, Harcourt, Brace and Co., 1932), p. 259.

13. The controversy has been admirably summed up, with full references, by Earl Miner, "The Death of Innocence in Marvell's *Nymph Complaining for the Death of her Faun,*" *Modern Philology,* 65 (1967), pp. 9–16, and by Ruth Nevo, "Marvell's 'Songs of Innocence and Experience,'" *Studies in English Literature,* 5(1965), pp. 1–21. I agree with the view that the theme of the poem is "the death of innocence," but cannot accept Miner's suggestion that the poem may also carry political implications related to the destruction of the old order by Parliamentary forces. A number of readers have, I think, been misled by the account of the word "troopers" in the *OED,* where we are told: "The term was used in connexion with the Covenanting Army which invaded England in 1640." But, as my next note makes clear, the word was also being used in the 1640's to apply to Royalist "Troopers."

14. See the use of the word "Troopers" in *The Parliaments Vindication, in Answer to Prince Ruperts Declaration,* by *S. W.,* London, 1642. This pamphlet reprints and answers the *Declaration*

in which Prince Rupert defends his army against the charge of committing atrocities: "But since it hath pleased my Lord Wharton to tell the whole City of London openly at Guild-hall, and since to tell it all the world in print, that one great cause of their preservation at Edge-hill, was the barbarousnesse and inhumanity of Prince Rupert and his Troopers, that we spared neither man, woman, nor childe . . . ." S. W. in his reply refers to "the barbarous inhumanity of Prince *Ruperts* troopers." (I owe this reference to my friend Daniel Woodward.)

15. Several commentators have pointed out analogies with the story of the stag of Cyparissus in the *Metamorphoses*, X, 106–42, and with the story of Silvia's deer killed by Ascanius, *Aeneid*, VII, 475–510. (See Miner, *op. cit.*, p. 13.)

16. T. S. Eliot, *op. cit.*, p. 255.

17. Hauser, *op. cit.*, I, 29.

18. *Ibid.*, I, 229.

Among the many studies of Marvell, I wish to express a general appreciation of insights gained from the following: M. C. Bradbrook and M. G. L. Thomas, *Andrew Marvell*, Cambridge University Press, 1940; Frank Kermode, "The Argument of Marvell's 'Garden' ", *Essays in Criticism*, 2 (1952), pp. 225–41; Joseph Summers, "Marvell's 'Nature' ", *ELH*, 20 (1953), pp. 121–35; Don Cameron Allen, essays on "The Nymph Complaining" and "Upon Appleton House" in *Image and Meaning*, Baltimore, Johns Hopkins Press, 1960; John Edward Hardy, essay on "The Coronet" in *The Curious Frame*, Notre Dame, University of Notre Dame Press, 1962; Lawrence W. Hyman, *Andrew Marvell*, New York, Twayne, 1964; Harry Berger, Jr., "Marvell's 'Upon Appleton House': An Interpretation," *Southern Review* (Australia), I (1965), pp. 7–32; Pierre Legouis, *Andrew Marvell, Poet, Puritan, Patriot*, Oxford, Clarendon Press, 1965; Harold E. Toliver, *Marvell's Ironic Vision*, New Haven, Yale University Press, 1965; J. B. Leishman, *The Art of Marvell's Poetry*, London, Hutchinson, 1966; Stanley Stewart, *The Enclosed Garden*, Madison, University of Wisconsin Press, 1966.

Index

Index

term applied to Marvell, 154,
156–8, 164, 169–70, 173–4,
185, 190
term applied to Milton, 102
Mantua, Duke of, 174
Margoliouth, H. M., 202 (n 1)
Marino, Giambattista, 102
La Galeria, 173
Martial, 64
Martin, L. C., 202
Marvell, Andrew, at Cam-
bridge, 152; career of,
compared with Crashaw's,
152–3
collected poems, 159
contrasted with Crashaw,
163–5
contrasted with Donne, 165–7
contrasted with Herbert,
155–6
influenced by Carew, 154
influenced by Cavalier poets,
153–4, 156, 162
influenced by Donne, 154,
164–7
influenced by Herbert, 154–5
influenced by Jonson, 154,
160, 164–5
Mannerist qualities, 154, 156–
8, 164, 169–70, 173–4, 185,
190
pastoral tradition, use of, 154,
156–9, 175, 177, 182, 184–5,
187
poems on Princess Anne, 152
political poems, 182, 187
portrait of, 150 (Fig. 30)
studies of, 204
wit, quality of, 186

Works:
"Ametas and Thestylis
making Hay-Ropes,"
158–9
"Bermudas," 175–7
"Clorinda and Damon,"
156–8
"The Coronet," 154–5
"Damon the Mower," 177–
8
"The Definition of Love,"
165–7
"A Dialogue between the
Resolved Soul, and
Created Pleasure," 158–
60
"A Dialogue between the
Soul and Body," 160–1
"A Dialogue between
Thyrsis and Dorinda,"
158
"On a Drop of Dew," 161–3
"Eyes and Tears," 163–5
"The Fair Singer," 154
"The Gallery," 173–5, 203
(n 8)
"The Garden," 171–3
"To his Coy Mistress,"
154, 161, 167–9
"To his Noble Friend Mr.
Richard Lovelace," 153
"An Horatian Ode," 152–
3, 171
"The Match," 154
"The Mower against Gar-
dens," 178–9
"The Mower to the Glo-
Worms," 177
"The Mower's Song," 177

Unfunny Money

Also by Gary Alexander

Pigeon Blood

Unfunny Money

Gary Alexander

Walker and Company
New York

First published in the United States of America in 1989
by Walker Publishing Company, Inc.

Published simultaneously in Canada by Thomas Allen & Son
Canada, Limited, Markham, Ontario

Library of Congress Cataloging-in-Publication Data

Alexander, Gary, 1941-
Unfunny money / Gary Alexander
p.   cm.
ISBN 0-8027-5724-3
I.Title.
PS3551.L3554U54   1989
813'.54 — dc19   88-32266
CIP

Printed in the United States of America
10 9 8 7 6 5 4 3 2 1

For Shari, Tracy, Michelle, and Rebecca.

The author apologizes to the Socialist Republic of the Union of Burma, the People's Republic of China, the Lao People's Democratic Republic, and the Kingdom of Thailand for geographic distortions and for encroachment of their borders. Tolerance is also asked for liberties taken with the topography and the climate of the region.

CAST OF CHARACTERS
(major, minor, and some cameo) with pronouncing guide
for Luongan names:

Bamsan Kiet (bomb-sawn key-yet), *Hickorn's
Superintendent of Police*
Captain Binh (bin), *Kiet's adjutant*
Sini (see-knee), *Kiet's half sister*
Thanh Dac (tawn doc), *Kiet's brother-in-law*
Lo, *the fishmonger*
Prince Novisad Pakse (nove-ih-said pock-see), *ruler of
Luong*
Gaston LaCroix, *manager of the Hickorn Continental
Hotel*
Ambassador Smithson, *U.S. ambassador*
Ambassador Shiherazade, *Soviet ambassador*
Cuong Van (cong van), *Luong's Minister of Defense*
Totisa Bu (tote-ih-saw boo), *Luong's Minister of Finance*
Fop Tia (full'p tee-ah), *Mayor of Hickorn*
Roland (Buzz) Wheeler, *Luong manager of Tropics Office
Products, Ltd.*
Freddie Pogue, *seller of bar and restaurant supplies*
Marsad Ref (mar-said ref), former army officer and now
"godfather" of Foh Ten
Dung Nha (dung nah), *former army officer who works for Ref*
Mr. Singh, *Indian tailor and moneychanger*
Heng Fri (hang fry), *Kiet's desk sergeant*
Tien (tin), *Kiet's late wife*
Fahwandi Kli Shabbir (Khalid O'Shea), *guru of the
Church of the Amalgamation of Enlightenment (CAE)*
Kanpurin Morajini (John Smith), *leader of CAE group in
Luong*
Kanpurin Sharla (Joyce Wilson), *CAE follower*
Kanpurin Rastafed (William Jones), *CAE follower*
Ril Thoi (rill toy), *Luong Rouge commander*
Ou Vang (oh vang), *bicycle manufacturer*

N

W ⟷ E

S

INDIA

CHINA

BURMA

Mandalay

LUONG

• Obon

LAOS

20° N.

Hickorn

VIETNAM

Vientiane

BAY OF BENGAL

THAILAND

Rangoon

Bangkok

CAMBODIA

• Phnom Penh

Ho Chi Minh
City

GULF
OF SIAM

The Kingdom of
LUONG

Prologue

IF THE KINGDOM of Luong existed, it would be mentioned in various almanacs and books of fact. Since Luong is, in this fiction, a small and obscure land, comment would be brief, as follows:

Population: 1,535,000 (1986 est.): Hickorn (capital) 211,000; Obon 54,200.

Geography: 41,214 sq. mi., slightly smaller than and roughly the shape of Louisiana. Landlocked. River valleys and jungle in the southeastern Hickorn district, mountainous terrain in the northern highlands (Obon district).

Climate: Tropical. Cool nights in the highlands. Torrid in the south. The wet season prevails from May to October.

Government: Type: Constitutional monarchy. Head of State: Prince Novisad Pakse; b. 1910; in office since 1954.

Economy: wood products, rice, tin, tobacco, opium. Minimal exports, but self-sufficient in agriculture. Currency: Luongan zin (405 zin/ = $1 US). Per capita income (1986 est.): $511.

Communications: Three radio stations, four newspapers.

Literacy Rate: 76%

History: Early tribes were conquered and assimilated by invaders. Luong became a French protectorate in 1889, but regained independence in 1954. Sometimes known as the Fourth Indochina, Luong avoided the warfare suffered by Laos, Cambodia, and Vietnam. Political apathy, weakness of Communist-led Luong Rouge insurgents, superpower indifference, and the neutralist posture of Prince Pakse are the principal reasons why Luong has enjoyed peace in recent times.

1

1

BAMSAN KIET, HICKORN'S superintendent of police, spent his annual two-week furlough, as always, with Sini, his half sister, and her husband, Thanh Dac. They were farmers who grew rice on the Ma San River's rich alluvial plain, twenty kilometers from the city. This isolation from crime and Hickorn's pace was glorious and cathartic, and Kiet could not wait to get there.

Perhaps it was eagerness to flee urban woes or perhaps it was the inflexibility that accompanied middle age, but Kiet had refused to change his furlough schedule despite the fact that the monsoons had passed unusually early this season. Kiet had arrived on the very day that dikes were being opened, paddies flooded. It was planting time.

All able-bodied members of a farm family participated in planting. Much needed to be done quickly. Kiet could not refuse. To do so would insult his relations and, worse, his ancestors, who had rightfully taught worship of the land and its bounty.

Kiet had been the only child of a peasant mother and a father who was a low-level governmental clerk, a mandarin to mandarins who processed documents for the French. His father died during Kiet's adolescence. His mother remarried a farmer and returned to her origins. Kiet was attending Luong University then and remained in Hickorn. The harsh, simple life of subsistence rice farming had somehow triggered his mother's fertility and she bore three more children, Sini being the eldest. This next generation proved prolific also, leaving the widowed and childless Bamsan Kiet as a conspicuous

3

offshoot on a growing family tree, a fleshy city boy who drove automobiles, talked on telephones, and captured thieves. He might as well have been taken from a Martian spaceship and adopted.

Kiet tried his best, for his obligation was woven into Luong's history. But he was of Caucasian height and bulk, an oddity amongst his short, lithe countrymen. With slacks rolled to his knees, bare feet and calves in water, torso stooped over to insert tender seedlings in the tepid muck, Kiet was never more aware of the disadvantages of size and softness. Carp trapped in the pond were tame and occasionally slapped against his ankles. At each slimy impact, Kiet prayed to no god in particular that they were just that and not vipers.

Sini and Dac and their five children skimmed through their task. Kiet trailed behind, woozy from pain and exhaustion. Sini revered her brother and said nothing of his performance. Nor, in the interest of family harmony, did Dac. He despised Hickorn and its sissified inhabitants, who wore shoes and had electricity. His polite silence was no comfort to Kiet. Dac was customarily sullen toward his brother-in-law, but this planting enlistment had turned him serenely smug. He could neither read nor write and the world ended at the boundaries of his property, yet he had learned to ridicule with the briefest glance.

It was a popular notion among intellectuals that too many Luongans had lost their kinship to the land and their ancestors and that they could immensely improve their well-being by communing with the soil. This wisdom emanated from Hickorn coffeehouses and upper-class academic types. Kiet, however, was more skeptical. His joints and muscles told him that his well-being had retrograded, drawing him perilously close to said ancestors. He further suspected that the simple life and the lack of technological luxuries such as plumbing did not necessarily bring an incandescence to his soul.

Thus, Kiet begged off a day early, citing a vague but urgent police matter. He staggered to his Citroen and returned to Hickorn, thinking of those poets, essayists, and profound thinkers who coined the romantic homilies. Best they not encounter the superintendent in a criminal-justice matter anytime soon.

Kiet told nobody that he was home. He wished to prepare a grand meal and enjoy it in privacy before resuming his duties. He loved fried shrimp, the exquisite freshwater shellfish dredged from the floor of the Ma San. The perfect accompaniment would be quantities of cold Golden Tiger beer, a smooth local brew inexplicably termed "amber death" by westerners.

He drove to the Royal Luongan Bank, withdrew adequate funds from his account, and went to the public market located on Ma San Boulevard, across from the river. Amidst a vast array of aromas and noisy haggling, the market sold produce brought in daily from the countryside, meat and poultry—live and slaughtered—and seafood.

Kiet walked directly to the stall of Lo, his favorite fishmonger. Lo offered Hickorn's freshest seafood, and Kiet saw his prize in galvanized tubs, layered on chipped ice. After two weeks of carp, steamed rice, and unidentifiable greens, his stomach growled in anticipation. Kiet exchanged greetings with Lo and asked for a full kilogram.

The quoted price, of course, was outrageous. There were no set prices in Hickorn. All goods and services were subject to bargaining. Kiet, playing his part, threw up his hands theatrically and cut the figure in half. Lo flinched as if he had been slapped and dropped ten percent. Kiet groaned and raised ten percent. They edged toward the ultimate middle ground, but when Lo refused to budge from three thousand zin, Kiet knew something was wrong.

"Two thousand a kilo is fair," Kiet said. "It always has

5

been. We joust, we dicker. It stimulates my appetite. Then I pay you two thousand."

"In the past, yes, Superintendent," Lo said nervously. "But you know how it has been in the last two weeks."

"No," Kiet said. "I don't. I have been away for two weeks, planting rice."

"Ah," Lo said, smiling. "I worried at the sight of you, Superintendent. I am glad to hear that you weren't crippled in an accident."

"Thank you," said Kiet, who was not smiling. His entire body ached. He had suspected that his posture was not entirely normal. He attempted to stand straighter, ignoring lightning bolts of pain in his back and upper legs. "Why can't I have the shrimp for two thousand?"

"Prices have gone suddenly wild in Hickorn. You must pay more for everything," Lo said shrugging. "If I could sell to you for two thousand, I would. At three thousand, my profit is nothing. If you were not my good friend and the police superintendent, I would have to hold at thirty-five hundred."

Hunger overruled pride and thrift. Kiet paid the three thousand, vowing to henceforth trade with another fishmonger.

Lo examined the money closely, placed a gentle hand on Kiet's arm as he picked up the bag of shrimp, and said, "Superintendent, I am so sorry. I cannot accept this money."

"Why not, please? Do you have a conscience after all?"

Lo handed Kiet two of the six five hundred–zin notes he had given him. "Here, look. Hickorn is flooded with it. I see some every day."

Kiet examined one. It appeared to be a perfectly normal piece of currency. On the face was the portrait of His Royal Highness, Prince Novisad Pakse. the borders were ornately scrolled. On the obverse was a depiction of the

6

Royal Palace. The bill was colored in greens, blues, reds, and golds.

Though worthless in international trade, the Luongan zin, in Kiet's opinion, was the most artistically engraved currency in the world. It was beauty, where the staid monochromatic American dollar was brutish power.

Kiet looked at the second bill. Then at the first again.

Lo laughed. "I know! You're testing me, aren't you?"

Kiet could only nod.

"Well, don't worry, Superintendent. I know what to look for. I won't be fooled, but I appreciate your lesson anyway."

Kiet put the money in his pocket and skulked out. Lo called after him, "Will you still be wanting shrimp?"

"Later, my friend," Kiet mumbled. "I have more merchants to test."

He did not look at the bills again until he got into his car. He hoped that he was wrong, that Lo was wrong, that they both had been mistaken. There was no mistake. The serial numbers on the two bills the fishmonger had refused were identical.

2

AVENUE ALEXANDRE LOUBET had been named in honor of a nineteenth-century French priest who romanized the Luongan language. The Chinese-like ideograms of the old written language were incomprehensible to European missionaries and, therefore, pagan. This change allowed the Christian Bible to be translated more easily into Luongan, thus saving untold souls from eternal damnation.

An important plank of Prince Pakse's foreign policy was the naming and renaming of Hickorn's streets. If, for instance, China fell out of favor, Avenue Mao Tse-tung might become Avenue Ronald Reagan. That redesignation was made last year in an elaborate ceremony. American foreign aid increased slightly as a result. Six months later, Rue Souvanna Phouma was no longer, replaced as Rue Chou En-lai. Phouma and Laos posed no threat to Luong's frontiers, and the forgiven Chinese were happy again. They soon rewarded Prince Pakse with a dozen unreliable tractors and an invitation to visit Beijing.

His Royal Highness, a Catholic, had never tampered with Avenue Alexandre Loubet's designation. His subjects were evenly divided between Buddhists and Catholics, and the exchange of religious views in Luong had not always been peaceful. An undercurrent existed that the seventy-seven-year-old Prince Pakse was wise not to inflame.

The address of Hickorn's police headquarters was 900 Avenue Alexandre Loubet. Two stories of massive, unembellished stucco, it had served for half a century as barracks and a command center for legionnaires. Its interior re-

8

mained spare and cold, barely changed from the days of French hegemony. Boots on hallway tile produced echoes and the place smelled of history. Kiet could almost hear voices—arrogant banter and commands and, toward the end, the quieter sounds of relief at being posted in Hickorn instead of Dien Bien Phu. Kiet liked the businesslike message headquarters gave to his officers and their reluctant guests.

Captain Binh was in Kiet's office. His delight at seeing his superior fell just short of an embrace. "Superintendent! I've been trying to reach you, but you've never told anyone where your half sister's farm is."

Binh, Kiet's adjutant, was acting superintendent in his absence. He quickly vacated the desk and the responsibility. Kiet settled gingerly into his chair. "The omission was intentional, but a timely rescue would have been appreciated. Next year I shall not repeat the error. I will even draw you a map."

"You are moving so slowly, Superintendent. Have you been in an accident?"

"In a sense. A protracted one." Kiet wore yesterday's shirt, slacks stained by agriculture, and sandals. In contrast, his young adjutant was perky and resplendent in a starched white uniform and mirror-polished shoes. Gold captain's pips gleamed on shoulder boards. His appearance and nervous energy were exhausting. "You wish to speak to me about crazed prices and counterfeiting, do you not?"

"So you've heard already. I don't know if the two are interrelated, Superintendent. I think they might be. Prices are inflated, yes, but my primary concern is the funny money. There are baskets of the stuff in the property room."

"Excuse me, Captain. Funny money? As in amusing? I lost considerable face giving counterfeit zin to Mr. Lo, a merchant I have known and liked for years. Neither of us were amused."

9

"No, no, you misunderstand. That's slang for counterfeit money," Binh said. "Funny money or queer. I was involved in a counterfeiting case in Washington. Can I tell you about it?"

Captain Binh had trained for a year in America's capital, with their District of Columbia police. He came home bearing tales of wondrous efficiency, of radio cars, computers and plea bargaining. His education had little practical application in Hickorn, but Kiet once again assumed the role of eager and patient listener.

"Please do."

"Well, one night we raided a dilapidated house on L Street. The suspect was printing perfect fifties and hundreds on a stolen photocopy machine, a state-of-the-art laser copier that printed in color on both sides of ordinary paper. The suspect was a parolee and a drug addict with no skills. My supervisor and the Secret Service agents who accompanied us said that anybody can counterfeit these days. Before high technology, counterfeiters were skilled printers."

"The zin notes I assaulted Mr. Lo with were drawn moments before from the Royal Loungan Bank," Kiet said wearily.

"They fool everyone. They are detected only if you get lucky and match serial numbers. That happens seldom."

"Lucky," Kiet said. "Are there any of these magical machines in Luong?"

"There must be, Superintendent, but none to my knowledge. We have checked newspapers, printing companies, and various government agencies. Their copiers are basic black-and-white and their presses are either offset or obsolete linotypes. The printing presses can manufacture passable queer, but we have no evidence they are being used illegally and I know of nobody in Luong capable of engraving the plates. I don't remember a previous counterfeiting case in Hickorn. Do you?"

10

"Before your time, there were a few pitiful hand-drawn efforts at forging zin. Also, some bogus French francs were smuggled in about fifteen years ago. But no, not on any scale. The official exchange rate is four hundred zin to one American dollar. The black-market rate is six hundred to one. Sadly, our zin is not worth the trouble."

"Until now," Binh said. "The quantities are enormous."

"Evidently so. Which denominations?"

Binh went to the property room, brought back samples, fanned out the wad on Kiet's desk, and narrated, "five hundred–, one thousand–, two thousand–, five thousand–, ten thousand–, twenty thousand–, fifty thousand–, and one hundred thousand–zin notes. We haven't recovered many in the upper ranges. They attract too much attention, I suppose. The two thousand– through twenty thousand–zin bills, however. Hickorn is clogged with them."

"There is no inkling to the source of this, uh, queer?"

"No, Superintendent. We just know that they are excellent forgeries and that they are everywhere. The black-market rate is now one thousand zin to the U.S. dollar and climbing."

"I'm gone two weeks and we're at an apocalypse." Kiet instantly knew he had said the wrong thing.

Captain Binh's expression tightened. Then he said, "I suppose it would seem that the criminals waited for your vacation before launching their scheme. How much simpler it was for them without Hickorn's police superintendent available to crush the plot."

"No, no," Kiet said, recovering. If Binh lost face because of the thoughtless remark and went into a snit, he would be useless for weeks. "I meant that it is a coincidence with abominable timing. I could have done no better than you."

"Oh, well—"

"Yes, true, and you possess the flexibility of youth. If you had not been in charge at the outset, confiscation of the bogus zin now in the property room would have been accomplished at a much slower rate. If I were more pliable, I would have postponed my furlough and the neglected muscles and ligaments in my body would not be swollen and aching. What else has transpired in my absence that I should know about?"

Captain Binh smiled, Kiet's slight already healed. "The religious sect that began proselytizing at the airport earlier in the month? They are still there, distributing pamphlets and asking donations from travelers."

Kiet paused to think. He remembered. Binh had brought the matter to his attention the week prior to his departure. Kiet had ignored the details. "Are they causing trouble?"

"No, but they are a nuisance. I personally warned them not to be overly aggressive, and they have been cooperative so far. On the other hand, Luong is trying to promote tourism. I don't believe this cult is a positive image to visitors."

"This is an American group, is it not?"

"Yes, but their leader is an Indian guru who really is not."

"Let it pass unless they break a law, Captain. In the late sixties and the early seventies, Hickorn International was a stopping-off point for any number of sects who were going to or from Katmandu or wherever it was their guru dispensed his infinite wisdom."

"Shouldn't we be doing something about them?"

Kiet considered the problem for a moment. "No. What you have already done is sufficient. These groups, they come and they go. I would not worry. Counterfeiting is our priority. what else?"

"Freddie Pogue is in town," Binh said with obvious distaste. "He was seen on the *terrasse* of the Continental. He stays there when he is conducting local business, you know. The man is scum."

Kiet agreed with Binh's evaluation of Freddie Pogue's

12

character. The Hickorn Continental was Luong's finest hotel. If a deal in the kingdom was to be cut, the Continental's open-air terrace was the place. Since absentee French owners opened it in the 1920's, innumerable arrangements had been struck beneath ceiling fans, Golden Tiger bottles or brandy snifters clinking to seal bargains that ranged from the innocuous to the obscene.

This was Freddie Pogue's natural habitat. Depending on the passport and other documents he carried on a particular visit, he was either an American, Canadian, or Australian citizen. Pogue had made a handsome living selling bar and restaurant supplies to American officers' and NCO clubs in South Vietnam during the war. He had rebounded nicely from the personal tragedy of the American escape and subsequent Communist unification, and was plying a similar trade to civilian concerns throughout Southeast Asia.

Kiet had long suspected that Freddie Pogue's wares extended beyond cocktail napkins, Scotch whiskey, and stainless-steel sinks. Everything from weapons to opium were thought to be in his catalog. Kiet doubted the latter. Golden Triangle warlords and corrupt Royal Luongan Army officers assigned to the highlands owned the drug trade. If Mr. Pogue had asserted himself as a narcotics player, Binh's reference to him would have been more respectful, as Luongans were loathe to malign the dead.

On the subject of arms, Kiet wasn't so certain. The gossip was difficult to disbelieve, but Pogue was slick. His police blotter was blank, clean. His soiled reputation was strictly speculative.

"Has he been behaving himself?" Kiet asked.

"I don't have the manpower to put surveillance on him, Superintendent. The counterfeiting has impacted our resources to the extent that routine patrol duties are neglected."

Impacted? Binh had brought with him from his District of

Columbia police experience the Miranda card and a technique called public relations. The first was a statement read by rote to killers and robbers. It was almost apologetic. You were telling them that they had rights and what those rights were. Public relations involved what police officers said to newspaper and television reporters. It was apparently mandated that you smile and swear that you were not doing your job if the killer or robber became injured in the course of the arrest. Something termed a civil lawsuit could drain your departmental budget if a criminal was damaged in the process of apprehension.

If this was not strange enough, Captain Binh articulated these modern views by using nouns as verbs. Peculiar verb usage had garbled his speech patterns and exact interpretations were often difficult. Impacted. Accessed. Programmed. Kiet was never precisely sure of the meanings.

He said, "I shall pay a call on Mr. Pogue. What else?"

"Minister Bu desires to see you at your earliest convenience."

Totisa Bu was Minister of Finance. Luong's economy and the Royal Mint fell under Bu's authority. Kiet knew why he had been summoned.

"What, then, Captain, is our plan for counteracting this funny money nonsense?"

"There are no clues as to the origin, but we're monitoring merchants and educating them," Binh said helplessly. "We're picking up the phony bills we find. Soon we'll need more baskets for the property room."

Kiet left for home and a hot bath, thinking about an Americanism Binh had once told him, a short parable about horses long since departed from their corral.

14

3

RUE WILLIE MOSCONI'S tag was as inviolable as Avenue Alexandre Loubet's, but for a different reason—not the politics of religion, nor politics in general. Adoration was the motive. Willie Mosconi was one of Prince Novisad Pakse's favorite billiards shooters.

If His Royal Highness's practice of renaming Hickorn's streets fueled skeptics, his passion for pocket billiards encouraged outright ridicule: an old man squinting over green felt, directing a shaking stick at colored balls; appointments delayed because a match with a Royal Palace servant had proven especially challenging; a senile monarch retreating from his duties, swaddling himself in a silly game.

Kiet knew better. Billiards intrigued him. The geometry required was exact, yet fluid and asymmetrical. After each shot, the configuration changed. Bank shots were frequently employed to attack the object ball from behind or at an oblique angle.

Kiet had witnessed His Royal Highness run table after table of nine-ball. Upon invitation, Kiet had played several games with the seventy-seven-year-old ruler. Prince Pakse had won with ease, Kiet getting only a single shot before the table was cleaned. When Pakse broke, the triangular rack of balls exploded every which way. From there he was a subtle predator. Colored balls fell obediently into pockets, and the cue ball always came to rest at a spot that doomed its next victim.

Kiet regarded the game and its devious precision as

15

analogous to Luongan internal politics. Novisad Pakse had survived in power for over three decades by maneuvering into a subtle advantage and dispatching rivals. If His Royal Highness was doddering and fuzzy-headed, Bamsan Kiet should be so enfeebled a quarter century from now.

Abstract thoughts of His Royal Highness sinking balls were more pleasing to Kiet than counterfeit zin and his upcoming appointment. They were on his mind as he slowed along Rue Willie Mosconi and parked at a restricted spot in front of the Ministry of Finance.

Immediately after Independence, the ministry, formerly a French bank headquarters, had been acquired on attractive terms by the Kingdom of Luong. Paris financiers were eager to flee a colonial economy handed over to the natives. The building's facade was a Greco-Roman mishmash of pillars and elaborate scrolling. Remodeling by the present tenants had been confined to neglect—soil, stains, and cracking stucco.

The ministry thus retained the desired effect of aloofness and superiority to the citizenry. Such was Kiet's opinion, an opinion reinforced whenever he was in the presence of Minister of Finance Totisa Bu. Kiet considered Bu loyal to His Royal Highness—he was a nephew, after all—and honest, but too professorial, too remote, too much the scholar to be an effective administrator.

Bu held an advanced degree from an American university that was a member of a select and botanical-sounding grouping known as Ivy League. He was grayish and frail, and wore three-piece suits, monogrammed shirts, and a gold pocket watch. He was something called a Yalie. Kiet sometimes had to remind himself that he was in the company of a fellow Luongan.

"Superintendent Kiet, I thank you for coming so promptly following your vacation," Totisa Bu said. "Was it enjoyable?"

Kiet began to speak, but Bu interrupted. "Excellent. It

16

seems that we have a mutual problem. Petty crime is not in my purview, but the counterfeit zin circulating in Hickorn is impacting our fragile economy."

"Impacting," Kiet repeated. "Mr. Minister, this crime is not petty. No crime is petty."

"Yes, from your standpoint I understand, Kiet. I need to know what progress has been made."

Kiet deflected the inquiry. "I hoped you might be of assistance, sir. The Royal Mint is part of your, um, purview."

"I've been assured by my mint director that every safeguard has been observed. I've personally inspected the facility and am convinced that our security procedures are adequate. No supplies are unaccounted for and no mint employees are on the premises beyond their normal shifts."

Kiet was not convinced, but if incompetence had been concealed, careers protected—in Binh's Americanized terminology, the covering of one's ass—it would be nigh impossible to prove.

"In fact," Bu continued, raising a finger, "to be totally fail-safe, I ordered cessation of currency production when the counterfeit notes were initially discovered. The Royal Mint is closed and under heavy guard."

"When was the first queer found?"

"Queer?"

"Excuse me," Kiet said. "Queer is law-enforcement slang for counterfeit money."

"Approximately two weeks ago."

Coinciding with my departure, Kiet again thought. "It is believed that the counterfeit zin is disrupting our economy. I have a slight understanding on a personal level, having been overcharged for Ma San River shrimp. What is the connection, please?"

"A common example," Bu said without interest. "The phenomenon created by the abundance of imitation zin in our marketplace is a classic variation of the inflationary gap."

17

Bu swiveled in his chair and plucked a book from floor-to-ceiling shelves. Kiet suppressed a groan.

"Here it is, Kiet," he said, opening the book to pages of fine print and line graphs.

"Of course," Kiet said, nodding.

"The entire spectrum of the inflationary gap theory is too complex for a layman," Bu said.

"Certainly," Kiet said.

"Basically, when the money supply exceeds the cost of available goods and services, a gap occurs."

"An inflationary gap," Kiet said.

"Excellent, Superintendent. Prices are bid up and the gap is filled. If the gap cannot be filled, the dynamic works like this. An excess in purchasing power causes endless price increases and an inflationary spiral. The generation of large amounts of counterfeit zin in Hickorn's modest economy is warping it."

"Spiraling it," Kiet said.

"Indeed. In Tokyo or New York, the introduction of this quantity would be of no consequence."

"The workmanship is good, too," Kiet said. "People either don't recognize a bad note or if they do they pass it to another who doesn't. Spending is reaching the panic stage. People are afraid their zin will be worthless tomorrow, so they spend it today. Is this accurate?"

"Yes, and the fault is partially mine," Bu said. "We print zin on plain bond. No threads in the paper, no watermarks. Some mints are experimenting with holograms now, did you know? Anything to thwart the counterfeiters."

Kiet did not know. He had never heard of a hologram. "I know. Perhaps it would be worthwhile to look into."

"Unless the counterfeiting is stopped in the near future, Kiet, the value of money saved will be destroyed and there will be no further incentive to save. Investment will dry up. Disaster, Kiet. Disaster! Economic disaster on the order of Germany's in the 1920s, when it took a wheelbarrow full of

18

marks to buy a loaf of bread. We are on the brink of hyperinflation.

"During the United States Civil War, another period of hyperinflation, a Confederate Southerner was quoted as saying, 'We used to go to stores with money in our pockets and come back with food in our baskets. Now we go with money in our baskets and return with food in our pockets.' Let me reiterate, Kiet. This breed of galloping inflation is just around the corner."

First it was hyper, now it was galloping. Kiet thought of Captain Binh's vanished horses, he thought of baskets in the property room. Thought patterns were spinning in his head. "I agree, sir."

"Then what is your program for elimination of the menace?"

"To capture the counterfeiters, Minister Bu."

"Specifically?"

"To capture the counterfeiters as soon as possible, sir."

Totisa Bu's eyebrows raised. "I had expectations that you would have a formalized and strategic approach on line."

"I do," Kiet said. "In Hickorn, rumors and gossip blossom like weeds. By and by, fateful words are spoken to the wrong person at the wrong time. We listen to stories, then we catch the criminal. That is how crimes are solved in Luong, Mr. Minister.

"My young adjutant, Captain Binh, studied police work in America. Despite shotgun microphones and science laboratories that can identify the birthplace of a fleck of lint, he admits that their finest crimebusting successes happen when a stupid mouth cannot stay shut."

Bu looked at him. "Your policy is to wait for a telephone call or a whisper of a bar-room revelation?"

Kiet felt himself reddening. "My policy is to aggressively pursue information. *Aggressively*, Mr. Minister."

Bu was oblivious to Kiet's anger. He gestured to his bookshelves. "All right, Kiet. We'll launch a two-pronged attack. You on the streets, me devoting my waking hours studying papers."

"Pardon me, sir?"

"Books, theses, dissertations, articles in journals. Anything dealing with the effect of macrocounterfeiting in a Third-World nation and a concomitant solution."

Kiet hated the reference to Luong as Third World. It was to him a pat on the lice-ridden head of a starving child. He forgave the usage by westerners. The term was integral to their briefing memoranda and travel brochures. From the lips of a Luongan, it was despicable. "And? . . . "

"I haven't found an applicable model yet," Bu said with a shrug. "I know I will, though."

Bu's frustration was Kiet's exit visa. He said thank you, he would be grateful for any help the minister could provide, shook his hand, and hurriedly escaped. Bu deemed himself Luong's foremost economist. Kiet had a different opinion. His next stop was the man who really was.

4

MR. A. SINGH, proprietor of Bombay Tailors, was not a Yalie. As far as Kiet knew, he was unlettered. He was also a liar, a cheat, a confidence artist, and totally amoral. Singh had no monopoly on these sins, but he exploited them to commercial advantage more skillfully than his peers.

If Totisa Bu's macros and hypers and spiraling gallops made perfect sense on the pages of books and manuscripts, A. Singh experienced harmony with paper too. but there was a significant difference. The paper with which he dealt was account books and currencies. His feel for trends and causes was less intellectual than visceral, his information immediate. It was the difference between thoughtful analysis and fast hands. In Kiet's view there was no question which man was Hickorn's premier economics wizard.

Kiet drove to Singh's shop on Avenue Dwight Eisenhower. The street was in the core of downtown, a lush strip of chic stores that Captain Binh categorized with a merged Franco-American word: boutiques. *Le Avenue*, as it was known to its patrons, catered to tourists, affluent Luongans, and western emigrants who could afford to live in the International District. Anything was available for a price, and the prices were dear.

Chinese and Indian merchants predominated on *Le Avenue*. The engines of our marketplace, Kiet thought as he parked. Our Asian brothers teach us the art of commerce and are kind enough to manage it for us.

Jewelry stores on each side of Bombay Tailors sported chromed trim and artsy, cursive neon in the windows. *Ear-*

21

repressible proclaimed one, *Time Eternal* the other. Kiet marveled that there were sufficient unadorned ears and wrists among Hickorn's wealthy to keep these thieves and their outrageous prices in business.

Singh's *Bombay Tailors* sign was a small painted board above a wooden door. The window glass was dusty, obscuring the displayed suits and slacks from passersby. No formal business hours were posted. An air of indifference existed, a contrast to the smarmy entrepreneurship of neighboring establishments. The image was intentional and Kiet was not deceived.

He entered to the jittery and blinding smile of Mr. A. Singh. "Superintendent, it has been too long!"

Singh was in his thirties, was short and pudgy. His hair gleamed and his eyes were perpetually moist. "Mr. Singh, we must talk."

"Always a pleasure, Superintendent. If I am being too personal, forgive me, but accept my sympathy nonetheless."

"Excuse me?"

"Your gait is unnatural, Superintendent. You walk with obvious discomfort. It would be inappropriate of me to inquire as to your affliction, but please be aware that I have access to catalogs to a variety of orthopedic aids, any of which I would offer to you at a substantial discount."

Kiet had a quick and delicious image of Singh in a paddy, planting rice seedlings, one-by-one, his back bent to the one-hundred-degree sun, his blistered feet adhered to the muck, an endless row in infinite acreage.

Kiet smiled. "I cannot pay your prices."

"Stockings, trusses, shoes, everything. Available instantly by air freight from leading European manufacturers. My charge to you, sir, would be, shall we say, less than nominal."

"Thank you for your unnecessary concern," Kiet said. "The last time we chatted, you tried to bribe me with a silk ascot."

22

Singh spread his arms and sighed. "Superintendent, you are devoted to your duty and you protect us from hooligans and burglars. You are misinterpreting a sincere expression of gratitude."

"Singh, if you really wish to make me happy, please discuss candidly what you know of this counterfeiting and inflation problem."

"Terrible, is it not? It is spreading in Hickorn like a medieval plague. I cannot quote a client an accurate price for a suit. From the time measurements are taken until the garment is ready, my costs will have—"

"Singh, if you ever knew a lapel from a cuff, the distinction has been forgotten. The clothing in your windows is manufactured in Hong Kong with 'Made In Italy' labels sewn in by the same underpaid seamstresses you employ to make alterations when you do sell the rare suit."

"Sir, I am a craftsman."

Without exception, their meetings were collisions, Kiet on police business, Singh ingratiating and defensive and full of denial. They were in the midst of a ritual. Singh would not cooperate further without an indication of respect.

Kiet took a deep breath and complied. "A skilled tailor, yes. I apologize for the aspersion. I imagine your apprenticeship was arduous and you have done splendid work as a journeyman. However, you are a businessman, too. A businessman must be flexible and diversified to survive and you have done so nicely in other areas."

"Thank you, Superintendent," said the appeased Singh.

"Your primary business is moneychanging and I know of no Hickorn money-changer who does a greater volume or is fairer with his customers," Kiet continued. "Trading of currency on the black market is illegal, but condoned. I am not here to harass you for that practice."

"Everybody does it," Singh added eagerly. "The influx of foreign currency aids our economy. Black market, may I say, Superintendent, is an ugly term. I prefer to think of myself as one who offers a beneficial and alternative method of exchange."

"Yes, yes," Kiet said. Enough. He was getting an oily aftertaste from the conversation. "The official rate given at banks and embassies is four hundred zin to the U.S. dollar. When I departed on furlough, the, uh, so-called black-market rate was six hundred to one. Yesterday it was one thousand to one. What are you paying now, please?"

Singh's shoulders slumped. "Ten-fifty and rising. I have no choice. Tomorrow, who knows? Eleven hundred? Twelve? It's crazy. I hate this uncertainty, Superintendent. If I gamble and stockpile one currency or another and the prices zoom or dip the wrong way, I am in trouble. I love stability. Oh how I love it!"

"As do I. Tell me what you know of the counterfeiting and perhaps stability can be reachieved."

"I swear, Superintendent, I know nothing. This counterfeiting and inflation, if it doesn't cease, I'm ruined."

The anguish in the Indian's face convinced Kiet that he was telling the truth. "Has anybody tried to pass funny money to you?"

"Pass what, Superintendent?"

"Funny money is law-enforcement slang for counterfeit."

"Yes. Some accidentally. Some not, I think. I have made a list of repetitive serial numbers. There are many in each denomination and I check every note carefully, but I know some slip by me."

"Who has been changing large amounts of zin for western currency lately?"

Singh pointed a finger upward. "Big transactions? The usual, Superintendent. Senior army officers, high-level bureaucrats, private businessmen. They cannot wait to transfer our feeble zin into hard currency and their Swiss bank accounts."

"Freddie Pogue?"

"Mr. Pogue is a faithful customer and a delightful gentleman. When he is in Hickorn, we do business in quantities that satisfy his living expenses. Relatively modest quantities."

"He is in Hickorn now," Kiet said.

"I did not know. I haven't seen him."

Kiet stared at Singh. Captain Binh had trained on lie detector machines at America's District of Columbia. There was a polygraph at headquarters. It had been a gift of the Soviet Union or the United States. Kiet couldn't remember which. The device was moldering in storage, diseased by neglect and tropical humidity. They plugged it in once and poof! Headquarters went without lights until an electrician was located. The best lie detector was the liar's eyes, Kiet believed. He read truth in Singh's.

"Larger-than-average bundles of zin for hard currencies, please. Who?"

"Superintendent, you are asking me to betray a professional confidence."

"Money-changing outside of authorized agencies is a crime per se."

"Have you never changed zin on the street?"

"Never," Kiet lied. "I am too busy to go through the procedure of having your doors padlocked, Singh, so please talk to me. Names and denominations."

"But you have never before arrested anyone for money-changing, Superintendent."

"Names and denominations."

"Mayor Tia. American dollars."

Kiet hesitated, collecting his thoughts. Since Fop Tia's election as Hickorn's first democratically selected mayor nearly four years ago, Tia had lobbied hard to transfer the Hickorn Police Department from an agency of the Ministry of Defense to an instrument of his own office. Kiet's powerful friends at defense had been able to forestall what he felt would be a disastrous merger.

Tia was a greedy and successful businessman, a commodities

25

broker who traded and speculated in lumber, rice, and tobacco. Upon his election, thanks to pressure from the United States Embassy, Tia had put his holdings into a blind trust administered by his partners. Tia's ambition then shifted from money to power, and much of his mayoral energy was devoted to expansion of his office's authority.

The democratic election process was alien to Luong's tradition of monarchal appointees—the mandarin ministers and functionaries who steered the nation under the patronage of royalty and their European masters. Independence had eliminated the French irritant, but little else had changed until recently, when western urging had yielded a compromise in which Parliament members and municipal leaders became choices of the electorate.

Kiet had no strong feelings about this new system, one way or another. Cronyism dictated power in the old process, graft in the new. No essential difference.

Nor had he begrudged Fop Tia's victory in the initial election. His opponent was also wealthy and unscrupulous. Both men had imported the quaint western customs of stuffing ballot boxes and buying votes through neighborhood committeemen. So when the total vote count exceeded by twenty percent the population of Hickorn—man, woman, and child—Kiet was neither alarmed nor incensed. Since the corruption quotient was roughly equal, he assumed that Tia's narrow margin was probably an accurate and largely apathetic statement of preference.

The next mayoral election was three months away. Hickorn's citizens were fed up with Fop Tia's shenanigans, and several challengers were building considerable support. Kiet knew them to be honest men. It promised to be an interesting and spirited race.

"Tia can buy lots of dollars on his mayor's salary." Kiet said cynically. "He is a masterful budgeter. I envy him."

"The blind trust is a sham, Superintendent. It is a piece

26

of paper. You know as well as I that Mayor Tia keeps an active hand in his commodities ventures."

"Yes, but not as active a hand as he would like. There are appearances to maintain. Have you heard how his business is doing? I've been told that it has declined since Tia isn't running it day-by-day."

"True. His partners are not as astute as he. And the inflation is surely harmful. If you contract to sell a kilo of rice for five hundred zin one month from today and the market price has increased to a thousand, ah, you are a big, big loser."

A cold fact that likely eliminated Mayor Fop Tia as a counterfeiting suspect, Kiet thought. "How much zin is our beloved mayor changing, please?"

"Superintendent, I have already violated my ethics beyond the point at which I will be able to sleep tonight."

Kiet hated it when a grown man whined at him. "Yes, yes, professional confidences and whatnot. I admire your integrity, Mr. Singh, but patriotism is at issue. Illegal gain is secondary to the destruction of our economy."

Singh stood mutely, unimpressed by Kiet's speech.

"You have admitted black-market money-changing to me." Kiet frowned and scratched a temple. "Let me think, do I have a padlock in the Citroën? Yes, I do. In the trunk. And a closure form to fill out and paste on your door? In the glove compartment maybe? I cannot recall. If not, we keep an ample supply at headquarters."

"Fifteen thousand dollars worth of zin every other day, Superintendent."

Bamsan Kiet's mouth fell open.

27

5

Once, hickorn city Hall had been merely that, a modest if garish structure that struck Kiet as the Ministry of Finance in miniature. It had been perfectly adequate for the French Governor General's deputies who presided over Hickorn's affairs, as it was for subsequent Luongan appointees. Ceremony dominated function, so an atmosphere of charming though cramped colonial decay took precedence over expansion of working space, for which there was no need, since principal mayoral duties consisted of greeting important visitors and the issuance of business licenses.

Mayor Fop Tia promised and delivered modernization. It came in the form of a bureaucratic Hydra. Tia closed City Hall and occupied a bland three-story office and apartment building on the corner of Mu Hickorn and Rue Ho Chi Minh. His newly formed Department of Engineering condemned it and chased out the tenants. Hickorn City Hall became the Hickorn Center of Public Administration, facilities with diminished charm but fifteen times the square footage.

Kiet had read the words of a British social scholar named Parkinson, who postulated that a civil service expanded by an inexorable rate of growth, irrespective of the work which had to be done. the Englishman was speaking directly of Tia, who created Departments of Community Service, Sanitation, Employment, Parks, Water, Purchasing, Weights and Measures, Planning, Liaison, Intergovernmental Relations, et cetera. The various departments washed Hickorn with tidal waves of paper. Citizens were growing sick of enduring interviews and filling out forms

28

for services they would never receive. Fop Tia's reelection prospects were indeed questionable.

Kiet parked, thinking also of Adolf Hitler. The German fiend had sought to rule the world through annexation and military conquest. He suspected Tia of attempting the same by adding desks. One morning the world would awake to discover that it was composed of Hickorn deputy water commissioners.

He went inside, looked for the stairs, then saw Hickorn's only Luongan-owned elevator. It was a curiosity installed by Tia at taxpayer expense and Kiet could never remember that it existed. He rode up with a comely and uniformed operator and a crush of clerks wearing starched white shirts and carrying briefcases stuffed with work they hadn't done during their long lunches and siestas.

Kiet got off on the top floor, announced himself to a secretary, and was asked to wait. He sat and studied the activity. There wasn't much. Municipal employees at desks were listlessly shuffling mounds of paper. The sheer bulk of the printed matter and documents seemed to overwhelm them and absorb their energy. The room was muggy and the ceiling fans provided minimal relief, their cooling breezes blocked by an invisible yet palpably real inversion layer of bureaucratic inertia.

Kiet noticed a number of sophisticated electronic machines. Postage meters, desktop computers, and photocopiers. All appeared fairly new. The gadgets, the elevator, the spread of officialdom in general —Kiet wondered at the cost. In his inaugural year, Tia had bamboozled Parliament into tripling his budget. It increased by fifty percent each year thereafter. Funding came through increased taxes on property and retail sales. Hickorn voters had cause to be angry.

Kiet was finally shown in to Fop Tia. The mayor was stumpy, his physique a replica of Mr. A. Singh's. He was dressed in a bright, orangish, open-collared jacket and matching slacks.

29

His shirt was sky blue, the top buttons undone. Gold chains rested on a hairless chest. Captain Binh had contemptuously described Tia's preferred garb as an obsolete North American fashion entitled Polyester Leisure Suit.

Tia's furnishings matched the man. Chairs, a sofa, and the desk were European imports, bright and modern pieces of glass, chromium, and leather. Tia and his surroundings were superficial and vaguely dangerous. Kiet settled into cold leather and faced a cobra.

Tia glanced at his watch. "Bamsan Kiet, hello. I'm short on time. I have a luncheon speech to deliver to a group of merchants. With reelection coming up, I have to do these things. I have to explain my accomplishments, which should be obvious. Democracy makes strange demands on a public servant. Life was infinitely simpler when I was a humble businessman. Politics! Is it worth the bother?"

Tia spoke rapidly, without taking a breath. His ending question was ludicrously rhetorical and Kiet ignored it. "I came home from furlough to find Hickorn in financial chaos."

"The counterfeiting, yeah. The perpetrators ought to be publicly executed. Tied and blindfolded in front of sandbags and shot."

"We no longer do that, but I share your sentiment," Kiet said. "The lack of identified perpetrators is another problem."

"Why come to me, then?" Tia asked. "If you were in my chain of command, we could be cooperating with efficiency, but you are not." Here we go again, Kiet thought. He said, "Mr. Mayor, I am abusing your valuable time because you know many people and have a sensitive touch on the pulse of Hickorn."

"If I could assist you, I would, Kiet. Use *your* valuable time to capture the counterfeiters."

"Captain Binh, my young adjutant, suggests that the zin notes could have been duplicated on an advanced photocopy device."

30

Fop Tia swept an arm toward his outer offices. "I have some and they are marvelous, but not good enough for forgery. They only aid me in serving my constituency."

"I wasn't accusing—"

"You're a fool if you are," Tia interrupted. "If these criminals impoverish Hickorn, I'm doomed on election day. I'm the mayor. I'll be blamed. Do you know what snow is, Kiet?"

"I have seen it in films and read of it in books."

"The mayor of Chicago was defeated and ousted from office because of snow. The winter of the election, that city was whipped with relentless blizzards. Chicago's snow-removal equipment was inadequate. They couldn't scoop aside one snowfall before the next storm deposited more. She didn't cause the inches and feet of snow, God is responsible for that, but she was blamed anyway."

God? Fop Tia had acquired religion shortly before his election. Which god and savior and prophet he believed in was determined by expediency and the moment. If Tia owned an icon, it would be a Buddha statuette draped with rosary beads.

"God did not print the phony zin, Mr. Mayor."

Tia replied by glancing at his watch again.

"Your machines look new," Kiet said.

"They are. Parliament's appropriations are stingier than everybody thinks. An American aid grant allowed me to move some of my executive management procedures out of the Stone Age."

"I envy those conveniences," Kiet said, sprinkling bait.

"If you were in my table of organization, I could make arrangements that would slake your envy. Those obstructionists at the Ministry of Defense who cling to their empire, Cuong Van being the worst, they might just release Hickorn Police if you said the right words. Your department isn't military, after all. You're a civilian, a servant of Hickorn's people, as I am."

The desired response—a hungry mouth clamped on the bait. "Putting it that way, Mr. Mayor, I see the situation in a new perspective. I am a flexible man, and as you know, Minister Van is an old and dear friend. I will discuss it with him when I see him next."

"Please do."

"By the way, just out of curiosity, who supplied you this splendid equipment?"

"Various vendors. My assistants in Purchasing buy them."

"From a local seller?"

Tia shrugged. "I don't know. I delegate authority. I'm too busy to look over the shoulders of my people."

Kiet could see out a window the National Cathedral across the street. It was an intimidating assemblage of stone, stained glass, and sharp spires. He knew the Christian God to be vengeful and ill-tempered, a carrot-and-stick deity who dealt in absolutes. There was no middle ground between eternal damnation and eternal salvation. Among His Ten Command-ments was a clause regarding "bearing false witness." Tia's office was at the National Cathedral's mid-level. Kiet won-dered how the mayor could tell such consistent lies in the presence of this ugly monolith.

"Would you mind if I asked the director of that department?"

"I would, Kiet. They're extremely busy, as you should be, searching for your counterfeiters."

"Currency exchange is becoming frantic," Kiet said. "Peo-ple are converting their money into dollars and pounds and francs, fearful that the zin they hold is counterfeit and worth even less than genuine notes."

Tia did not emote. "I know. It is unfortunate. Now, excuse me, Kiet. I have a speech to make."

Kiet thanked Fop Tia for his time and left. He hadn't expected Tia to fall on his knees and confess the fifteen thousand every other day, but by spitting out the bait on the business machines—deflection of a harmless question—he had qualified himself as a serious counterfeiting suspect.

6

THE PAY TELEPHONE in a kiosk outside Hickorn's Center of
Public Administration miraculously worked on the first try.
The city's phone system had been installed by the French, and
the major improvement since had been conversion of slots
from franc denominations to twenty- and fifty-zin coins. Busy
signals and otherworldly beepings were the norm.

"Superintendent, Ambassador Smithson himself called,"
Captain Binh reported.

"My checking in with you has to be an omen," Kiet said
sarcastically. "The American Embassy is my next order of
business."

"It must be extremely important," said the excited Binh.
"It's his practice to have clerks and attachés leave mes-
sages for you. He says he needs to see you ASAP."

Kiet was too insulted to reply. In Luongan, *asap* meant
dog excrement.

Binh laughed. "No, Superintendent, it isn't *that*. ASAP
is an English acronym for as soon as possible."

"I know," Kiet said, relieved. "I was just mulling over
the urgency. Did Mr. Smithson elaborate?"

"No. He said it was a matter of national security and
hung up."

Kiet told Binh he would call in later, then drove to the
new American Embassy, which had been dedicated by
Prince Pakse six weeks ago. It was four stories, the same as
the Soviet Embassy, but precisely one meter taller. The
architectural style was that of a shoebox placed on end.
Sunlight throbbed against steel framework and mirrored

glass. Cynics had dubbed it the Glass Palace. Kiet was reminded of Fop Tia's furniture.

Kiet hadn't been inside the new embassy before. When he walked through the brass-sashed, smoked-pane, automatically opening doors that spread with a whoosh, he departed the comfort of ninety-degree temperature–ninety-percent humidity and entered Antarctica. Goosebumps appeared on his skin like a pox. These Yankees and their air-conditioning addiction. Break out the Glass Palace's windows and the climate of the entire region would change. Give it a year and the children would be ice skating on the streets.

A toothy young man in a navy blue suit materialized and took Kiet's hand. He hadn't heard the approach because of soft, stringed music that drifted from everywhere despite the apparent absence of speakers. At least in the old embassy you froze in silence punctuated only by typewriters.

"Superintendent Kiet, I presume? Jerry Wainwright. Political attaché. The ambassador is expecting you."

Kiet's fingertips stung. He withdrew his hand.

Wainwright chuckled. "Static electricity. There's a payback when you suck the mugginess out of the air. Let's route you up to the ambassador."

He patted Kiet on the shoulder, led him to an elevator, Hickorn's second elevator, told him to take it to the top, proffered a finally non-electrical handshake, and said to have a nice day. Serenaded by the same violins, Kiet rode upward, making a mental note to ask Binh about the technology of musical buildings.

Kiet remembered how hard it usually was to get an audience with the ambassador. Smithson's sole concern in Luong seemed to be communism and the Luong Rouge guerrillas, who made periodic nuisances of themselves by attacking convoys and ambushing Royal Luongan Army patrols that foolishly wandered too far from their highland garrisons.

Ambassador Ritchie, Smithson's predecessor, an appointee of a prior American president—a peanut farmer from their subtropical province of Georgia—had also been single-minded, but fixated with human rights. Once Kiet persuaded Ritchie that he did not use cattle prods in his interrogative process and that his jail housed only generic criminals, they got along famously. Kiet missed him.

Smithson was an incredibly tougher nut. Kiet did his utmost to please by asking serious questions and furrowing his brows during lectures on the domino theory. He could not, however, buy Smithson's paranoia about a communist menace, or his insistence that guerrilla activity was escalating, soon to sweep into the cities and destroy democracy. They had come to coexist, though, Smithson satisfied that Kiet was a competent crime solver who never overlooked the possibility of Marxist chicanery.

"Superintendent Kiet, how nice," he said with disguised urgency. "Come in, come in."

The ambassador was lean and fiftyish, gray-maned and immaculately attired in pinstripes. He was a member of a foreign power clique known as Ivy League Eastern Establishment. Kiet could not imagine him ever sprouting a pimple or dangling a participle.

He gave Kiet some Luongan currency and said, "Tell me what you think of these."

Kiet examined a dozen twenty thousand–zin notes, taking his time. He wanted to be totally sure of what he was seeing before offering a reply. Smithson's exhibits tended to preface object lessons, which degenerated into the dreaded lectures on communism.

"There are two pairs with identical serial numbers," he said.

"It logically follows that they are counterfeit, does it not?"

"True. Some of them, anyway."

"You can't tell which are good and which aren't?"

36

Kiet shook his head no. "They are excellent forgeries. Where did you get them, Mr. Ambassador?"

Smithson cleared his throat and leaned back in his chair, fingers woven together on a flat stomach. "A staff member brought them to me. Call it a fortuitous intelligence-gathering situation."

Kiet dared not call the "intelligence-gathering situation" what it really was: an underling, perhaps the unctuous Mr. Wainwright, had changed dollars on the street for Smithson with A. Singh or one of his colleagues, the practice being too sordid for the ambassador himself to indulge.

"You and your staff member are very alert, sir. I applaud you."

"I felt it best to advise you personally, Superintendent. In confidence, of course. This may be the tip of an iceberg or it may be an isolated instance of somebody taking advantage of a foreigner. If the former, it's certainly a situation you'd wish to nip in the bud."

Kiet searched his mind for a diplomatic response. Two weeks of financial anarchy in Hickorn and Smithson had not *known*? He and his nation's spy satellites and CIA network hadn't an inkling until he'd sent out a flunky with a portion of his ambassadorial paycheck?

"If I may be candid, sir."

Smithson nodded grimly. "Please do. Nothing you say will leave this room."

"We have had a sprinkling of recent counterfeiting complaints. We are investigating."

"If these were normal times, I wouldn't understand. The Luongan zin isn't worth the paper it's printed on."

Bamsan Kiet did not need to be reminded by this individual that his country's currency was wallpaper. "In sufficient quantities, Mr. Ambassador, anything has value. In what context, please, are these abnormal times?"

Smithson smiled tightly and winked. "The Rouge have been quiet recently. Agreed?"

37

Kiet agreed. The last Luong Rouge engagement with the Royal Luongan Army had occurred five or six weeks ago. The army units stationed in the highlands, at Obon, were timid. Seldom did they dispatch patrols into the countryside, almost never at night. Their operations were reactive, a face-saving counter to Rouge aggression, interruptions to the routine business of trafficking opium delivered across the northern borders by Golden Triangle warlords.

The Rouge and their infinitely patient leader, Ril Thoi, held confrontations to a minimum. Kiet had grown up with Thoi and knew his revolutionary fires to be undiminished since the beginnings of the movement in the 1960s. But Thoi had a problem in common with Kiet and his police department: budget.

Thoi believed that his revolution should be spotlessly indigenous, an uprising of the peasantry against the decadent shackles of oppressive constitutional monarchy. He, therefore, refused any and all gifts from Communist superpowers and from his Socialist brothers in Vietnam, Cambodia, and Laos, who had themselves accepted plenty of SAM missiles, AK-47s, and resident advisers. If you had to climb into bed with a foreign master, Thoi often said, you couldn't see the romance of his ideology in the dark, you only felt what was being done to you.

Aggravating Ril Thoi's stunted revolution was a lack of monarchial oppression. Prince Pakse taxed his peasants equitably. They ate their fill of crops grown and sold the surplus without unfair levies. Discontent was just another deficit in Ril Thoi's revolutionary budget.

"A skirmish ten kilometers out of Obon," Kiet recalled. "Two government troops wounded, a guerrilla killed."

"A search-and-destroy mission, but piddling. Am I right?"

"Yes." Kiet knew the unofficial and correct version. The Rouge had blundered into a rendezvous of Luongan troopers and Chinese drug traders, whose mules carried saddlebags of

38

raw opium. The soldiers and bandits had protected their profits with the ferocity of a tigress defending her cubs.

"The lull before the storm is my perspective."

"Excuse me, sir?"

"Rouge printers have taken a quantum leap from propaganda pamphlets, haven't they?"

Kiet was catching the drift. "Mr. Ambassador, every Communist leaflet I've seen is somewhat crude."

"Past tense, Superintendent. Before the introduction of Soviet printing hardware. What better way to waltz in and take over than after inundating Hickorn with counterfeit money. The Rouge can't overcome Luongan democracy with muscle, so they switched their tactics to a softer form of terrorism. Orchestrate an economic collapse and march in without firing a shot. Maybe I'm getting ahead of myself, this counterfeiting menace as new as it is, but it's a theory that should be prioritized."

This was going badly. Kiet had dragged himself here to research western printing technology in Luong, and Smithson was presenting fantasies of Russian photocopiers being parachuted into the highlands.

"Minister of Finance Bu and I talked earlier," Kiet offered. "He believes the motive is sheerly criminal and mercenary. Further, he explained a phenomenon he termed an inflationary gap. This is what happens when a money supply is increased significantly. Hypergalloping inflation occurs."

"Bu's a good man, an egghead from my old alma mater. We're fellow Yalies, you know. Boola boola. But between you and me and the gatepost, Superintendent, Totisa keeps his head buried too deeply in his books."

Boola boola? A pagan chant somehow associated with Yalieship and the botanical Ivy League? The recognition code of a secret society? Kiet did not care to pursue this puzzle. "Mayor Tia, likewise, implies that the counterfeiting motive is greed. He is worried that the consequence to Hickorn's economy will destroy him politically."

39

"I can't heap enough kudos on Fop Tia," Smithson said, shaking his head in admiration. "That gentleman is a manager. In a very short time, he's completely transformed Hickorn into a systems-oriented jewel of municipal organization. It's amazing!"

"Amazing," Kiet repeated.

"Mayor Tia's fears may be premature, though. I have no intention of allowing the counterfeiting to go beyond its embryonic stage and jeopardize his chances at the polls."

Kiet suppressed a groan. He did not reply.

"I was posted in Saigon in the 1960s, you know. The Vietcong destroyed the credibility of that city's leadership through urban terrorism. Bombings and sapper attacks and the dissemination of fear. As I earlier stated, Ril Thoi and his thugs are too weak to accomplish their evil goals with bullets and plastique. It makes more and more sense for them to take a subtler approach."

Kiet said nothing.

"Well, we can squelch that little scheme in a hurry. Minister of Defense Cuong Van is a close friend of mine. I'll get on the horn and set up a meeting. Once we've pinpointed the source of the counterfeiting, surgical strikes on key positions will bring their evil game to a swift end."

Kiet visualized the highland army commanders and the lip service they would pay to Smithson's request, even if it was ordered by Cuong Van. They were too consumed with their opium to risk casualties in quest of phantom laser printers.

"On the outside possibility that the machines originate in Hickorn, Mr. Ambassador, who might market them?"

Smithson opened his top desk drawer. "You're stretching, Superintendent. That's a long shot."

"I must be thorough and explore everything, sir."

"I understand. They say that the vast majority of all police investigations result in dead ends. But no stones can be left unturned, can they?"

"No, sir."

Smithson handed Kiet an embossed business card. On its corners were the cities of Singapore, Kuala Lumpur, Hickorn, and Bangkok. In the center: *Tropics Office Products, Ltd.* Roland (Buzz) Wheeler, Luong Regional Manager. 423 Avenue Hai Ba Trung, Hickorn. Telephone 23.769.

"You have had transactions with them?" Kiet asked.

"No. We aren't permitted to purchase durable goods on the economy. We requisition equipment from State. Mayor Tia may have bought from this outfit. Fop and Wheeler are friends. He introduced Buzz to me at a party."

Buzz. A strange nickname, thought Kiet. His English dictionary defined it as a persistent vibrating sound. He remembered a drinking session with Captain Binh, in which his adjutant, in a giggly tone after consuming two Golden Tigers, had confessed to having a "buzz on."

"If I may ask, Mr. Ambassador, what is your impression of Mr. Wheeler?"

"A nice fellow, fast-talking and witty, but a bit too breezy for my taste. Too much the salesman and hustler."

Kiet stood. He and Smithson promised each other full cooperation on the counterfeiting menace.

When Kiet reached the door, Smithson said, "Take care of that lumbago."

"Excuse me?"

"You're listing to starboard."

Kiet began to explain. Smithson cut him off. "I threw something out playing polo and my back's never been the same. One of the hardships of this tour is that Hickorn has no chiropractors. The next best thing is regular massages. It worked wonders for me."

"Thank you for the information, sir."

"And try not to catch a chill. It's murder on your joints."

7

THE INTERNATIONAL DISTRICT was a residential enclave for upper-class Luongans and wealthy foreigners. Compounds and villas were not walled but were separated from the masses by spiked, wrought-iron fencing as tall as any man. Vegetation—palm trees, shrubs and hedges, rainbows of perennial flowers—put one to mind of a manicured jungle.

Avenue Hai Ba Trung ran east and west. Its name was Vietnamese, for the three sisters Trung. His royal Highness had granted the designation as a sop to militant Hanoi. Centuries ago, the Trung heroines had commanded an army that repelled Chinese invaders. As the women's exploits were pre-Marxist, domino theorists and the hearty capitalists living along the street were not offended.

Four-twenty-three was located closer to downtown than the International District's pricier far limits, but from what Kiet saw as he stopped, he would take it. A two-level stucco house, spacious but not oppressively large. Wrought-iron gates that were swung open. A BMW automobile parked in the courtyard. To a side, a pool of tubby goldfish were supplied recirculated water by a urinating concrete cherub. If fortune ever granted him ownership of this property, he would strongly consider remodeling that bizarre touch with a sledgehammer.

A bronze plaque on the vestibule announced *Tropics Office Products, Ltd.* Kiet pushed the doorbell button. Chimes clanged inside. He waited. No answer. He rang again. Still no answer. He tried the door. It was unlocked, as was the inner door.

42

Kiet entered what had once been a living room or a drawing room. It was now a merchandise showroom. Machines big and small, performing functions known and unknown to him, rested on floors of polished hardwood and on Persian throw rugs. The larger devices were freestanding, the tinier displayed on tables. Some, presumably microcomputers, had television screens. Others, perhaps copiers, came equipped with slots, bins, and colorful keypads. Familiar logos and brand names of multinational corporations were well represented. As in the U.S. Embassy, musicians entertained from an unseen phonograph. This was a presentation of drums and horns that he recognized as pretty good jazz. He guessed that Wheeler lived here too, the upstairs being his private quarters. Whether he did or not, Tropics Office Products, Ltd., was no slapdash bazaar at the public market.

Kiet noticed that one end of the room had been partitioned into a business office. Its door was ajar. He could see the edge of a desk and a pair of crossed feet. The feet were encased in shiny loafers connected to legs and creased slacks. A western business executive in repose, he thought. It surprised him that he didn't smell cigar smoke.

"Hello," he said.

Silence.

"Mr. Wheeler?"

More silence.

Kiet went into the office and discovered why the man lounging at his desk didn't rush to greet a potential customer. He was seated in a swivel chair, arms akimbo, chin vertical. He had been shot in what remained of his face. How many close-range rounds it had taken to make him indistinguishable as a human being Kiet could not say. On the desk was a perforated bedroom pillow, an impromptu silencer. Mr. Roland (Buzz) Wheeler, he assumed.

Kiet took a deep breath, closed his eyes, and backpedaled. Squeamishness at the sight of gore was Bamsan

43

Kiet's deepest secret. Knowledge that blood and guts wrenched the stomach of Hickorn's ranking law-enforcement professional would result in an irreparable loss of face. Luongans were gentle people, but they would not tolerate sissies in positions of police authority. Men assigned to shield them from the unfeeling were expected, to a reasonable degree, to be similarly remote. If the truth were ever revealed, a child shoplifter would resist his attempt to arrest.

The brutality of the murder reminded him of Marsad Ref. Former Royal Luongan Army Colonel Marsad Ref was the most vicious man he had ever encountered. To fire five shots into the face of a man when one would suffice was his style. His motive would be fun, not meticulousness.

Less than a year before, through a complex scheme of smuggling, intimidation, and murder, Ref had almost turned the Kingdom of Luong upside down. Kiet and Binh had captured him in a Hickorn Continental hotel room as he prepared to assassinate His Royal Highness and Ambassador Smithson, who were below at a street-renaming ceremony. Ref wore a wig and the scruffy fatigues of a guerrilla. His assault rifle and sniperscope were Chinese made. The Rouge were, of course, to be blamed. And there would be a power vacuum Ref intended to fill, regardless how bloody rival factions chose to make it.

The two police officers then bundled up Ref and secreted him out of the hotel in a laundry cart. They took him to the Foh Ten Bridge and forced him to cross it, unarmed and without money. Foh Ten, also called Dragon's Bile, was a dreadful slum, Hickorn's shame. Its inhabitants were survivors, predators who fed on the lives and possessions of others.

Kiet's decision to release Marsad Ref into Foh Ten was based on two reasons: expediency and self-righteous cruelty. To hold Ref under arrest and endure a lengthy trial was perilous. He and his supporters were too clever and

44

volatile. A coup d'etat commanded from a headquarters jail cell. An assault on the jail to release him. Further assassination attempts by followers. Judges and jurors terrorized into voting an acquittal. The possible horrors were endless.

Thus an ironic justice was conceived by Kiet. Army deserters who Ref had brutalized while posted at the Royal Luongan Military Academy existed in Foh Ten in some numbers. The count of civilian rascals holding grudges against the colonel was also high. Marsad Ref should have been quickly consumed in his new environment. Kiet's conscience had not permitted him to administer a bullet to the head of the monster while he was trussed in the trunk of his car at the foot of the Foh Ten Bridge. He came later to regard it cowardly to take the other approach, transferring the responsibility for justice to anonymous psychopaths. He agonized that his twin rationales had blended, that he was dumping a problem and hoping that justice would *not* be swift. He dreamed of Ref and when he did he was finished sleeping for the night. One evening he dreamt that Ambassador Ritchie was seated on the edge of his bed, narrating videotapes of Ref's torture by vengeful thugs, chastising him throughout for his hypocritical stance on human rights.

He need not have lost the sleep. Marsad Ref was not consumed by Foh Ten, he now *ruled* it. The thievery and prostitution and power games within and the stolen goods that were brought from Hickorn proper, the essence of Foh Ten's economy, were *his*. Captain Binh said that Ref had become Foh Ten's "godfather." The word had no counterpart in the Luongan language. Binh's definition of a regional crime superintendent was the antithesis of the natural separation of the word into deity and head of family. No wonder westerners do not understand us, Kiet thought for the millionth time. Kiet inspected the body again, albeit briefly. This was Ref's handiwork, although it probably wasn't. The colonel had not been sighted outside

45

Foh Ten since his banishment. He had been recently moving into extortion of Hickorn small businessmen, but had been doing so via outside contractors, criminals of modest capabilities who foresaw Ref's eventual expansion and desired to be part of it.

Kiet shuddered, aware that Marsad Ref hadn't cornered the market on sadistic homicide. He needed a bathroom in a hurry. Afterward, he telephoned Binh and asked him to come over, refusing to say why. Kiet hoped he had spoken in a calm, measured, professional tone. But he couldn't be sure. That uncertainty was almost more distressing than discovery of the body.

8

CAPTAIN BINH ARRIVED in twenty minutes. Kiet had gotten his nausea under control and wandered through the villa, determining by ransacked cupboards and drawers in other rooms that the killer or killers had searched the place. A back door leading into the alley was wide open. Kiet further decided that he had interrupted a search in progress.

Binh zeroed in on the body, the victim, the fascinating pathological puzzle. Kiet waited elsewhere. Binh emerged from the office with a wallet, deducing from identification therein that the deceased was indeed Roland Wheeler.

"I attended several autopsies in D.C., Superintendent," Binh said. "I learned a lot about pathology as it applies to murder. Even as a layman I can confidently state that Mr. Wheeler was killed within the past hour. There is no rigor mortis yet. And, see, if you will, that the surface blood is in gelatinous clumps and not entirely clotted."

Gelatinous clumps. Kiet did not move forward. He was on the opposite side of the showroom, a perspiring palm laid casually on some sort of postal metering doohickey, eyes focused on a harmless point above Wheeler's door opening and the ghoulish Binh. "Yes. I observed that. Excellent, Captain."

"The pillow was used to muffle the gunshots. I doubt if the neighbors heard anything. They didn't contact us if they did."

"Your conclusions are, as always, correct and insightful. We'll continue searching the premises on the hopeful assumption that the killer or killers did not find what they were looking for."

Binh reached for a telephone. "I'll get a forensic team over and additional officers to canvass the neighborhood."

"No," Kiet said. Binh's "forensic team" would trample through, wasting department film and smearing fingerprint powder about until the interior of the building looked like it had been whitewashed. To preserve professional harmony he kept that reason to himself, but divulged the important one. "I want this crime to temporarily remain our secret."

"Superintendent—"

"Does anyone at headquarters know why you're here?"

"No, they couldn't. You didn't tell me why you needed me. Your voice was strained, so I knew it was something major. I maintained confidentiality."

"I knew you would and I know you're also aware that rumors and gossip in Hickorn travel like pollen."

"Yes, but the sooner we gather evidence, canvass for witnesses, and put out an APB, the better our prospects of an arrest."

An APB too. Hickorn's theaters featured old American cop movies. Kiet visualized Yankee police work as boxy Ford sedans and dragnets and roadblocks in a black-and-white world of tommy guns and double-breasted suits. Naturally, today's methods absorbed by Binh in the District of Columbia had advanced—the forensic laboratories and computerized APBs and whatnot—but his young adjutant's enthusiasm and instincts seemed to parallel those of western fictional detectives more closely than prior to his training. "The evidence, the primary evidence, is what we seek. Do you have an ax in the trunk of your car?"

With a puzzled frown, Binh nodded yes.

"Bring it, please."

Binh did.

"Come. I thought I smelled varnish in an upstairs bedroom."

The bedroom with the faint varnish odor had a wall-length, built-in closet of glossy teak that was identical to

48

others on the floor, but the room was unusually compact.

"The intruders fled before they had an opportunity to come upstairs," Kiet said. "Everything is in order."

Binh sniffed. "I smell it too."

He then tried the folding doors. One bank of three opened easily. The other two wouldn't budge. "Locked, Superintendent. Or they are dummies."

He felt and knocked and tugged on the decorative fascia, saying, "On a drug raid in Washington, we were stymied until a loose brick in a fireplace was pulled out. Lo and behold, it was connected to a rope that released an adjacent veneer of wall paneling. Ingenious! Inside was five kilos of pure cocaine."

"Yes, yes," Kiet said. "Please use the ax to unlock this mystery."

The partition between the real and false closet was thinner than the doors. Binh chopped through it and saw wires and cables and metal tracks.

"This section is designed to slide upward, Superintendent," he said between gulps for breath. "It's electrically powered. I'll bet I can trace where it's activated. Perhaps a fake light switch."

Kiet was too excited to spoil Binh's fun. "Splendid idea. Later, though."

He assisted in removing the splintered wood. The exposed cavity revealed a photocopier the size of a kitchen range, an ordinary paper cutter, and two large cardboard boxes. The copy machine was on casters. They wheeled it into the bedroom and slid out the heavy boxes. One was filled with blank paper, the second with sheets of zin notes, six bills to a page.

"Millions and millions worth of queer," Binh said in whispered awe. "If you had walked in on them twenty minutes after you did Superintendent, this would be gone."

Kiet plugged in the copier. "Speaking of activating things—how?"

"Simple." Binh took a thousand-zin from his wallet, inserted it in the slot, and pushed a button. After three minutes of whirring and buzzing, the NOT READY light went out, and a perfect duplicate of the bill was excreted into a tray.

"See," Binh said. "Both sides. Wheeler did six bills at once to save time and to fill a blank sheet, but the principle is the same."

"Plain bond paper, as Minister Bu said genuine zin is printed on," Kiet said, mesmerized. "You merely cut it to size and spend it."

"Superintendent, my forensic team?"

"Instant money," Kiet went on. "Extraordinary."

"Superintendent?"

Kiet snapped out of it, lifted the box of counterfeit, emptied it onto a bed, grunted, and said, "Patience, Captain. First we count and collate."

"Count and collate?"

"The paper cutter, please. We'll finish that chore for the late Mr. Buzz Wheeler."

Hickorn is situated between the equator and the Tropic of Cancer, at nineteen degrees north latitude. In the tropics, there is no twilight; the word is not even in the Luongan vocabulary. When the sun sets, it is as if a blanket is thrown over it.

Ten minutes to seven, the funny money was cut and arranged to Kiet's satisfaction. Out the bedroom window, the sudden blackness was accentuated by street lights. A line of moons on the horizon, he thought. There was a symmetry to the timing of task completion and otherworldly imagery that he couldn't quite define.

He had sent Binh to Wheeler's office for more rubber bands to wrap the money. Binh returned, wrinkling his nose, saying, "Superintendent, putrefaction is happening. May I call—"

Kiet cut Binh off with a hand wave before he was treated

50

to details of decomposition. "Soon. Now, what do we have? Eight different denominations, about one hundred different serial numbers for each. The matching serial numbers that alerted Ambassador Smithson and myself were statistical accidents. This run seems to be concentrated on the biggest denominations."

"Greed," Binh said.

"Greed and maybe urgency. A final printing if they realized that the magnitude of the scheme was causing it to collapse onto itself. A tally, please?"

Binh added columns of figures on his notepad. "A third of a billion zin, Superintendent."

Kiet saw that the captain's hands were trembling. "Don't forget that it's only paper."

"I'm trying."

"Three hundred and some million zin convert to three hundred and some thousand U.S. dollars," Kiet said.

"Not the actual value if it were traded in bulk," Binh said. "In America, counterfeit greenbacks are sold to fences for a small percentage of face value. The rule of thumb is ten to twenty percent, depending on quality."

"Very well, Let us assume a conservative ten percent and a net profit of thirty thousand dollars," Kiet said. He then told Binh of his conversations with A. Singh, Totisa Bu, Fop Tia, and Singh's admission that Mayor Tia had been exchanging zin for fifteen thousand U.S. dollars every other day. "A reverse transaction. People customarily buy zin with dollars. If Tia and Wheeler manufactured this amount in a two-day span and split evenly, your computations jibe."

"What was Wheeler doing with his share?"

Kiet shrugged. "Doubtlessly the same, with Singh or a fellow leech. I was ignorant of Wheeler when I spoke to Singh, and he isn't inclined to be a conscientious citizen and volunteer information."

"I refuse to believe that Freddie Pogue's appearance in town is a coincidence," Binh said.

51

"You may be right," said an equally unconvinced Kiet.

"I have it!" Binh cried. "Fop Tia conspired with Wheeler to print queer and laundered it through his business partners and his ward heelers to prop up his faltering commodities firm and to provide a campaign chest for an election he is in danger of losing and it had gone too far, Wheeler so greedy and so out of control that inflation was damaging Tia's business and his public image to the extent that he had no choice but to have Wheeler murdered."

Kiet digested the soliloquy. Americans had taught him to summarize problems in vast, rapid-fire sentences. He dismissed the reference to laundry as babble induced by fatigue, but his theory was nevertheless logical. "Splendid, Captain, although the killing, the, uh, corpse, the manner—Marsad Ref has not strayed from Foh Ten, has he?"

The euphoria of Binh's inspiration faded from his face. From the outset, he had disagreed with Kiet's decision to release Ref into Foh Ten. But his dissent had been silent, manifested by curt replies whenever Ref's name was mentioned and by sullen expressions. A Luongan, even if tainted by twelve months of police department labor unions and internal-affairs snoops and citizen review boards and ombudsmen, could not dishonor a superior with mockery and insubordination. To do so would dishonor himself.

"Not to my knowledge," Binh said coolly. "I can't give you a guarantee. Ref is slippery. When I saw Wheeler, Ref came to mind too."

"A name we will record in our mental lists along with Freddie Pogue's," Kiet said. "This is becoming complicated."

Binh cupped a hand to his cheek. "Superintendent?"

"Yes, yes. Telephone your forensic team."

While Binh was downstairs calling, Kiet loaded the funny money back into its box. Binh came up the steps, footfalls sounding like a minor stampede. "Superintendent, there is a free-for-all at the airport!"

"Excuse me?"

52

"A brawl. Every officer not on patrol duty is at the scene or enroute."

"Including your forensic team?"

"Unfortunately."

"The worst of luck," Kiet said, rolling his eyes in feigned exasperation. "Everything is falling on our heads simultaneously. What type of brawl?"

"The religious sect I briefed you on yesterday. Apparently they accosted a group of stopover travelers. A cultist was caught in the act of pickpocketing. All hell broke loose."

"Take an end of this box. A third of a billion queer zin is heavier than it looks."

"Superintendent, doesn't this situation have priority?"

"You said yourself that no help is presently available. We'll load this in a car, go to the airport, and when we've investigated the spectacle, we'll commandeer your forensic experts and resume the investigation."

"The body?"

"Mr. Wheeler is indisposed. He will wait. Come."

9

HICKORN INTERNATIONAL AIRPORT was located four kilometers north of downtown, on Richard Nixon Boulevard. The road was a smooth four lanes separated by a brushy median—Luong's closest facsimile to a freeway. It had been constructed with American foreign aid funds, a sleek thoroughfare designed to rush airlifted assistance into the capital in event of Communist shenanigans. The airport was not one of the world's busiest, and Nixon Boulevard traffic was proportionally light. In the late hours, upper-class youths raced their motorbikes and sports cars. The danger to anyone but themselves was so slight that Kiet did not assign officers to police the insanity.

The airport terminal was a seedy stucco arrangement connected to the control tower, which jutted upward on the south side. At night, not much could be seen except an electronic glow inside the tower's four walls of blue glass and backlighted lettering above the terminal entrance that proclaimed, "H CKO N."

Despite this gentle shabbiness, Hickorn International was truly international. The Ma San River was widest at Hickorn's docks and played out into malarial tributaries near the Thai border. But for paths in mountain passes and rough trails hacked through double-canopy jungle, the only way out of Luong was up.

Binh drove too fast in the narrow labyrinth of business-district streets. This was expected and Kiet braced an elbow against his door to protect against concussions and shattered collarbones as the Citroën and its worn-out suspension slid and swayed. He clung to the front of his seat with white-knuckled hands when they sped onto Nixon, and Binh pressed his foot to the floor, shouting over the whining and shuddering of the machine that this was an excellent opportunity to "blow out the carbon."

Meanwhile, Kiet had subdued his terror sufficiently to quiz Binh on the religious sect.

"They identify themselves as the Church of the Amalgamation of Enlightenment, Superintendent."

"Amalgamation?"

"That's the central feature of their faith, so they say. It means to merge or unite. They claim their religion combines the positive attributes of every other, and therefore is the answer to true enlightenment. Those are their words, Superintendent. The church is incorporated in Delaware."

The last sentence didn't logically follow. Kiet let it pass and said, "They use the airport for their fund-raising activities, you told me."

"Yes. They give flowers and pamphlets to travelers and request donations in return. Proselytizing at airports by sects out of the religious mainstream is very common. When they aren't at the airport, they're downtown, begging food for their own needs."

"Excuse me," Kiet said. "Why don't they buy food with the money they raise at the airport?"

"It isn't allowed. It's all sent to America, to their guru."

"I remember you saying that he was an Indian who was not an Indian. I was too busy at the time with counterfeiting to pursue that riddle."

"Their guru imitates the Hindu fakirs in his dress and his preaching techniques. He is really an American of half-Irish, half-Pakistani descent named Khalid O'Shea. In the cult he is the Fahwandi Kli Shabbir. He is extremely wealthy, but is presently serving time in Lompoc for mail fraud and income-tax evasion. I learned this from contacts at the U.S. Embassy. The Church of the Amalgamation of

55

Enlightenment is a source of considerable embarrassment to them."

"What, please, is a Lompoc?"

"A minimum-security prison in the State of California. The bulk of the inmates are swindlers and check forgers and lawyers. Some of the Watergate felons did time there. They have fences instead of walls, and the prisoners live in dormitories. I hear they have tennis courts. This guru was sent to Lompoc because he isn't dangerous and because it was his first offense."

Kiet did not understand. Either a prison was a prison or it was not. This Lompoc seemed to be a compromise that rested offenders from the pressures of their criminal careers and encouraged them to repeat upon release. Luong's only tennis courts were behind the walls of International District villas. He wondered if Lompoc guards were permitted to play. He withheld further questions about the amalgamated zealots and the promise of further bewilderment. He would see for himself.

Hickorn International's terminal lobby had the look and aroma of a gymnasium. Airline counters to one side. Open space and scuffed tile in the center. Benches, lockers, and public toilets on the opposite side.

The scene struck Kiet as the aftermath of a savage and disputed basketball game. He noticed streaks of blood on the floor. Western tourists stood at the ticket counters, airport security personnel and uniformed Hickorn police officers close by, as if referees. Seven people knelt on a bench, hands joined. They wore silken robes decorated like camouflage fatigues. Their heads were shaved and they were humming in unison. Referees overseeing *this* group outnumbered their colleagues three to one. Their holsters were unsnapped.

"Were they armed?" Kiet asked Binh.

"No. I'm certain they weren't. They claim the colors, the

56

greens, blues, and browns in their robes symbolize sea, sky, and earth," Binh said. "They appear paramilitary, but they aren't."

"What are they humming?"

"Nothing in particular, Superintendent. A singsong they call a mantra. It gets them in touch with their alleged essence."

"Amalgamating," Kiet said, groaning. "Age range, twenties and thirties. Four males, three females?"

"Five and two, I think, Superintendent. The cultist on the extreme left is a man."

"His mouth and one eye are swollen and he is handcuffed. The pickpocket, I presume."

"We'll find out fast."

Binh scanned for someone in charge. A Hickorn patrol sergeant was watching the captain and his superintendent. An airport security sergeant too. Binh wagged a finger at the latter, the man with primary responsibility here. The incident had certainly caused him humiliation. A snub would be crushing. Kiet approved of Binh's sensitivity.

The sergeant approached in short, hurried steps and saluted. Binh returned the salute and asked, "Who is the victim?"

The sergeant pointed at a stout red-faced Caucasian with a gray brush cut. Kiet had already observed the man, the most agitated of the lot, massaging his knuckles. "His name is O.A. Munger, sir. He is in a tour from Beijing that is changing planes to Bangkok. The monk in handcuffs took his wallet. Mr. Munger felt a hand in his pocket. He chased the monk and tackled him. They fought. The monk's friends came to his aid. Mr. Munger's friends came to his."

"A free-for-all," Binh said.

"Yes, sir. We were able to separate them before any more blood was shed."

"Except the monk's," Kiet said.

"Yes, Superintendent. Mr. Munger is extremely strong. It took four of us to remove him from the monk."

Kiet looked at the westerners. Tension was apparent and it worried him. "Is the cocktail lounge open?"

"No, Superintendent. I ordered it closed due to the trouble."

"Splendid. Correct for that moment, but please have it reopened. It is a handy release valve that will put added distance between the tourists and the cultists."

"You the head honcho at this Chinese fire drill?"

O.A. Munger's hand was on Kiet's arm. Luongans disliked being touched by strangers, and Kiet slapped it away as if it were an insect. He looked at Binh for a translation. Binh nodded yes, Kiet was the head honcho.

"Hey, don't get testy, champ," Munger said, taking a prudent backward step. "Our plane's lifting off in an hour and we need to wrap this thing up. Our itinerary don't call for delays in unauthorized countries."

"We would not want you delayed here . . . " Kiet said, adding for the sake of diplomacy, "unnecessarily."

Munger wrung his right hand and flexed his fingers. "Hit that sucker a couple good ones."

The gesture seemed to be of pride rather than pain. Munger's breath was a wilting blend of stale bourbon and generic halitosis. "Sir, has your property been returned to you?"

"Yep. The fag just got my wallet. We're on a twelve-day See Asia thing we won for having top volume in the western zone. Wholesale auto parts is what I'm talking about. They told us before we left about rinky-dink places like this, how nine-year-old pimps would snatch your watches right off your wrist. Didn't think some white guy, goddamn pervert or not, would be taking a shot. We're not gonna have to hang around for a trial or anything, are we?"

Kiet addressed the sergeant. "Do you have written statements?"

"Yes, Superintendent, from Mr. Munger and witnesses."

"Then you are free to leave Luong, sir."

"He'll get what's coming to him?"

"He will receive a fair trial."

"They're supposed to be religious, you know," Munger said. "They was pushing their leaflets on us the minute we stepped off the fucking plane. I'm a God-fearing Christian. These yo-yos, they don't even believe in Jesus. How come you tolerate atheists like this?"

Kiet said nothing.

"Luong is a free country, sir," Binh said sharply.

"You ought to have a death penalty for this kind of stuff. Look at 'em, off in their trances! Fucking commie zombies—"

"Orville."

A chunky woman with frizzed hair and a cigarette impaled in the corner of her mouth was tugging at his shirt.

"This here's the little woman," Munger said in introduction.

"They just unlocked the lounge, Orville. The bartender says he knows how to make mai tais."

"Thank you for your cooperation, Mr. Munger," Kiet said.

"I'd hang around if I could," Munger said in tow, looking back.

"Appreciated," Kiet said.

"You got an electric chair, you need a volunteer to throw the fucking switch, I'm your boy."

Mrs. Munger cackled and slapped her husband on the rear. Kiet exhaled relief as the tourists filed into the bar. He suggested to Binh that they interview the opposing basketball squad, although he didn't state his request in those terms. Kiet and Binh walked to the cultists. Surprisingly, they broke out of their spells without coaxing. Their eyes rose and froze intently on Kiet. A member of the sect stood and bowed.

"I am Kanpurin Morajini, leader of our mission," he said to

Kiet. "I apologize profoundly for the action of my brother. Kanpurin Rastafed has disgraced us."

He was half a head taller than Kiet and as thin as any Foh Ten wretch. His shaved scalp and drawn cheeks resembled a skull more than a face. "Identification, please."

"Yes, Fahwandi."

Kiet glared at Morajini before inspecting the cards given him. Binh said, "He did not call you a profanity, Superintendent. I'll explain later."

A driver's license issued in the State of Oregon, a Social Security card, and a thick plastic rectangle with raised letters and overlapping orange moons identified the alleged Kanpurin Morajini as John R. Smith.

"My father canceled my MasterCard some time ago, Fahwandi. I retain it only to prove who I am in contexts such as this."

"Your two names are quite different," Kiet said.

"I was conferred my true name by our gossamer master Fahwandi Kli Shabbir when I elevated my being in this life to an enlightened plane."

Fahwandi again. Kiet attributed Morajini/Smith's confused use of the title to malnutrition and narcotics addiction. The Katmandu guru seekers of the 1960s and 1970s ingested an astounding variety of chemicals in their quest for nirvana, and the Church of the Amalgamation of Enlightenment was as bizzare as its predecessors.

"Is the pickpocketing charge to be denied?"

"No, Fahwandi. Our Kanpuri have diverse backgrounds. Enlightenment is a fragile state, and past lives unfortunately overlap. I was an aeronautical engineer, for instance. Kanpurin Sharla was a bank employee named Joyce Wilson."

Morajini had gestured to a lovely young woman with green eyes and a sprinkling of freckles. She was smiling and her eyes were locked on Kiet. He felt himself blush and said, "Your Kanpurin Rastafed?"

60

"He was a thief," Morajini said matter-of-factly.

"Who is he?"

"William N. Jones," said the sergeant. "According to an expired State of Illinois driver's license."

Rastafed/Jones was continuing the humming noise that sounded like "ommmm." He too was fixated on Kiet, in a disjointed gaze that made the superintendent shiver. "Have you interrogated him?"

"We tried," said the sergeant. "If you ask me, his brain is dead."

Morajini said, "Kanpurin Rastafed is purging. If a Kanpurin is inherently weak, the plane that separates his base life from his enlightened is a film of thin ice."

"Mr. Jones has fallen though?" Kiet said.

"He has, Fahwandi," Morajini said, bowing. "He is as contrite and mortified as I, I assure you. Through cleansing meditation, he is—"

"Refrigerating the plane," Kiet finished. "He must come with us regardless."

"I am yours to comply, Fahwandi."

"You and your followers will accompany us, please. You cannot stay at the airport tonight. I do not want more trouble."

Morajini bowed and went to his people. They got up without argument. Kanpurin Sharla and another assisted Rastafed/Jones to his feet. The seven followed Hickorn police officers out of the terminal. Kiet took Binh aside and said, "A night in jail will do them good. They need a clean bed and a meal."

"Very generous," Binh said coolly. "You and I are returning to Wheeler's?"

Kiet realized he had been justifying his decision to his young adjutant and was mildly angry at himself. "Yes. But you have a point to clarify regarding the Fahwandi business?"

In Binh's hand was a rolled-up pamphlet. "I've seen this literature of theirs before, but I hadn't paid much attention

61

to—well, tell me what you think of the photograph on the cover page."

It was a picture of the gossamer master Fahwandi Kli Shabbir in the camouflage garb. He was seated cross-legged on an ornate high-backed chair. A colorful tapestry provided the backdrop. Incense burned in brass urns at each side of the chair. Shabbir's features were Oriental. He was middle-aged and meaty. Bamsan Kiet could have been looking at himself in a mirror.

"A remarkable resemblance, is it not, Superintendent?"

Kiet groaned.

10

KIET'S EXTRATERRESTRIAL IMPRESSION of nighttime Hai Ba Trung Street was obliterated by the blinking red lights atop police cars. The activity was at 423, Wheeler's villa. The moons on the horizon, the street lights, were congregation points for snoopy neighbors, vantage points near enough to observe but far enough to avoid personal involvement. Flashlight beams cut through the side yards as if scythes. An officer, pen poised at notebook, was interviewing a man in the courtyard. The man, a Caucasian, was in his underwear and smoking a cigarette.

"Oh my God," Binh said.

"I agree," Kiet said, stepping out of the Citroën, thinking that every serviceable headquarters vehicle not at the airport must be present.

He was familiar with the interviewee, an antique Frenchman named Andre Lupien. Lupien had been manager of the Michelin rubber plantation before his retirement. An *engagé*, haughty with the affluence of his International District life, he looked somewhat ridiculous in jockey shorts and undershirt. The sight of stooped posture, lumpy leg veins surrendered to gravity, and slack skin pleased Kiet.

"Kiet, what is Hickorn, Chicago or Marseilles? Burglars can loot our finest neighborhood?"

"Monsieur Lupien lives across the street, Superintendent," said the nervous officer. "He heard noises and saw lights go on. He telephoned us."

The officer and the Frenchman were agitated, though distressingly calm under the circumstances. Inside was a

63

mutilated and rotting human body. Kiet played along. "Was anyone discovered in the house?"

"No, Superintendent. They made their escape before we arrived."

Kiet and Binh could not look at each other. To leave a capital crime scene unguarded violated the procedures of any police department.

Lupien said. "They were making a terrible racket, waking the dead."

"Did they come in a vehicle?" Kiet asked, almost wondering if Lupien's saying could be taken literally.

"Not that I saw."

"Another neighbor heard loud racing noises in the alley, Superintendent," the officer said. "And the back door has been kicked in."

Lupien coughed a harsh cigarette cough and said, "It was primitive, Kiet. Animals crashing into a home and doing what they wish with a person's belongings."

Kiet thought it ironic that a crime against property was detected in some detail, while the earlier grisly one escaped all notice.

"Thank you for your cooperation, Monsieur Lupien," he said, hopeful that the expression of appreciation would dismiss him.

It did, but not before a parting blow. "Any time, Kiet. Do what you can, will you, to confine your burglars to their own native quarters. This is an alarming precedent. Peace of mind is taken for granted in the International District. For the price, we are entitled."

"I am as disturbed about this as you are, sir," Kiet said for entirely different reasons. "This case has our utmost priority."

Kiet gestured to the officer to go inside, to lead a tour. The showroom was undisturbed, but Wheeler's office was in shambles. Desk drawers pulled out, contents scattered. Same with the filing cabinets. There was no body, however, and not a speck of blood.

64

"Obviously they were ransacking for valuables," the officer said. "The remainder of the villa is in similar condition."

"Yes," Kiet said, nodding numbly.

"The putrid odor, do you smell it, Superintendent?"

Kiet had. He was now breathing through his mouth.

"It's as if the residents were careless about leaving food exposed and removing their garbage, but the kitchen is sanitary."

"Peculiar," Kiet said.

The officer consulted a notebook. "The occupant is Roland Wheeler, an American bachelor who sells the office machines we see. The neighbors say he is leasing the villa and has lived here for about nine months. Their relationship with him was polite. You know how these International District people are, Superintendent. They're wary and snobbish. Wheeler was an American who rented instead of buying. They regarded him as a transient who was ostentatious with money."

"Ostentatious. How, please?"

"His automobile. That BMW is new. This villa too, of course. He threw big parties that lasted late and loud."

"Did the neighbors identify party guests?"

"Monsieur Lupien sniffed noisily and said they were *nouveau riche* merchants without substance and grabby politicians."

"Specifically, please."

"Mayor Tia was the best-known name. Some of his cronies in his business enterprises and at City Hall."

"The Hickorn Center for Public Administration," Kiet corrected.

He turned to Binh, but he was gone. To avoid generating a conversation with the officer on Fop Tia, he watched police officers with notebooks, recording their observations. Uniforms without notebooks and pencils were crawling on the carpeting with tweezers and daubing fingerprint powder on doorknobs. Trolling for evidence. Binh's legacy from the New World, he thought.

65

"Where is the captain?" he finally said.

The officer replied by cocking a thumb upward. Kiet trudged the steps. He found Binh in the reworked bedroom. He was seated tensely on the edge of the bed, hands clasped.

"The copier is gone, Superintendent."

Kiet sat beside him.

"It would be," Kiet said. "It would be."

11

NEXT MORNING, ON the verge of noon, Heng Fri was the desk sergeant on duty at headquarters. He was Kiet's age and beyond, a gaunt and wrinkled department veteran who wore a perpetual gap-toothed smirk. A cynic with a high regard for law and order, he was a loyal, honest policeman and a useful instrument for the humbling of suspects brought in to be booked. One look at Heng Fri and a criminal with lies and apologetic tales to tell knew that he was in for a hard tribunal.

"Bamsan, these lunatics of yours, if you don't release or shoot them soon, you will have to ship me to the asylum they escaped from."

Kiet's mouth was parched. His brain throbbed, poisoned by the residues of last night's Golden Tiger. The first three beers had softened the edges of a horrendous day. The remainder of the six-pack blurred them. He vowed once more to establish sensible limits on his drinking.

"Excuse me?"

"The loons you arrested. I came on duty and there they were on the floor of their cell, chanting in a circle. These camouflage uniforms of theirs, they are *so* delicate and glossy. Is this an advance party of invading homosexuals?"

Very carefully, Kiet shook his head. "No. You know what they are, Fri. Save your humor."

"I knew they stayed at the airport and in town. I could ignore them there."

"Are they making trouble?"

Heng Fri said, "They're suspiciously obedient, but it is

the chanting that is driving me mad. Unlock the jail door and you can hear for yourself. They're inhuman, Bamsan. They don't sleep."

"Chanting is part of their religion," Kiet said.

"Oh? And *you* are the Gautama Buddha?"

Heng Fri had been raised as a Buddhist, but for as long as Kiet had known him, the sergeant had rejected the teachings of all gods and wise men as he did the stories of prowlers apprehended with skeleton keys and crowbars. "Explain, please."

"The chanting. Key-yet, key-yet, key-yet—"

Kiet raised his hands to stop him. Fri's seniority and their abiding friendship had granted him the privilege of occasional mockery. "Is Captain Binh in?"

Heng Fri's smirk heightened. His face seemed constructed at forty-five-degree angles. "Your prodigy, the boy wonder of criminal science?"

The paranoiac qualities of Golden Tiger hangover were renowned. Westerners who cursed the brew "amber death" attributed it to formaldehyde allegedly used to halt the fermentation process. Whether Kiet's gloom was chemically induced or environmental, he desired to be elsewhere. "Your opinion of my adjutant is on record. Yes or no?"

"The offices. His or yours. If you can do miracles, Bamsan, shut off that record player. I'm really sick of their tune."

Kiet met Binh in the hallway. He heard it too. "Key-yet, key-yet, key-yet . . . "

"Superintendent, they are—"

"They certainly are. Bring Morajini to me, please."

If Kanpurin Morajini/John Smith's bowing servility at the airport had annoyed Kiet, the genuflection at his desk was utterly embarrassing, a deep and prolonged gesture worthy of homage to an empress dowager. "All right! Stand upright or be seated. Stop the silliness!"

"Fahwandi—"

68

"Superintendent, damn you!"

"You are the living reincarnation, Fahwandi."

Kiet groaned and looked at Binh, who shrugged and said, "I cannot reason with them either."

"How can one be alive and simultaneously reincarnated from himself?" Kiet demanded.

"We thought it impossible that our gossamer master Fahwandi Kli Shabbir, even in his omnipotence, could achieve so marvelous a wonder but, Fahwandi, since we cast our eyes on you, our faith is affirmed a thousandfold. He has channeled his being, his essence, to us through you."

"Channeled," Kiet muttered. Another English noun transmuted into a verb. "I resemble your leader in a brochure. You are being silly."

"Resemble, no. Identical, yes, Fahwandi. Too identical for you to be but a gift from our persecuted Fahwandi. His power is celestial and he has made you our gossamer master until the satanists unshackle him."

"Persecuted!" Binh said angrily. "That creep broke laws. He cheated the Internal Revenue Service and solicited money under false pretenses, stupidly using the United States Postal Service. That ugly guru of yours is a con man, Smith. It's about time you faced up to the fact you and the slobs with you have been screwed."

"Ugly?" Kiet asked.

"In the moral sense, Superintendent," Binh answered quickly.

"Your pickpocket must stay for his trial. The rest of you are free to go," Kiet said.

"What are your instructions, Fahwandi?" Morajini asked serenely, oblivious to Binh's tirade.

Kiet had an idea. "The money you raise, what happens to it?"

"Each penny, each franc, each yen, each zin, is an offering to our Fahwandi. Since the great satanic persecution,

69

his financial needs have multiplied. The avarice of lawyers appealing his conviction—"

"Hah! Your guru owns a chain of pizza parlors, real estate throughout America, and an offshore bank in the Caribbean that handles the dirty money you bilk people out of. You have your nerve pleading poverty."

Binh was shouting. The sound waves reverberated in Kiet's skull.

Kiet shushed him with a finger to his lips. "You requested instructions from me, Kanpurin Morajini. Fahwandi Kli Shabbir's holy ministry is worldwide, is it not? His message is to be spread everywhere, yes?"

"Yes, Fahwandi."

"I therefore order you to resume proselytizing at Hickorn International Airport. Once you have raised the cash to buy airplane tickets for you and your disciples, you will venture forth and continue our crusade."

"Ah," Binh said, smiling.

"Bangkok is the closest destination and the cheapest. The Thai will welcome your gospel. They are probably unenlightened."

"Yes, Fahwandi."

"Furthermore, when you are hungry, I decree that you spend necessary funds to feed yourselves at the airport restaurant. Do not waste time begging on Hickorn's streets to satisfy your basic needs."

"Fahwandi, I am not contradicting you, but our gossamer master has always commanded that we propel monies toward the central vortex of enlightenment."

"That is inoperative for the moment," Binh said in gleeful enjoyment. "The living reincarnation requires flexibility in thinking, Kanpurin."

Morajini looked at Binh, then Kiet, who bowed his head, authenticating his assistant's statement.

Kiet got up and shook Morajini's hand. "One additional small point. Why do the Kanpuri shave their heads?"

70

Binh snickered. "Lice control."

Kiet glared at him.

"The Fahwandi's hair grows luxuriantly as does yours, Fahwandi Kiet. Shaving our heads is an expression of love, a symbolic comparison to the thick locks of Fahwandi, a comparison of the ignorance of acolytes to the wisdom of the gossamer master."

"That is undemocratic. Please let it grow. I think my Kanpuri will be more attractive with hair," Kiet said.

"Done, Fahwandi. Our razors can still shave facial hair?"

"Please."

Kiet sent Binh and Morajini to the cells to retrieve the followers, sans Rastafed/Jones, the wallet snatcher. Kiet watched them march out: six pathetic drones. He averted his eyes as Kanpurin Sharla/Joyce Wilson passed. As at the airport, the admiration in her expression was too much like adoration, and Kiet sensed that it was as sexual as spiritual.

The unattractiveness of bare pates was less important to Kiet than the sect's obedience to their substitute guru. It would be a test to prove if Morajini was sincere. The terminal would be spot-checked for acceptable behavior and stubble.

After the departure of the Church of the Amalgamation of Enlightenment prisoners, Kiet and Binh discussed Kiet's discovery at Wheeler's villa of the deceased's wild parties that conspicuously included Mayor Fop Tia. Kiet asked if there were favors to be returned by any member of Tia's burgeoning staff. Binh knew of several deputy commissioners of whatever who had had minor legal scrapes that were processed charitably because of previously clean records. Kiet suggested that they be approached and asked to notify Binh or himself if a significant change in Tia's routine or schedule was detected. Binh agreed enthusiastically. Neither man uttered the word blackmail. Binh nagged again about Freddie Pogue. Kiet, feeling like a henpecked husband, promised to act.

The *terrasse* of the Hickorn Continental Hotel was a

71

chapel of intrigue to some. Political positioning and money were the idols worshipped and traded. The devout multiplied numbers on cocktail napkins and guaranteed promotions of cousins to this job or that.

To Kiet, the *terrasse* was Hickorn's foremost restaurant. Its specialty was the fried shrimp denied him two days earlier by the counterfeiting revelation and his humiliation at the stall of Lo, the fishmonger. Ma San River shellfish were rushed to the Continental's kitchen and fried in peanut oil and sesame seeds.

Kiet cringed at the price. the printed figure had been crossed out and a higher amount penciled in. The penciled one had been crossed out too and a yet higher price was scribbled above it. Kiet had two plates of shrimp anyway. And a medicinal dosage of Golden Tiger. His hangover was cured. He was as content as he had been in days.

Freddie Pogue walked in and took a table by the sidewalk. For a hustler, an appearance on the *terrasse* at luncheon time was mandatory. You were making yourself available.

Pogue was in a certain syntax a Far-East Bum. The insult was conferred by other itinerant Caucasian salesmen who mistakenly believed themselves superior to their peers. These were men who denied or had forgotten their pasts, men to whom the future was an abstraction.

Kiet held this prejudice and wasn't interested in fine distinctions. *Anybody* with blue eyes, a briefcase, and a smile was a Far-East Bum. He could not comprehend any American or European who went *engagé*. Why did they not yearn for their homelands? What, after all, was so awful about the country of one's birth? If Kiet were forced to leave Luong for more than a single month, he would become a melancholy wreck.

Freddie Pogue fit his stereotype—middle age, midsection bulk, a netting of ruptured nose capillaries, and the western peddler's uniform of slacks, white shirt, Rolex watch, and cologne.

72

Pogue saw Kiet and had a Golden Tiger sent over. Kiet raised the bottle in thanks and instructed the waiter to deliver Pogue a drink with his compliments. Kiet knew his preference to be gin splashed over ice. Pogue bragged to waiters that his years in Asia had made him immune to *tourista*, informing them arrogantly that it was needless to lie about the ice being frozen from distilled water.

Kiet waited. Eventually, Pogue picked up his drink and came over. This was important and Kiet would have waited until the sun went into nova. Freddie Pogue had surrendered to suppliant status. The interview would be conducted in Bamsan Kiet's territory.

"Chief, you're looking chipper."

Pogue was the only person on earth who corrupted superintendent to chief. Kiet rose halfway and took his grasp.

Pogue sat heavily. "Relatively speaking, you're looking chipper, I should say. We're getting to be a pair of old geezers, aren't we?"

There was no way to answer that question with dignity, so Kiet didn't.

"You look a bit stiff, old chap, is all I'm saying. No insult intended."

Kiet could not determine Pogue's accent of the day. He was dragging his vowels into diphthongs, so it might be Canadian. The man was in many ways a chameleon. "None taken. I have been planting rice. It is wondrous for the soul."

Pogue drained his glass and looked at Kiet blankly. "A healthful if distasteful pursuit, I dare say."

"Does Hickorn's healthful climate bring you here, Freddie?"

Pogue clapped his hands, summoning the waiter and another gin. "Oh, no. I have no time for health. My business obligations are too pressing."

"Which are, please?"

"Restaurant and bar supplies, Chief. As always. I'm not making many sales, though. My clients are clutching the

73

tail of the zin and hanging on for dear life. They're having a wild ride. I can't quote a price for product that's delivered in eight weeks. I bloody can't! I quote high to protect myself. Johnny Walker Red is six thousand a liter wholesale. In two months it might be ten thou. Maybe higher. I quote twelve to cover my arse. They say sorry and goodbye, baby."

"Counterfeiting," Kiet said, as if anteing the word in a poker game.

Pogue lifted a finger. "There it is, Chief. I changed money for my modest living expenses an hour ago. Twelve hundred to one. And I haven't the slightest if the notes in my pocket are real or toilet paper."

"Commodities of value demand hard currency," Kiet said. "In my uneducated opinion, you might be as immune to local currency fluctuations as you say you are to intestinal disorders."

Pogue roared in wheezing laughter. "Chief, I marvel at your memory. My *tourista* story to these native waiters, it's true."

He slapped an undulating gut. "Nobody jerks Freddie Pogue around. I'm a *native* anywhere I am. I'm a citizen of the world, Chief. They play me for the hick from Winnipeg, they pay. They buzz-buzz in their jabber and think I don't know. I speak the languages, even down to the dialects. Blindfold yourself and I'd have you believing I was Luongan."

Pogue was diverging, taking the wrong road. Kiet said, "Guns, Freddie. Armaments, munitions."

"Hypothetically?" Pogue asked without body language.

Kiet did not answer.

"Who in tranquil Hickorn could be a client? The Rouge mine the Obon highway and toss grenades now and then. What else, Chief? I know of no market."

"Marsad Ref may have ambitions."

Pogue frowned, scratched his brow, then snapped his

74

fingers. "Ref. Yes. The renegade colonel sequestered in Foh Ten. I've never met the gentleman, but they tell me that if you're on the wrong side of him, you won't live long enough to dread your nightmares."

"How long will you be in Hickorn, Freddie?"

"I'm committed to a trade show in Penang in four days. Are you giving me restrictions, Chief?"

Pogue's reaction had been measured and theatrical, the craftsmanship of an accomplished liar. Kiet slid back his chair, saying, "No. Luong is not a police state."

"And an enchanting land it is, Chief."

"An enchanting land with laws. Enjoy your visit, Freddie."

12

IT WAS KIET'S intention to devote the following day to managerial tedium, disposition of the mundane work that had grown in teetering piles on his desk since his departure on furlough. There were no breaks on the counterfeiting case to distract him, nor had Buzz Wheeler's body been rediscovered. Nobody had even filed a missing-person report on the late office-equipment sales man. His death remained a secret shared with Binh and the killers who had so thoughtfully cleaned up after themselves.

Kiet's thoughts wandered to the concept of purgatory. While that belief applied to the intermediate state of a tainted soul, a place of temporary punishment before gaining passage to Heaven, Wheeler's earthly remains were also enduring a delay. Antisocial types had inserted a phase between homicide and proper burial. He wondered if Wheeler was a religious man, specifically a Roman Catholic.

He banished the thoughts and attacked the documents. A requisition request from Heng Fri for a padded seat cushion, no reason stated. Kiet initialed his approval. It was a small chunk out of the department's budget. Bargain ammunition. Fri, a humorless joker, was sure to continue taunting Kiet with the cultist's worshipful chant. Endlessly. In a crowded squadroom. Kiet would counterpunch with sympathy about Fri's hemorrhoidal inflammations. Splendid.

Theft and sale of a carton of inner tubes from a bicycle shop by a youthful employee. Complainant petitioning to drop the charges. His daughter and the accused were married last Saturday. Kiet speculated if her wedding gown concealed the bulge of expectant motherhood. He signed.

A pedicab driver and owner quibbling over apportionment of fares. Owner shoved driver. Driver, who chewed betel nut, spat in owner's face. Kiet wrote a terse memo and a routing slip, directing the squabble to the Hickorn Center of Public Administration. If Fop Tia did not have a Department of Transportation Arbitration, this was a wonderful impetus to establish one.

Kiet answered a knock at his door with a grateful "Come in." He welcomed a respite from musty paper and bad typing. The visitor was Mr. A. Singh, proprietor of Bombay Tailors. Singh was dressed as if for a formal occasion, in a beige Nehru jacket, heavily creased brown slacks, and black patent-leather shoes.

Singh had never graced headquarters voluntarily. His pliant face was a confused waxwork of rage and anxiety. Kiet pictured an irate and confused cobra storming a mongoose den.

While Kiet was fumbling for a greeting, Singh sprinkled his desk with currency. "Superintendent, I have been cheated. I ask that you look at these."

Kiet suppressed a smile. "Cheated, Singh? *You?*"

"Am I not entitled to report a crime, Superintendent? I too am a resident of Hickorn."

Singh's whimpering tone was disagreeable. Kiet counted and examined the money—twenty U.S. fifty-dollar bills. They looked authentic, but the feel was wrong. The paper was plain bond. He held one up to the light; it had none of the telltale colored threads.

"Where did you get these?"

"Yesterday evening, they were brought to me in exchange for Swiss francs."

"Your currency service is diverse, Mr. Singh, but I imagine that your rates on one hard currency to another are less favorable than at banks or embassies."

"I must charge a slight premium for asking no questions, Superintendent."

"Slight," Kiet muttered. "Where, please? From whom?"

"A Russian I have dealt with in the past."

"And you didn't immediately recognize these for what they are?"

"They were inserted into a larger quantity of real fifties, as one might shuffle marked cards into a deck."

"A sizable transaction, then."

Singh nodded. "I have dealt with the man before. I regarded him as honorable, as I only counted what he gave me. I cannot believe the audacity of what occurred half an hour later."

"Please tell me," Kiet said wearily.

"A second Russian brought me an identical sum of fifty-dollar bills to change. They were all counterfeit."

"And you refused them?"

"I did, Superintendent," Singh said, his posture stiffening. "I told him to take his future business elsewhere. I am an honest businessman."

"Of course you are, and they were testing your gullibility. Who were the Russians?"

"Their first names are Ivan and Sasha. Those are the names they gave me, but all Soviets are KGB, as you are aware. They were probably aliases. Both men are attached to the embassy. I learned that once when Ivan came to me driving a staff car."

Kiet sighed heavily. The toes of his shoes touched the cardboard box under his desk, the box of bogus zin taken from Wheeler's villa. His stomach was knotting with the knowledge that the Union of Soviet Socialist Republics had become another factor in this hideous mess. Wheeler's disappeared photocopier was in the possession of the Bolsheviks and they were playing with it.

"What would you like me to do for you, Singh?"

"I sustained a loss of one thousand dollars, Superintendent. I'm a victim of a fraud. I'm filing charges. I want arrests made. I want compensation."

Kiet thought he understood Singh's indignation. A swin-

78

dler being swindled was like a thief whose booty had been stolen. It was a sense of violation, an enormous injury to professional pride. While Kiet understood, he did not sympathize. He dug through desk drawers and found the department's lengthiest incident report form.

"Fill this out, Singh. Go to the Soviet Embassy, file a complaint with them, and ask them to forward copies of their report to me. Then go to our Foreign Ministry and repeat your tale. Supply me with a copy of their affidavit and we can possibly proceed. Diplomatic immunity is involved here. It can be tricky."

"But I thought diplomatic immunity applied only to minor offenses such as tearing up parking tickets."

Kiet recalled Binh speaking of foreign diplomats and their automobiles in the District of Columbia. They parked them where they wished for whatever duration they chose and the authorities were helpless to police their rudeness. Instruments called parking meters were ignored. Kiet hoped to see such a machine some day. His curiosity was less than compelling, however, toward other elements of western culture such as television, celebrity magazines, and the mass-produced cheeseburgers Binh so dearly missed.

"Singh, we have no parking ordinances in Hickorn. If you take the slot of someone important and he screams loudly enough, we will impound the offending vehicle. Diplomatic immunity as a total concept is more difficult. If Ivan or Sasha had shot you, we could act, but it wouldn't be easy. Your weeping relatives in India could experience a delay before you were avenged."

"My money," Singh said sadly. "My thousand dollars."

"I will do what I can, but you must cooperate."

"How?"

Kiet crumpled the incident report form and dropped it in his wastebasket. "Keep your mouth shut about your problem for the time being. Your situation has a wider scope."

79

"Inaction isn't cooperation," Singh said, brightening at the prospect of information. His hand grazed the back of the chair beside him.

Kiet sat rigidly, fingers clasped on his desktop, informing the tailor that he had not been invited to stay for a conference. "I will be in touch when there is a development of mutual interest. By the way, is Mayor Tia still seeing you?"

Singh had retracted the hand. It was joined behind his back with the other. He was not a happy man. "Not since we spoke at my shop."

"And how is our beloved zin doing relative to the dollar, please?"

"Abysmally, Superintendent. I was forced to offer twelve-fifty this morning to complete a minimal transaction."

"We will be talking soon, Mr. Singh," Kiet said. "I promise."

Bamsan Kiet lived on the corner of Rue Willie Mosconi and Avenue Che Guevara, in a moderately prosperous neighborhood of merchants and clerks. His property was walled, making it by Luongan definition a "villa." Its builder was a tax administrator in the last governor general's civil service. He was a Frenchman and a middling bureaucrat with social ambitions, a pretentious sort who believed he had erected a miniature estate by surrounding himself with concrete. The walls served a second function—alleviation of paranoia. In that era, the Viet Minh were conducting their revolution in both the countryside and the cities of Indochina. The tax man wrongly feared that Hickorn colonials would also be prey to bombings and kidnappings.

The house itself was a modest four rooms, extremely comfortable by Luongan standards, but hardly an object of envy by the moneyed. So small was the lot that the two meters of wall and wrought-iron spikes atop it cast continuous shadows on the courtyard and grounds, making the hobbyist pursuit of horticulture impossible. This had been

80

and remained Kiet's sole objection to the place.

Kiet had lived in the villa with his beloved wife, Tien, until she perished in the cholera epidemic of 1966. He had lived there alone since.

He went home early today, in the midafternoon, not for a siesta—a Hickorn custom of which he was in the minority for not practicing—but because a neighbor had reported a suspicious individual loitering at his gate. Binh had told Kiet triumphantly that this was Block Watch in action.

Block Watch was an American process of monitoring one another's home, on guard against the sociopaths and narcotics addicts who burglarized private residences with horrifying regularity. Kiet had vetoed Binh's proposal for a Hickorn Block Watch, citing the Luongan's inbred nosiness. He pointed out that housebreakers were frequently detected by neighbors scanning for adultery and disgusting personal habits. A formal Block Watch would require an expensive information campaign and the inevitable paperwork, where the same end was reached accidentally in the pursuit of gossip material. Binh had pouted. Today he crowed and Kiet let him, although his opinion of the subject was inalterable.

He did worry during the drive home. His first major policy change after promotion to superintendent was elimination of siesta by department personnel. An excessive number of crimes against property occurred in the torrid midday when Hickorn rested. If criminals insisted on plying their trade in fiery weather, as if vampires emerging from their coffins at sundown, Kiet and his people would be vigilant, figuratively bearing mallets and wooden stakes.

Afternoon burglaries declined significantly. Hickorn crooks resumed a nocturnal regimen, the risk of heatstroke doubled by that of jail being intolerable. So who was the suspicious party? And why was said suspicious party so readily noticed by neighbors who should be snoring under ceiling fans?

81

Kiet saw. It was a Kanpurin. The sect member sat on broiling pavement, back resting on his iron gate. The sky was cloudless, and unfiltered sunlight made the Kanpurin's camouflage robe appear metallic. At least this cultist had a trace of common sense, he thought as he got out of the car; he was balancing a newspaper on his head as a sun shade.

He was a she. Kanpurin Sharla/Joyce Wilson. She looked up at him blankly and tried to speak. Kiet amended his observation of common sense. Damn her, her lips were cracked and while she was perspiring the sweat on her face was a thin patina, not a normal flooding. Her complexion was chalky.

"Come," he said, extending his arms.

She took his hands. Hers were soft, dry, and incredibly warm. He hoisted her upright, cupped her waist, and unlatched the gate. He carried her inside, thinking indifferently of the gossip grist he was creating.

Kiet kept his home shuttered at daytime and it stayed rather cool. He seated her on his sofa and hurried into the kitchen for liquids. He took a jug of boiled water from the refrigerator and filled a tall glass. Though he was offended by westerners' snide cracks about Hickorn's water system and he believed health officials who began disinfecting it after the epidemic that claimed Tien and certified it safe henceforth, he had not drank from a tap since her death. Nor would he ever.

He held the glass to Sharla's mouth, tipping and lowering it, metering her intake.

"Stay quiet and drink. Continue at this rate. No faster. If you gulp, your retching will interrupt every siesta in a five block radius. Understand?"

She nodded that she did. Kiet poured some water for himself. It refreshed at the beginning, but the final swallows tasted flat. He switched to Golden Tiger and watched, nurse to patient. In an hour she had finished four glasses of water. She was alert and color (for a Caucasian) had returned to her cheeks.

82

Kiet initiated a conversation by simply asking why.

"You have a counterfeiting case, I'm told. I was passed a bad fifty."

"An American fifty-dollar bill?"

She took the crumpled bill from a pocket sewn into the strange robe. "Ulysses S. Grant and all the trimmings. The engraving is perfect but it's printed on typing paper. In my past life I was a bank loan officer. In Oregon where I met Kanpurin Morajini. I was an assistant vice-president of a branch. The paper is a dead giveaway. Any teller with a week's experience would detect it."

"How did you find my home, and why didn't you bring the bill to headquarters?"

"I asked where you live, Fahwandi. The airport people knew. Hickorn is really a very small town, isn't it?"

"Too small at times. The second part of my question, please."

"You, Fahwandi, are the living reincarnation of our gossamer master. Fahwandi Kli Shabbir has channeled his essence to you."

"I have been so informed."

"The karmic powers that delivered us to you were again invoked when the counterfeit money was donated to me, Fahwandi. It was a sign that I contact you personally, but not in the hubbub of your police station. Enlightenment and truth seek the vortex."

"I know nothing of enlightened vortices, but if I am your fill-in guru, will you accept a command?"

"Absolutely, Fahwandi."

"Stop calling me Fahwandi. My name is Kiet."

"Kiet," she said, savoring the word.

"Splendid. And I shall call you Joyce instead of Sharla. Who passed you the bill?"

Kiet's cat, his housemate, came into the room. The obese animal glanced indifferently at his master, jumped onto Joyce's lap, and went to sleep.

"Nice kitty," she said, petting it.

"Not nice. It's a stray that adopted me. In the monsoon season it cries like a baby until I let it in and it sleeps on my bed. In the dry season it ignores me unless I forget to feed it."

"Well, it's still cute. What's its name?"

"I haven't named it. That is my punishment for its arrogance. The prior owner of the bill, please?"

"Oh. Sorry. A young tough. He was dressed scruffily. He came out of the airport bar and I think he was drunk. He asked me who we were. I told him. He spoke broken English, but I believe I communicated the cogent points of our faith. He made obscene remarks to me and tried to fondle my breasts. The other Kanpuri saw and came to my aid. He wadded up that fifty, threw it at me, and walked off before there was trouble."

Splendid, Kiet thought. The Russians are circulating dollars. Drunken goons too. What next? Baskets full of dollars tossed from an airplane above Hickorn? "Could you identify him from a photograph?"

"Yes, I'm sure. His hateful face is imprinted in my memory."

"Good. We keep an album of our favorite clients. Mug shots, as my adjutant says. Incidentally, how goes the proselytizing?"

"Wonderfully, Fah—Mr. Kiet."

"Kiet."

"Kiet. Kanpurin Morajini is excited about your directive. We are working eighteen hours a day to achieve our financial goal, and the airport restaurant food you ordered us to eat is fairly good."

"Splendid. Soon, you should have the funds to fly off and preach your ministry to the Thai."

"Oh yes," Joyce said, her voice animated. "Morajini calculates it won't take longer than seven or eight months."

"Excuse me?"

"You're frowning, Kiet."

84

"Seven or eight *months*?"

"Kanpurin Morajini was inspired by your command to spread our holy ministry worldwide."

"I remember speaking those key words, but not in that precise—"

"Morajini says that the channeling was imperfect and that Fahwandi Kli Shabbir really desires that the funds for a worldwide gospel be obtained in Hickorn."

"Static in the channeling transmission, as it were."

"Oh yes, Kiet. You have granted us the luxury of eating restaurant food and growing out our hair, Kiet. An around-the-world airline tour is the ideal progression. Thanks to your wisdom, we can evangelize the blessedness of pure enlightenment without dissipating so much energy in quest of our creature essentials."

Kiet closed his eyes. He had dynamited his own plan by spoiling the cultists, by insisting that they live like human beings. He thought of Binh's scorn for their jailbird guru and said, "We have a contradiction. If Pan Am luxury travel packages are ordained as holy, why did Kli Shabbir not state that poverty is a sin to you in his basic doctrine? Why did he send you out to live like animals?"

Joyce licked her damaged lips and smiled. "Fahwandi teaches that a tenet of enlightenment is the growth of one's day-to-day knowledge and the surprises that accompany it."

Kiet was becoming angry. He pictured Khalid O'Shea/Fahwandi Kli Shabbir swatting fuzzy balls on the tennis courts of the Lompoc, a smirk on his face as his sentence ran down and dividend payments swelled his fortune. "Knowledge? You beg money to enrich a felon. You embrace me as a guru because I resemble the swine. Excuse me, but ignorance is the more apt term."

Joyce answered with a broadened smile. Kiet compared it to the mindless beatitude of the 1970s hippies, the Katmandu pilgrims.

He cooled his anger with a swig of Golden Tiger and asked, "What do you people actually believe in?"

"We believe that what is is. The gossamer master teaches us to take what is positive from other religions and philosophies and distill it into pure enlightenment, while discarding the negative. He connects us with our higher selves, our omniscient oversouls. He has taken us on a spiritual journey. He has made us happy."

Joyce lost Kiet at "oversouls." He was developing a headache, and it wasn't from the Golden Tiger. "So he broadcasts gibberish? He tells you you are happy and therefore you are?"

"The next word I expect to hear is brainwashing," she said, her smile locked.

"It's your brain," Kiet said. "How did an intelligent and attractive young woman named Joyce Wilson come to join the Church of the Amalgamation of Enlightenment?"

"The intelligent and attractive young woman you refer to is not so young," Joyce said. "She is thirty-three. Her past life as a rising bank officer was unfulfilling. Lack of fulfillment in her marriage is an understatement. She solved that problem with divorce. She thought marital freedom would open the doors of fulfillment. It didn't. She drank too much. She foundered. She met Kanpurin Morajini in a shopping mall. He gave her pamphlets and hope. She accepted a higher plane of existence. Then, recently, Morajini and his acolytes were deemed by the gossamer master to be an especially enlightened group. They were honored by being dispatched to the underdeveloped nations of the world."

"An expensive mission," Kiet said. If she followed "underdeveloped" with "Third World," he would consider banishing her. "You cannot hitchhike from the Province of Oregon to Luong."

"It was expensive, Kiet. I got the house in the divorce and the best car. I sold them. I felt fortunate to be able to contribute my equity."

86

She hesitated, looked around, and said, "Your home is lovely. I know you've been a widower for ages, but I intuit a feminine touch."

"I don't move furniture."

"Not in twenty-some years?"

"I employ a maid," Kiet said defensively. "She cleans and shops for me."

Joyce laughed. "I didn't mean you're messy. My garment is sticking to me. May I take a shower?"

"If I'd arrived an hour later, you would have been a prune. Perspiration is a healthy sign. Yes. Certainly."

She showered and returned to the living room wrapped in a towel.

"Kiet," she said.

He was too stunned to answer.

She lifted her arms and the towel fell. She walked into Kiet's bedroom.

Since Tien's death, Kiet's sexuality had swung crazily between phases of promiscuity and celibacy. In his younger days, Luongan women considered his size and girth as Buddhalike and, therefore, extremely attractive. Of late, his periods of celibacy had extended into a life-style. The disorder of indiscriminate sexual conquest required too much energy and was vaguely degrading. It had been months.

Kiet went into the bedroom. Very gently they became lovers.

"I apologize for my haste," Kiet said.

"Don't," Joyce said. "The Fahwandi is fast too, but—"

"You and Shabbir?"

"He beds all his female Kanpuri. He says it is a parallel to Catholic nuns marrying Jesus. He is mechanical. As acolytes we are vessels. But you are loving and sensitive."

The moment did not permit Kiet to express further contempt of the guru. "Enlightenment," he muttered.

"Morajini wants me and persists, but I refuse. There has been no one in my life—this way—for a long, long time."

87

"Sleep," the substitute Fahwandi commanded through a yawn.

They did. Kiet awoke minutes before sundown. Harsh, horizontal rays penetrated cracks between the curtains. He saw that the stubble on Joyce's scalp was red. Inexplicably, this aroused him. He awakened her with soft, patient caresses.

13

JOYCE SLEPT LIKE an angel, curled in a fetal position, her lips twitching periodically. Her snoring was a contented hum. She was beautiful, innocent, childlike. At dawn Kiet crept out of his home, a thief in the night, a burglar fleeing the burgled. He shut his front door as if it were constructed of nitroglycerin.

Of the seductions in his history, this was the most shameful. Subsequent to Tien's death, fueled by self-pity and testosterone, he had taken what was given. He was the aggressor and the couplings were honest. Pleasure was the expectation and no false promises were made.

Joyce had been the aggressor and she was his first Caucasian. Perhaps this was the problem. Respectable Luongan women responded as lustily as any, but never until the male demonstrated his intentions. Binh's descriptions of modern American women he had intimately known were evidently true. Carnivorous, he called them. Kiet did not consider himself a bigot, but he was willing enough to listen to stories of erotic misbehavior by westerners.

No! Shabby rationalization, he decided as he drove the empty streets. The guilt was his, not hers. Women had accepted him for many reasons, but not because he was an earthly deity. He was as fraudulent as the jailbird Shabbir. He could have insisted that she put on her clothing as he had insisted that she cease addressing him as Fahwandi. He hadn't.

Headquarters was quiet. Thankfully, a deferential young sergeant was on the desk. Kiet doubted if he could tolerate

Heng Fri now. He told the sergeant that he was not to be disturbed and resumed work on the paper backlog.

Shortly before Binh was due in, he exited a side door. He wasn't in a humor to see anybody familiar. He lingered for an hour at a café, sipping tea and eating croissants. The presence of Hickorn's police superintendent made the proprietor more than a little nervous. The restless and brooding Kiet was surely on a surveillance, poised to seize a felon.

At the earliest appropriate time, he paid an unannounced visit to the Soviet Embassy. The structure was imposing: gray concrete, four tiers of tiny, smoked windows, a thicket of antennae and satellite dishes on the roof.

The guards appeared innocuous in comparison, but Kiet knew better. They wore shortsleeved khaki devoid of insignia and caps adorned with a silver star mounted in a red band. If they were armed, their weapons were discreetly hidden in the gate shack. This Boy Scout image was the idea of the past ambassador, Kalashnikov, an effort to sell Russians in Luong as harmless guests instead of piranha.

But Kalashnikov had departed Luong in disgrace. Officially, he was on an "extended furlough." Circumstantial evidence had linked him to Marsad Ref's assassination and coup attempt. The Soviets were frustrated with Ril Thoi, the Luong Rouge leader; the man was too independent to be a reliable puppet. Kiet felt that Kalashnikov's infatuation with Ref was based on the questionable premise that he was a Fidel Castro type, who could be purchased after the revolution. No matter. Kalashnikov's furlough was indefinite. Rumors placed the former ambassador in Vladivostok processing in-country travel permits.

Kalashnikov's replacement, Shiherazade, was his utter opposite. Kalashnikov was a vulgar ox of a man, Shiherazade slim and urbane. He reminded Kiet of the American university professors who conducted field studies of the Indochinese

90

nations in the early 1960s. They researched communist insurgencies and made voluminous and faulty recommendations for eradication of the menace. The scholars were earnest and polite. So was Ambassador Shiherazade.

Kiet met him once, when he was supervising security at Hickorn International. The occasion was Shiherazade's welcoming to Luong. Kiet gauged him as a disciple of the incumbent General Secretary of the Central Committee, that easygoing fellow with the birthmark and the wife who frequented Paris salons. Shiherazade had a warm and constant smile. His teeth were perfect. Kiet pictured them in His Royal Highness's neck.

Kiet showed identification to the guards and requested an audience with the ambassador. On a subject of mutual urgency, he said. The guards spoke in jerky KGB-taught Luongan. Politely.

Messengers shuttled back and forth. Quizzical eyes never veered far from Kiet. Was he a defector? If so, from *what*?

In thirty minutes, he had clearance and was escorted into the monolith. They walked stairs to the ambassador's top-floor office, regrets stated about the elevator—Hickorn's third—being temporarily out of service. Kiet was not surprised. The air-conditioning system was audible, but the results were nil. The interior of this concrete block was near steamy. These Bolsheviks and their machines were a contradiction, he thought. America chilled their diplomats into ice cubes, but the most frigid nation on earth could not. He was not complaining, however. The ninety-degree–ninety-percent humidity climate was agreeable. And there were no invisible violinists either.

"Superintendent—Kiet, is it?—an unexpected pleasure."

Shiherazade greeted Kiet with a cheery smile and a limp handshake. Kalashnikov had enjoyed squeezing a palm into pulp and calcium dust.

"I apologize for my impromptu appearance, Mr. Ambassador."

Shiherazade waved arms as if fanning the stale air. "No apologies. You cited urgency. Urgency supersedes protocol. The Soviet people welcome the opportunity to assist our hosts. Sit down and rest, Superintendent. The spare part to repair our elevator should arrive in today's pouch. It is I who should apologize for your inconvenience. The steps are steep."

Kiet sat. He was leery of anyone so gracious. He surveyed the portraits on the walls. Gorbachev's was the largest, of course, mounted directly behind the ambassador. Brezhnev and Chernenko too. Lenin. Stalin. And Khrushchev? Wasn't he absent when Kiet was last here? He couldn't remember. It was impossible to keep track of which dead Bolshevik was a saint and which was a running-dog revisionist.

Kiet tried to sound scholarly. "As you certainly know, Mr. Ambassador, Hickorn is inundated with counterfeit Luongan zin. The havoc raised includes an upward spiraling of prices, an inflationary gap."

Shiherazade's sleeves were rolled up, his tie loosened. He was fiddling with a pencil, squinting into space, lost in serious thought. He looked like a western business executive digesting a minor marketing problem.

"A capitalistic economy is fraught with dangers," he said. "Laissez-faire systems are counterrevolutionary and easy to abuse. Authorities with the best interests of the state at heart are compelled to be reactive to the avaricious. Outlaws manipulate the weaknesses of profit-motivated imperialism.

"The financial suffering of your people is unknown in the Soviet Union. The ruble is not bartered like a slave in Zurich, London, and New York temples of money. The state determines the ruble's worth and establishes fixed prices for goods and services."

The professorial image had returned. Kiet thought of Minister of Finance Totisa Bu. He asked, "Isn't there counterfeiting in Russia? Aren't queer rubles ever passed?"

"Never in my experience. The penalty for counterfeiting the ruble and distributing it is an effective deterrent."

"Which is?"

"A firing squad."

"Our sentences are less severe."

"Prince Pakse should explore the advantages of the Marxist dialectic, Superintendent. Centralized leadership is equipped to smash criminal trends without the need of bowing to reactionary influences."

The pedantic Shiherazade's reference to His Royal Highness indicated that he was steering the discussion into a debate of political philosophies. Kiet was a detective, not a political scientist. He changed the subject. "I regret, Mr. Ambassador, that the printing apparatus responsible for the bogus zin is presently being used to manufacture American fifty-dollar bills."

"An unfortunate complication," Shiherazade said sympathetically. "I relate to your sense of urgency, but frankly, I am puzzled why you are bringing the matter to my personal attention."

"Yesterday, sir, an alleged Soviet national exchanged counterfeit U.S. fifties for Swiss francs. The bogus bills were inserted into a wad of real money and were not discerned until later."

Shiherazade's mouth fell dramatically. "At the Royal Luongan Bank?"

"No sir. On the street. With a black marketeer."

The ambassador smiled keyboards of white porcelain. His head moved lazily from side to side, a metronome. He was in perfect control. He was a marvelous actor. "Unlikely, Superintendent. Improbable. Our foreign service selects people of the highest integrity. They—we—are dedicated to serve our hosts. You have been deceived. The imperialist dedication to wealth should be your clue."

"A second alleged Soviet national approached the black marketeer thirty minutes thereafter," Kiet continued. "He requested an identical exchange. The buyer had by then discovered the hoax and was alert. These fifties were one hundred percent phony. They were visually correct, but duplicated on ordinary bond paper. He refused them."

"Do your alleged Soviet nationals have names?"

"Ivan and Sasha."

Shiherazade laughed. "In Russia Ivan and Sasha are very common names. Ridiculous! An obvious plot to discredit us. Ambassador Smithson is obtuse and antagonistic. This scheme stinks of him. It has his signature all over it."

Kiet's trap was set, spring-loaded jaws ratcheted wide. He baited it. "Exactly, Mr. Ambassador! I knew before I imposed on you, but I am an investigator. I require confirmation of my suspicions. A Soviet Embassy employee—let alone two of them—would not be so stupid as to walk into the shop of a crafty shark and attempt to trade a counterfeit currency of shoddy quality, a copy of a currency printed on unique paper, a currency a blind man would reject. And the person ordering such stupidity would be, in my view, a moron."

Ambassador Shiherazade tripped the bait wire in silence. His smile held in position, but his eyes were no longer involved. Kiet's insult had lowered the room temperature twenty degrees.

"Is there anything I can do to assist you, Superintendent?"

"Thank you for the generous offer, sir, but no. I knew that you could not be a part of this mess. I had to ask the questions, though, and I felt an obligation to inform you."

"I am grateful for the information."

Gratitude probably wasn't the right word, Kiet thought. The ambassador's smiling gaze was fixed on him. He was a genial statue. Kiet suppressed a shiver.

14

KIET WAS BROWSING through his album of favorite clients when Captain Binh entered his office.

"The mug book," Binh said. "Are you looking for anyone in particular?"

"I'm just trying to narrow down a category," Kiet said. "How many photographs do we have? The album is growing thick."

"Hundreds."

"And how many of them could we classify as drunken, scruffily-dressed, young toughs?"

"Hundreds."

"Regretfully so," Kiet said, closing the album.

"While you were out this morning, Superintendent, I received a missing-person report. That freak Morajini reported one of the two women in the cult missing, the one they call Kanpurin Sharla."

"Oh," Kiet said.

"I checked my notes on the airport incident and jailing. Her real name is Joyce Wilson."

"Yes," Kiet said.

"Morajini claims that Sharla left the airport yesterday afternoon to deliver important evidence to you regarding the counterfeiting. Morajini's probably a congenital liar, but what could his motive be?"

"He was telling the truth." Kiet then summarized Joyce's visit and his own to Ambassador Shiherazade. He omitted details not pertinent to the counterfeiting case.

"Wilson is still at your home, Superintendent?"

"Yes," Kiet said. "She was badly dehydrated and hasn't completely regained her strength."

"Compassionate of you, Superintendent. Can she identify the man who gave her the fifty-dollar bill?"

The word "compassionate" was spoken so hollowly that it suggested skepticism. Binh knew of Kiet's legendary sexual past. While Binh accepted Kiet's inclinations as dormant, he was also a male of the species whose District of Columbia year had shed the Luongan prejudice against cohabitation with other races. His question, his shift to police business, was fast. The face-saving process was avoided.

"She says so." Kiet took an envelope out of his desk. It contained more photographs.

"Marsad Ref's followers? You've shown me those."

"Alleged followers," Kiet said. "Junior officers who worked for him in Obon before his relocation to Foh Ten. Nine of them altogether. They vanished one by one. They were written off as either deserters or casualties of the Rouge."

Binh nodded. "There's been no trace of any of them. It makes sense. Wilson's drunken Luongan throwing around queer fifties."

"The partnership of Ref and the Soviets need not have ended when Ambassador Kalashnikov was called home to Mother Russia. An unidentified thug, A. Singh, Ivan, and Sasha. Roland Wheeler's splendid and missing copy machine. This challenges the probabilities of coincidence."

"Ref and the Russians," Binh said, nodding grimly. "Same song, different verse."

An inexplicable colloquialism on music. Binh was a fan of contemporary American rock and roll. Kiet too, though more selectively. He was fond of Slim Whitman and the Kingston Trio. But this was no time to delve into the remark's meaning.

"I think we should concentrate on these pictures," he said. "If the results are negative, we can try the big album."

"The mug book."

96

"Yes. The mug book." Kiet gave him some photographs from the envelope. "I have several copies of each. Please take yours to Hickorn International and interview the cocktail lounge employees. According to Joy—the Wilson/Sharla individual—our subject received his lubrication in that bar. I will do likewise with Wilson and bring her to her cohorts. You and I will meet at the airport."

"Her medical condition permitting?" Binh asked gingerly.

Kiet cleared his throat and sorted the photos. "I have every confidence it will."

On his trip home, Kiet prayed to any deity who would listen for the absence of domestic bliss. If Joyce was polishing furniture tops, a fragrant meal simmering in the kitchen, things would be difficult. If she was also seductively semi-dressed in a romantic mood, things would be impossible. Because of his agnostic contempt for the world's religions, he did not anticipate good service.

He had no cause to pester the gods. Joyce was seated on the sofa fully clothed in her camouflage gown. Dust had not been disturbed. The only smell in his kitchen was his cat's, who slept there in the dry season when he was inclined to spend his nights at home.

Joyce was staring at an empty corner of the room. "It's weird, Kiet, the conditioning I can't blot out of my former being," she said. "There's nothing in that corner."

"There never has been," said the puzzled Kiet. "I have no appetite for elaborate furnishings."

"Back home, a void in a living room corner is a television set in the repair shop."

"Luong has no television stations," Kiet said, adding defensively, "We have cinemas and radio stations."

"I know, but my ingrained consciousness had me waiting for a serviceman to return it." She made pushing motions with a thumb. "Punching the remote control. Is that weird or is it weird?"

97

Who could guess the nature of this remote control? Kiet was not disposed to try. He gave her the photos and asked her to search for a familiar face.

She returned the third of nine. Suddenly. No hesitation. "Him."

"Positively?"

"Well, he's clean-shaven in the picture. He had a beard, a Vandyke. He was wearing flat-lensed glasses."

Kiet was skeptical. "You saw through his disguise quite easily."

"Can I tell you a story, Kiet? I was new in banking, a management trainee working as a teller. The ink on my college diploma wasn't even dry. A customer came to my window with those same flat-lensed glasses. It was almost closing time and there weren't any other customers. It was on a Friday. Friday is a big payday and we still had a lot of cash in the drawers. I got scared. I pushed my alarm button."

"He robbed you?"

"No. He just asked me to change a hundred-dollar bill into twenties. I did and the cops rushed in with their guns drawn. They arrested him at the door."

"A false accusation. Did you lose your job?"

"No. I got a letter of commendation. He was a rapist and cocaine pusher who had escaped from prison."

"The flat-lensed glasses gave him away to you?"

"No. The eyes behind them. They made my skin crawl. This picture, they're identical eyes. This is the man. Who is he?"

"His name is Dung Nha," Kiet said. "He was a captain in the Royal Luongan Army stationed at Obon, in the highlands. He was a close subordinate of a former army colonel who is a subject of some interest to me."

"Why was this Dung Nha individual in disguise?"

"He is believed dead, the victim of a Luong Rouge ambush. No body was found, but enough personal effects were left at the ambush scene to validate a version of capture and subsequent execution by the guerrillas."

"He staged his own death? Why?"

"He and some of his junior officer colleagues too, we believe. I can't answer why."

"You can't or you won't?"

"Both. I have to go to the airport to meet my adjutant, who is showing copies of these photographs to cocktail lounge employees. May I offer you a ride?"

Joyce smiled. "Getting rid of me?"

"Your leader, Morajini, reported you missing. He is concerned about you."

"And jealous too, I'll bet."

Kiet said nothing.

"No strings attached, Kiet."

She was looking at him like she had last night when she shed her bath towel. The strings phrase was obviously slang, another American corruption of the British language they called their own. It required a response from him, but he was not any more willing to give one than he was to enter a dark room blindfolded.

"Cat got your tongue?" she asked coyly.

He glanced about. His nameless cat was nowhere to be seen. Today seemed to be developing into a conspiracy of foreign dialects.

"Kiet," she said, standing up, "what I'm trying to get across is that from now on our relationship will be on your terms. Okay? My intrusion into your home and your bed was wrong. It isn't the Kanpurin's place to initiate, to force destinies. It was selfish of me to seek pleasure while my fellow Kanpuri are hard at work to attain a glorious goal. Deny it all you want, but you are my Fahwandi, the gossamer master I can see and hear and smell and touch and love."

"As opposed to the Fahwandi halfway across the world in the Lompoc," Kiet said with resignation.

"Yes." She kissed him. "To the airport, Kiet."

Kiet caught his breath. "To the airport."

The thrice-weekly Thai International flight from Bangkok was in. A KLM jumbo jet was touching down, probably for a short refueling stopover. Tourists and businessmen bound for glittering destinations in Europe and Asia would have an hour or so to absorb their fill of Luong's local flavor. Local traffic too, including the perilous Royal Air Luong Hickorn-Obon shuttle, an antique Douglas DC-3 with oil streaks on its engine nacelles as thick as asphalt.

Kiet saw that the Church of the Amalgamation of Enlightenment Kanpuri were busily proffering pamphlets, nirvana, and the opportunity to make tax-deductible contributions. Hickorn International was as bustling as it ever was. But as usual, there was a dearth of affluent travelers, the type who clutched attaché cases fashioned from the hides of endangered species, the type who walked at a running pace, the type who would donate coins and the occasional bill to be rid of the nuisance and save a minute. The money crowd was greatly outnumbered by Luongans awaiting the Obon shuttle, people who were not clutching attaché cases. Their carry-on luggage was as often as not sleeping rolls and cages of live chickens. They were not good candidates for tax evasion and enlightenment.

Kiet groaned. Morajini's "seven or eight months" was a fantasy. At this rate, it would be seven or eight *years* before they were guzzling champagne in first class, enroute to dispense their gospel to heathens worldwide.

Kiet released Joyce to her cultist band with a neutral and perhaps too-loud "Thank you for your cooperation in our investigation." She winked at him. He blushed. Several of the Kanpuri rushed to her, hands fluttering, expressions mindlessly joyful at her deliverance. Morajini was in a hard stance in the path of two young and stoic Japanese who wore white shirts and dark ties and clutched elephant-skin briefcases. He noticed Kiet and took time from his prime prospects to glare.

100

Kiet turned his head, allowing the hatred and jealousy to glance off a cheek, and strode into the cocktail lounge. The bar smelled like all bars, of stale tobacco and sweet alcohol concoctions, and had plenty of glass facing the runway so the patrons could view aviation and remember where they were. The view today was of heat waves shimmering off runway macadam, the jungle beyond, and four operable aircraft.

Captain Binh waved excitedly. Kiet took the barstool next to him. Binh slapped a photo down. Kiet looked at it. He nodded.

"The Wilson/Sharla woman picked out Dung Nha too?"

"It is unanimous," Kiet said.

Binh snapped his fingers at the bartender who brought two Golden Tigers. Kiet saw the empty in front of Binh and hoped it was his first. After two he was giggly, after three catatonic.

Binh paid the bartender and said, "Tell Superintendent Kiet what you told me."

"It won't be any different. What I told you hasn't changed in an hour."

An hour, Kiet thought. This will be Binh's third Golden Tiger.

"Tell him, my man."

The bartender rolled his eyes at Kiet and began. "This guy in the picture. He's been in maybe twice a week for the last month. He is a dedicated drinker, Superintendent."

"Meaning?"

"Meaning he's obnoxious and gets asked to leave or his buddies coax him out."

"His buddies?"

"He's usually alone, but sometimes he has a friend or two with him."

"Describe the friends, please."

The bartender shrugged. "Rough guys. Young. I don't know."

101

"Has he ever been with a chubby, middle-aged, red-faced Caucasian male?" Kiet asked. "He drinks gin over ice and brags that he is invulnerable to local water."

"You just described Freddie Pogue," the bartender said.

"Do you know Pogue?"

He laughed. "All Hickorn bartenders know Freddie Pogue, and he drinks here a lot."

"Pogue and this man, together?"

"No."

"Talk about the individual in the picture, please."

"I can't say much. He was a drinker, as I said, but not the kind of drinker who babbles at his innkeeper. Him and his friends talked amongst themselves, but they did it at a table. I never overheard."

"The subject in the picture, he never talked to you?"

"Sometimes. Just shooting off his mouth."

"In what manner, please?"

"He bragged about how he'd be a big man in Hickorn soon."

"A big man, how?"

"He didn't say. A couple of days ago, though, he bought a round for the house with—Superintendent, am I in trouble?"

"Not as long as you continue speaking candidly."

"With an American fifty-dollar bill."

Kiet looked at Binh. Binh's eyes were glassy, abnormal.

Binh averted his glassy, abnormal eyes and said, "In case Nha walked in and I was drinking a Coca Cola, wouldn't that be suspicious? Policemen on duty drink Coca Cola."

"Incognito, yes. Relax, Captain, I am not being critical."

Binh sighed in relief and began giggling. He had forgotten that he was in full uniform.

"Coca Cola would have interfered with the advantage you would require for covert observation," Kiet continued, recalling a Binh Americanism about inhabitants of glass dwellings.

"What should I do?"

Binh's eyes were as liquid as the beer remaining in his bottle.

102

"Stand by," Kiet said, slipping off the stool with an idea.

"To what purpose, Superintendent?"

Binh deserved a holiday, Kiet thought, a day devoted to pure dissipation. "Police presence. Law and order."

"This saloon is safe," Binh said solemnly.

Another Americanism came to mind. Kiet said, "Have a nice day."

15

ON A CIRCULAR concrete pedestal in the intersection of Avenue Irving Crane and Mu Pakse was a bronze statue of Prince Savhana, romantically savage atop a rearing horse, sword poised to decapitate enemy infantrymen. Prince Savhana and his soldiers had repelled a Chinese invasion one-and-a-half centuries before the birth of Jesus of Nazareth. The battle was the Kingdom of Luong's last military triumph.

At one corner was a wayside. Its grass, shrubs, and flowering trees were immaculately tended. Wrought-iron and teak benches were provided for passersby. The ironwork was sanded and painted annually, the wood varnished. Such was the reverence for Luong's hero of heroes.

Bamsan Kiet sat on a bench next to a smallish man, short and slender with hair as thin as his eyeglasses were thick. His appearance was an accidental deception. The man was recently retired as commanding general of the Royal Luongan Army. In the 1950s, he had excelled at center-forward on the Luongan national soccer team. His body had not deviated a kilogram in weight or a degree in muscle tone since. Nor had his tenacity. The man was the object of Kiet's idea. He was Minister of Defense Cuong Van.

When Kiet had telephoned Van and requested a meeting, Van had suggested this innocent site: two important officials and old friends joining for midday refreshments and relaxation in the cooling shade of ancient glory. Pleasure during the meeting was a minor consideration, but it wasn't to be entirely overlooked. Kiet brought sandwiches and a thermos of iced citron soda.

"A welcome interim, Bosha," Cuong Van said. "Apparently I've been mistaken in the notion that my job is the supervision of our armed forces. Lately I have been placating diplomats. I sometimes ask myself why we have a Foreign Ministry."

"Oh?" Kiet said, filling cups.

Van sighed. "Ambassador Smithson, that pompous bore, he wants me to defoliate the highlands to expose the Rouge and their Soviet-made machines that print the counterfeit zin. I praise Buddha that there are no nuclear weapons in our country.

"I had been trying to get through to your headquarters when your call came in. The lines had been jammed all morning. You have a miraculous talent with our telephone system. A complaint about you was relayed to me by the Foreign Minister himself."

"Oh?" Kiet said, unwrapping the sandwiches.

"The new Russian shark, Shiherazade."

"Yes."

"He has lodged a protocol protest through channels. If he can be believed, you arrived at his embassy earlier today without an appointment and made provocative statements."

"We had a cordial conversation," Kiet said. "Evidently Ambassador Shiherazade is a back-stabber."

"He alleges that you besmirched him and his mission with accusations of black marketeering and counterfeiting, Bosha."

No Luongan dictionary listed the word "bosha." It had regional origins—Hickorn and Luong's south—and was a distortion of *bo shau*, a literal phrase for stunted growth. In the vernacular, bosha was runt. Kiet had not spurted in height until late adolescence and his *lycee* classmates, Cuong Van included, thus tagged him. Later in life, Kiet had come to accept it from old pals as an affectionate diminutive.

Kiet spoke meticulously of everything he had experi-

105

enced since his furlough. He spoke uninterrupted for twenty minutes. Perhaps the sheer quantity and the complexity of the fact patterns caused him to neglect a few irrelevant points, among them Joyce Wilson's fluttering towel and the wonderment associated with red stubble.

Bamsan Kiet and Cuong Van had been faithful friends for four decades, forty percent of a century. Van looked at Kiet and said, "Are you in love with her?"

"No, but she is responsible for a certain awakening."

Van threw a crumb of sandwich bread to a crowned pigeon, fattening somebody's meal. "Forgive me, Bosha. I should not have pried. When we sit and eat and talk, I think of our boyhood when our brains were behind our zippers."

"You're reading my guilt, Cuong. Joyce has idealized me as something I am not. I took advantage of her brainwashed conditioning."

"You said sweet things to the ladies. We all did."

"I was young and skinny and had muscles. I sold myself as worthwhile. Now that I'm not young, skinny, and muscular, I am a god."

Kiet shook his head and bit into his sandwich.

Van raised fingers as he recited names. "Fop Tia, Marsad Ref, Dung Nha, Freddie Pogue, Roland Wheeler—Will you ever again see Mr. Wheeler's remains?"

The prospect was not conducive to hearty consumption of food. Kiet put aside his sandwich and said, "No. The Ma San River is home to a hundred varieties of fish, half of which are carnivorous. I am not anticipating a corpse."

"My latest experience with inflation resulting from counterfeiting was this morning," Van said. "We're entertaining Malaysian general staff officers. How these foreign VIPs land in Hickorn with nothing in their pockets but American dollars, I will never comprehend. As a courtesy, I dispatched an aide to change money for them. The rate was incredible. Thirteen-fifty to one. I concur, Bosha, that this inflationary gap Totisa Bu defined will bathe Luong in fire and anarchy as readily as napalm."

"Who do you use for courtesy money-changing?"

"Singh. His rates are the best and he won't pass you counterfeit."

"A splendid choice," Kiet said.

Van took a piece of paper from a pocket and wrote the names of suspects and supporting players, spacing them throughout the page. He began drawing lines between the names, but he was scribbling and erasing more than connecting. "Bosha, my mind is set on a conspiracy, a consortium of greed."

"Mine too, Cuong."

"My lines refuse to intersect," Van said, tearing the paper into thin strips. "Ref and Dung Nha, yes. Wheeler and Fop Tia, yes. Shiherazade as a provocateur, Singh an accommodating middleman, Pogue an unknown ingredient. My lines are a maze."

"Crime centered on love and money is easy to solve," Kiet complained. "Foreigners invariably add business and politics and complications. Pogue and rumors of arms trading is a special worry. He would dismember his mother and sell the parts at the public market if there was a demand."

"I've heard the gossip," Cuong Van said. "We've been paying extra attention to our munitions inventory. I'm confident our pilferage is nil, but importing arms wouldn't be difficult for a man of the world like Freddie Pogue. Money has been known to temporarily distract Hickorn International Customs officers."

Kiet nodded in agreement. "Spread enough money around and there would be a blindness epidemic. And Marsad Ref is the logical client for guns and explosives in quantity."

"True," Van said. "My sources say that his goal is to establish a criminal network imitative of the Hong Kong triads. Anything promising a big profit would be controlled by him. Extortion, smuggling, theft, contract murder, to name some."

"Hickorn's Mafia godfather," Kiet said.

Cuong Van squinted. "Who?"

"Never mind. It is an American institution."

"Recommendations, Bosha?"

"I would like very much to interview the deceased Captain Dung Nha."

"Paraphrasing Ambassador Smithson, who presided at Nha's memorial services, the Captain Dung Nha who died so heroically defending our constitutional monarchy against the godless Communist Luong Rouge?"

"Yes, him," said a smiling Kiet.

"Nha is a psychopathic drunkard, but he has a human emotion we can exploit. He is dedicated to his widow and three fatherless children. They live in Obon and my staff informs me that he maintains regular contact with them."

"Splendid," Kiet said. "Are they being paid survivor benefits?"

"They are. Modification of pension requirements might just coax the martyred captain into the light of day."

"Resurrection from the grave?"

"A miracle. Yes. Give me a day to work on it. And from your domain, Bosha? I know you're plotting something evil."

"That carton of counterfeit zin under my desk is about to be circulated."

"A double-edged attack," Van said eagerly. "A method of intersecting the lines on my scratch pad."

"Hopefully."

"Fop Tia is your subject, I presume."

"His reverse transactions with Singh imply panic."

"An extended international trip contemplated?"

"Possibly. It is a decision of burning the funny money in headquarters' incinerator or underneath the mayor's tail. My Captain Binh has people watching for a run to the airport."

108

"An illegal decision, Bosha?"

"An expedient decision, Cuong. By tomorrow the zin will be devalued to fourteen hundred per one Yankee dollar. Minister Bu spoke of Germans rolling wheelbarrows of marks to the bakery. By next month only weightlifters will have the strength to haul sacks of zin to a market to buy a kilo of rice."

Cuong Van rose from the bench. "I'm already overdue for an appointment with the Malaysians. They've been asking to pray at a mosque. Hickorn has no mosques. Their second choice is to go shopping. It seems that gold jewelry and perfume is unreasonably priced in Kuala Lumpur."

"Underpriced treasures on *Le Avenue*?"

Cuong Van shrugged. "They'll learn the bad news for themselves as we swelter. I'll contact you in a day or two when we know if our traps clamped onto and chopped off any toes."

"Toes and feet," Kiet said.

"Satisfy my curiosity, Bosha, what do your lady friend and her cult believe in? Being their secondary guru and an infidel besides should give you an insight."

"They tell me that their Fahwandi connects them with their higher selves, their omniscient oversouls. He has taken them on a spiritual journey and has made them happy."

"Nonspecific and mindless euphoria. The—what were they?—hippies, weren't they on the same quest?"

"Nirvana," Kiet said.

"Nirvana," Van repeated, his voice leaden with fatigue. "There are worse objectives."

16

THE EMPHASIS OF a medical school's curriculum is a factor of the environment and life-styles of the population it is pledged to heal. Luong University's College of Medicine is modest, parochial. Cardiology, oncology, and psychiatry are taught as survey courses; students wishing to specialize in those disciplines complete their education abroad. The college's parasitology department, however, is as sophisticated as its counterparts in the industrialized west.

Parasitic diseases such as malaria and typhus persist, and every Luongan physician is trained to astutely diagnose and treat them. But a hypertension patient is as likely as not to be prescribed herbs. No pyschoanalysts practice in Hickorn, no stress therapists, no sports medicine experts. Supply and demand rule.

Bamsan Kiet's mind drifted to Luongan medicine as he awaited Mayor Fop Tia's reflex to his scheme. Time Urgency—Captain Binh had brought some home with him from the District of Columbia, like insect larvae imported in a shipment of guavas. Kiet subscribed to the overseas edition of *Time* magazine. He had read in it that Time Urgency was a symptom of Type-A Behavior and that Type-A Behavior deposited layers of plaque on one's coronary arteries, gradually restricting the flow of blood.

Thereafter, Kiet worried whenever his young adjutant glanced at his watch. If modern medical science could be trusted, each glance attracted cholesterol molecules to his arterial walls. He did not worry that Fop Tia was a compulsive watch-glancer. Tia had always been a Luongan mutation in that regard, aggressive and fidgety and ruthlessly ambitious. If the fire Kiet ignited overloaded his cardiovascular system, it was not his fault, absolutely not.

Kiet compared Time Urgency and Sheer Panic. The first was a dilute solution, the second its concentrated essence. Sudden results were anticipated, but Kiet was shocked when Captain Binh came into his office in *ninety minutes* and said, "We have to go. Now. Please hurry."

Ninety minutes after taking the box of counterfeit zin to Mr. A. Singh, proprietor of Bombay Tailors. Requesting that he dispose of the queer. In bulk. Immediately. Unloading it for what it is, asking an attractive five percent of face value. Singh's agonized protests. Kiet thanking Singh in advance for his cooperation.

In the Citroen, Binh said, "Fop Tia received a caller, Superintendent, a business crony. The meeting lasted but a minute. Tia ran out as if the Hickorn Center of Public Administration were on fire."

"Fire," Kiet said, smiling. Sheer Panic.

"My contact tried to telephone but the lines were jammed as usual. He owns a motor scooter, so he drove to headquarters."

"Your contact, a deputy commissioner of whatever, is dependable?"

"Oh yes, Superintendent," Binh said with a chuckle.

Kiet knew that Binh had the goods on the fellow. He did not care to know what. "Which direction was Tia headed?"

"Toward his home."

"Splendid. To the airport, please."

Binh started the car. "Superintendent, shouldn't we be trailing him?"

"My hunch is that he is packing. If we head to his home, he may well pass us going the other way."

Kiet's hunch proved correct. Fop Tia's red convertible turned from Avenue Che Guevara onto Richard Nixon Boulevard, the airport thoroughfare. The little Fiat fishtailed. Its exhaust was pumping blue smoke and the Citroen was so close—three car lengths behind as they entered Nixon from Mu Pakse—that Kiet could hear transmission gears grinding.

"Fantastic luck," Binh said, maintaining the three-car-length interval.

"Guesswork too," Kiet said. "I have been studying airline schedules for this occasion. A Singapore carrier services Hickorn once a week, making a loop via Bangkok and Penang. Today is the day. It is Tia's soonest opportunity to escape."

Fop Tia stopped outside the terminal entrance, took a small suitcase from the trunk, and quickstepped inside. "A loading zone," Kiet said. "He is abandoning his car."

When Tia was out of sight, Binh parked behind the Fiat and opened his door.

"No. Not yet," Kiet said.

"Superintendent, we can't—"

"We won't. The flight departs in one hour. Boarding will begin in thirty minutes. Tia will be busy buying his ticket and bribing Customs employees to ignore his baggage."

"Extremely light baggage," Binh said. "Why shouldn't we bust him now?"

"Busting, as you put it, a man of his prominence requires delicacy and timing. Do not forget, Captain, that Tia has power and influence. If there is a confrontation and airport security officers are brought into it, we could lose our quarry."

Binh drummed the steering wheel. Kiet looked at him. Binh stopped and stared at his watch. Kiet asked Binh to notify him when twenty-five minutes elapsed. He closed his eyes and meditated. This Time Urgency malady could be contagious.

Binh nudged him. Kiet knew that it was the exact instant of his instructions. Binh confirmed the exactness by thrusting his arm in Kiet's face and tapping his watch crystal,

112

demonstrating the second hand crossing the twelve.

An airline clerk handed Fop Tia his ticket as the two policemen approached. Tia was dressed in his customary style, the Polyester Leisure Suit fashion Binh scorned. The color of the day was green. Armpit perspiration had rendered that area the hue of moss. Gold chain snaked in and out of a canary yellow shirt.

Kiet scanned the terminal floor. The Church of the Amalgamation of Enlightenment was scattered, proselytizing. He saw Joyce. Her back was to him and she was engaged in ardent conversation with two elderly Chinese women, presumably passengers of the Singapore airliner, who had disembarked to stretch their legs. Whether they liked it or not, they were being joined in an effort to also stretch their consciousness.

There seemed to be an excess of persons draped in camouflage silk. He counted. Nine. The pickpocket was still in jail. An overage of three. He scanned again. The surplus trio had hair. They were Luongans, newly enlisted Kanpuri. Kiet groaned.

The mayor spotted Binh and Kiet, and ignited the politician's smile. "Well, gentlemen, are you traveling somewhere too?"

Kiet observed that the knuckles of the hand grasping the small suitcase were ivory white. "No. And you, sir?"

"Bangkok," Fop Tia said. "A trade conference of Southeast Asia mayors and entrepreneurs. A component of my job is promotion of commerce, you know."

"Spare us a moment, please," Kiet said.

"My flight—"

Kiet wrapped an arm around Fop Tia's chubby shoulders. "Please, Mr. Mayor," he said gently. "You will not miss your airplane."

Tia's eyebrows flared in exasperation, but he permitted the policemen to escort him to unoccupied benches by the lockers. Kiet exhaled in relief. He had counted on the mayor being too rushed to raise a commotion.

"This had better be damned important."

"It is and I applaud your bravado," Kiet said. "You are a splendid actor, Mr. Mayor, but listen to me. Your assassin or assassins did not betray you. They did not find Roland Wheeler's secret storage compartment after they murdered him. They did not remove the counterfeit zin and sell it to A. Singh. The contrivance was ours and the patriotic Mr. Singh was pleased to oblige."

Tia laughly loudly. "Kiet, you're too old for your job. Your brain is starved for oxygen. You're going senile."

The insult angered Binh. He said, "Wheeler tried to sell you his newest state-of-the-art laser photocopier, which you didn't purchase for the Hickorn Center of Public Administration, although the technology inspired a lucrative plan where you and Wheeler would print counterfeit zin and divide the proceeds fifty-fifty, providing money to compensate for the financial reverses of your blundering commodities partners and funds for your upcoming campaign, but then Wheeler went berserk, out of your control, became too greedy and dealt queer on his own in such quantity that our economy was affected. You had him whacked out to save yourself."

Whacked out? No time to increase my vocabulary now, Kiet thought. Nor to be critical of the vast, strident sentence. The point was made. He smiled serenely, immensely proud of the lad.

"This boy of yours, Kiet," Tia snapped, jabbing a plump finger at Binh. "He has a disrespectful mouth. The first thing on my agenda after the Bangkok conference is the discharge of this brat. You can't save him. Cuong Van can't save him. I have friends. Your job is precarious too, old man. You can clean out your desks together."

The jabbing finger belonged to the hand that had gripped the suitcase. Kiet grabbed the case, quickly and deftly for an old man, and slid it between his legs. He broke the latches with a pocketknife and said, "Excuse me, *after*

114

the Bangkok conference? Will that be in this century? And aren't you traveling rather lightly, Mr. Mayor?"

"Give it to me!"

"Your grasp was too intense. Blood to your fingertips was pinched off. Be grateful. I saved you from gangrene."

"Kiet, you bastard!"

"Underwear? A change of clothing? I am curious, Mr. Mayor. How can the wardrobe required for such an elegant conference fit? Does—the name of the miracle fabric, please, Captain?"

Binh beamed. "Polyester."

"Yes. Polyester. Does polyester compress, Mr. Mayor?"

"Kiet, you are a dead man."

"Am I? The mayor's hitsters will work while he is in Bangkok increasing Hickorn's trade?"

"Hit men, Superintendent," Binh corrected.

"Hit men. Yes. A contract criminal who works on credit for a disappeared boss is unique to my knowledge. How much money is in here, Mr. Mayor? A quarter of a million? Half a million? Every dollar you gained in the venture? Let us dump it on the floor and count. People will see what sort of underwear their mayor is taking to Bangkok. They may have as many questions as I do."

"Kiet, we are reasonable, intelligent men," Tia said, his voice raspy. "I think we can strike a satisfactory arrangement."

"A deal?" Kiet whispered, leaning forward conspiratorially.

"A wonderful deal, Bamsan."

The sudden first-name familiarity was offensive. Kiet winked. "Captain Binh is included, of course."

Tia's politician smile exploded on his face. He slapped Binh's thigh and said, "Forget what I said. You're a good boy. If I had ten of you working for me, I could fire the rest, right?"

"Right," Binh said evenly.

"Splendid," Kiet said. "Please tell me who you hired to kill Roland Wheeler."

115

Fop Tia frowned and wiped perspiration from his forehead. "Kiet, I thought you just agreed to a deal."

"I did and this is it, Mr. Mayor," Kiet said. "You will confess and name your accomplices, please."

"I don't know what you're talking about."

"Liar!" Binh shouted.

Kiet frowned at him and touched a finger to his lips. Binh was unusually testy, his eyes reddened. Kiet attributed his agitation, in part, to yesterday's Golden Tiger. He said to Fop Tia, "I will amend the offer. Answer a simple question and you can board your Bangkok airplane."

Tia brightened and reached for the suitcase. "A wise choice, Kiet."

Kiet pushed it deeper under the bench. "Tia, we know you had Wheeler killed. We know my lucky interruption of your hitlings—"

"Hit men, Superintendent."

"Yes. My interruption of their search for the funny money and the magical machine. What I do not understand is why they disposed of the body when they came back later for the machine and, fruitlessly, for the money. They must have known I discovered the corpse."

"Perhaps," Tia said, measuring his words, "perhaps different parties, perhaps different factions."

"A different faction employed by a different person?"

Tia made firm eye contact with Kiet. "Perhaps. Theoretically."

A separate Soviet–Marsad Ref–Freddie Pogue axis. An unsurprising complication. Tia had just confirmed it. Kiet was convinced of his truthfulness and further convinced that this was to be the extent of the confession.

Kiet got up. "I'll accompany you to the boarding gate. Come. I would not want you to miss your flight."

"My luggage. Give it to me."

"No. It stays. Its contents will be donated to the Royal Treasury."

116

"You're bluffing."

Kiet gave the case to Binh. "I am reluctant to initiate a riot, but if you force me, Tia, we will litter the premises with American dollars. How many people are in the terminal, I wonder? Fifty? Fifty witnesses that Mayor Fop Tia wears rectangular green underwear."

"All right, all right," Tia said as he stood. "You win."

They walked to the gate. Passengers were climbing a portable staircase, entering a Boeing 727. Tia said to Kiet, "With your department under me, we could do some good, profitable work together. That arrangement remains possible."

"Have a pleasant journey," Kiet said, not meaning it. "And do have a nice day."

Kiet and Binh watched the jet take off and bank southward toward Thailand. They went out to the Citroen. Binh said. "An accessory to murder is going free."

The bitterness in his voice summoned memories of Marsad Ref's reprieve. "We took his power and his money, Captain. They are as precious to him as his freedom."

"He should be facing a firing squad," Binh said.

"Yes, certainly. His accomplices too. A pleasant but unfortunately unrealistic fantasy. The actual hitters were probably nameless scum paid a few zin, recruited by Tia's subordinates. Proof in a court of law would be difficult. If we went by the rules, Tia would have a splendid chance of being exonerated. The folks who visited Wheeler's villa while we were answering the cult disturbance are the key players in the mess, them and their leaders. Tia and Wheeler started the enterprise. Others, far more dangerous, took over."

"Agreed, but still . . . " Binh's voice tapered off into a pout.

"Besides, Captain, Hickorn benefits mightily."

"How so, Superintendent?"

"The upcoming mayoral election. The candidates will

not be competing with an entrenched incumbent. To use polite terminology, Fop Tia is in exile. Regardless how venal and unpopular you are, incumbency is an advantage. Our next mayor might be an honest man."

"Well, okay, I guess I sort of see your point."

"Thank you." They got into the car and Kiet opened Tia's suitcase. The contents were as expected, but this correct assumption did not mitigate the shock. In breathless silence they gawked at twenty-, fifty-, and hundred-dollar bills.

"Awesome," Binh finally said.

"Not a cubic millimeter of space available for under-shorts," Kiet said. "I suspect that Tia intended to buy basic necessities in Bangkok."

Kanpurin Morajini exited the terminal, blinked and swiveled his head. He spotted the two police officers in their Citroen and shuffled toward them. Kiet groaned, counted a thousand dollars, presented the money to Binh, and said, "Please go downtown and give it to Singh in exchange for the queer zin."

"Why?"

"Compensation for the inconvenience we imposed on him."

"Ah," Binh said. "The exact amount of the Russian's queer fifties."

"I promised Singh justice. Ambassador Shiherazade will be billed later in some form."

"Then how will you get to headquarters, Superintendent? Taxicab?"

"No. In this vehicle. I did not see Fop Tia remove the keys from his convertible. In my view, the automobile is impounded property."

Binh licked his lips. He did not rebut. Kiet noticed as Binh raced away, smoke emitting from the exhaust and the rear tires, that he was not wearing his cap, *was* wearing sunglasses. Kiet motioned to Morajini to join him in the car.

"What can I do for you?"

118

"I misjudged you, Fahwandi," Morajini said, bowing his head.

"Quit bowing. The steering wheel will give you a concussion. And call me Kiet!"

"Kiet. My hostility of the day past was deplorable."

"Excuse me?" Kiet's innocence was, of course, a lie.

"Satanic speculation about you and Kanpurin Sharla seeped into my consciousness. I was wrong. Sharla has never been more serene and level."

"Oh?"

"Sharla spent the night at your home. My mind generated despicable thoughts. Paranoiac seepages from my former, unenlightened self eroded my plane. I had lost faith in the immaculacy of channeling, in the chastity of your delivery to us by Fahwandi Kli Shabbir."

"It happens," Kiet said, nodding in commiseration. "Rats nibbling on the wiring and whatnot."

"Will you forgive me? I realize that you didn't despoil Kanpurin Sharla."

"I didn't?" Morajini wasn't looking at Kiet. His gaze was frozen on the Citroen's instrument panel, as if exorcising monsters from the speedometer.

"Satanic persecution of the Fahwandi is relentless, Kiet. It coagulates. It amplifies. Silica absorbs the energy and scatters erratic wave patterns."

"Silica?"

"Trees are full of silica crystals, Kiet. The planet's land mass is dominated by trees."

"I understand now," Kiet said.

"Sharla vows that you did not try to deprogram her, and I trust her words."

Deprogram? A deviate sexual practice? He and Joyce had coupled conventionally. "You can trust her words, Morajini. By the way, how goes your preaching?"

"We have enlisted Luongan acolytes. I am pleased by our progress."

"In the context of fund raising, please."

Morajini shook his head. "Luong is a healthy and happy land, Kiet. Luongans do not starve, but there is not an abundance of discretionary income."

Kiet lifted the lid of Tia's suitcase and took out what he could wrap a hand around. It was only money. He said, "Worldwide evangelism is expensive. I am honored to channel this to you."

"I am speechless," Morajini said.

Kiet wondered how he could be speechless, yet simultaneously speak. "There are conditions. You will depart on the next international flight anywhere. Late this evening, Air India comes through Hickorn, then to Calcutta. Be on it. Enlighten the Subcontinent masses. Secondly, your Luongan recruits stay. Their conversion was hasty. If upon contemplation they remain faithful, they can join you. Finally, keep me informed of your location. After the pickpocket has paid his debt to our society, we must know where to ship him."

Morajini stepped out of the car and bowed.

Kiet waved.

"Believe me, deprogramming was my only concern about Kanpurin Sharla, Kiet. Her heart is compelled to follow the path subscribed on her enlightened plane. If the path does not intersect with mine, I am compelled to accept this linear inversion.'

Kiet said nothing.

"I am happy for the carnality with which you anointed her, Fahwandi. We all are."

Morajini's smile was beatific. Kiet blushed. He started the Citroen and made a mental note to investigate the meaning of deprogramming.

"Have a nice flight," he said.

17

Episodes of that day merged into the next. The episodes were linked, important.

Kiet went from the airport to the Ministry of Finance. He donated Fop Tia's suitcase to Minister Totisa Bu, who counted the dollars slowly and affectionately, then gave Kiet a receipt for $212,550 US. Bu told Kiet that his research on macrocounterfeiting in Third-World nations had proven barren. There were neither historical precedents nor applicable scholarly theorizations. Kiet expressed disappointment and asked if the dollars would be beneficial to Luong's wounded economy and the hypergalloping zin. Bu said that an injection of hard currency could do no harm. Monies of the world's wealthy nations stabilized, akin to fresh mortar in crumbling brickwork. Incredibly, Totisa Bu did not ask where Kiet had obtained the $212,550.

Tia's Fiat convertible was at headquarters. It smelled of brake linings and radiator fluid. Kiet imagined a horse flogged into exhaustion. Captain Binh was inside, in conference with a Royal Luongan Army colonel and a deputy minister of defense. They were scribbling on a blackboard, listing names in blocks—surveillance teams, Binh explained—and circling points joined by slashing chalk lines—primary coordinates, he further explained. On a table was an overflowing carton of two-way radios—state-of-the-art walkie-talkies, said Binh—of Korean manufacture, Japanese distribution, a USAID gift to the Ministry of Defense.

The deputy minister of defense, who apparently outranked the uniformed colonel, gave Kiet Cuong Van's best regards and his regret at being indisposed for this conference. Something to do with a Malaysian brigadier general and a star sapphire.

Kiet was praised for his disposal of Fop Tia, then briefed. Cuong Van had executed his role in the two-pronged subterfuge by moving the widows and children of missing and presumed-dead army officers from Obon to Hickorn for their protection. Interception of a Rouge communique led Intelligence to believe that families of the martyrs were in danger. The Communist thirst for atrocities had no civilized bounds. The innocents would be safer in Hickorn.

Since Dung Nha was presumably living in Foh Ten, he would be irresistibly tempted to see his beloveds. Distance and limited travel options rendered Obon inconvenient and hazardous. Nha would leap at the good fortune of their relocation. A company of crack troops was undertaking the surveillance. they were already assembling, in mufti, monitoring crucial positions: the Foh Ten bridge, the apartment house in which Nha's loved ones were lodged, the Soviet Embassy, the airport, the Hickorn Continental Hotel.

Kiet was impressed. He was also superfluous. He had been slightly miffed that the strategy session had gotten underway without him but the reason was obvious. Etiquette dictated that seconds in command coordinate with seconds in command. Cuong Van was hamstrung by a brass hat, perhaps filling a jewelry order for a Kuala Lumpur mistress. Preservation of face dictated that Captain Binh be given principal responsibility.

Kiet occupied himself with paperwork, keeping out of the way, looking in now and then, accepting with good nature morsels of information as the plan jelled. By sundown, they were ready, sentries in position, the colonel and deputy minister gone to supervise the troops and to brief Cuong Van.

122

Kiet and Binh spent the night there. An unavoidable inconvenience, Binh told Kiet. Hickorn Police Headquarters had been chosen as Command Operations Center, he said proudly. The COC. Nha could move at any time, necessitating the twenty-four-hour vigil.

The only sleeping quarters were vacant jail cells. Kiet could extend his arms and touch opposite walls. His bunk was plywood the size and shape of a coffin bottom. His toilet was a hole in the concrete floor. There were no windows. Lights in the hallway burned all night.

Kiet eased himself prone, he and his walkie-talkie, a definitely inferior alternative to his own bed and his sullen cat. Prisoners taunted the superintendent and his adjutant. Kiet told them pleasantly that if present company was offensive they could be transferred to the maximum-security wing, where the thumbscrews and testicle electrodes were kept. No such wing existed, but the deception worked.

The prisoners fell silent and went to sleep. Because they did, Kiet could not. Apparently, loud snoring was an abnormal quirk of criminals. Binh, in the adjoining cell, appeared to be immune. He contributed a nasal racket of his own, the radio hissing and crackling on his heaving chest.

In the early morning, Kiet gave up. He shut his cell door behind him with a thunderous clang, reveille for his tormentors. They answered with a gratifying chorus of moans and obscenities. He staggered to his office, the Command Operations Center. The COC.

Binh was already on duty, crisp and energetic, freshly changed into starched and gleaming dress whites. He sat in front of the blackboard of hieroglyphics, a notepad and walkie-talkie before him. Kiet would have hated him for his industrious perkiness if it were not for a steaming pot of coffee on the desk and the realization that he had not heard Binh leave the jail cell. It therefore followed that he had actually *slept*.

Slightly refreshed now, Kiet poured a cup, gulped life-sustaining caffeine, refilled, and sank into his chair.

Binh said, "I received no transmissions during the night, but I may have dozed off. Did you, Superintendent?"

"No."

"Time to rattle some cages."

"Yes?" Kiet said.

"Tiger One to field Tigers. COC standing by. Game activity update. Reply in sequence."

Tigers Two through Six reported no activity on Game. The voices were fuzzy, as if Hickorn telephone callers.

"A code we devised, Superintendent. The odds are long that Nha or any of Ref's other goons are monitoring this frequency, but if they are, the communications will sound harmless."

Harmless, Kiet thought? Game being tracked by half a dozen Tigers? "Impressive," he said, unimpressed.

"Tigers are posted at key spots. If Nha crawls out of his burrow, we'll know."

"Will he be apprehended on sight?"

"No. We're anticipating that besides visiting his wife he'll do business for Ref also. Tiger One is five armed soldiers. Nha will be busted at the bridge upon his return."

"Splendid," Kiet said, impressed this time.

Just then, "Tiger One, this is Tiger Two, over."

Tiger Two's voice came through the electronic fuzz anxious and high-pitched. Binh said, "Tiger Two, Tiger One. Go ahead."

"Game crossed Checkpoint Alpha, headed for Core. Mode is Motor Two."

"Roger," Binh said. He called Tigers Three, Four, Five, and Six, and relayed Tiger One's message. He explained to Kiet, "The field Tiger units haven't the range to reach each other, but COC's location, us, here, is central and covers the Grid."

The majority of Binh's words seemed to begin with capital letters. His inflection on them was giving Kiet a headache. And who was Roger, where did Roger insert himself in this drama between Game and Tigers? "What is Checkpoint Alpha and Core, please?"

Binh gestured to the blackboard. "Checkpoint Alpha is the Hickorn side of the Foh Ten Bridge, the locus of Tiger Two. Core is downtown. Motor Two is a two-wheeled motor vehicle, a motorcycle or scooter."

"Of course," Kiet said.

"I was schooled in the structured surveillance grid system in Washington. We interdicted a big cocaine buy once. I got to ride in the COC."

Kiet tried to picture headquarters on wheels. His imagination could not make it roll. "Rode?"

"We had a van. It was packed with radio gear. It gave off lots of heat. The climate of the van was like Hickorn's. We couldn't use the air-conditioning because of the noise. Everybody but me roasted."

"A rolling COC. Convenient," Kiet said. He stared at the incomprehensible shorthand on the blackboard.

"It's all right there, Superintendent."

"Yes, I see. Now what?"

"We stand by."

Kiet preferred to sit by.

After ten minutes, Tiger Three reported that Game had gone into his wife's apartment. Ten minutes later the Nha children came outside with rubber balls and toy cars. They played on the street for an hour, scampering to the curb when the infrequent automobile passed. Nha's wife yelled at them from a window. They went inside. Nha emerged and sped away to Core on his Motor Two.

"A conjugal visit," Binh said.

"Nha, the devoted family man," Kiet said.

Fifteen minutes went by. Tiger Six checked in. He had Game.

Binh answered Kiet before he asked. "Six is stationed at the La Toh."

Kiet knew the La Toh to be a neighborhood bar on Passage Luther Lassiter, a long and narrow café with steel and Formica furniture that was dragged onto the sidewalk during the dry season. Melancholy Luongan love songs wafted from a phonograph. La Toh's kitchen specialized in *zhae*, a peppery meat and noodle soup. They served glasses of Golden Tiger with ice cubes, refrigeration being an unaffordable amenity.

"Dung Nha the drinker," Kiet said, remembering. "Dung Nha, the early drinker."

"He adopted it as his Hickorn watering hole," Binh said. "He'd drink with his army pals on the Continental *terrasse* and retire to the La Toh when the parties broke up. He could drink himself into a stupor and nobody in the Obon command would be the wiser."

Kiet's stomach growled. He slapped it and said, "Nha may be a while."

"Breakfast? I'm not hungry."

"A malnourished adjutant is less than useless. Bring your talking radio."

They ate rolls and marmalade at a vendor's stall two blocks toward town on Avenue Alexandre Loubet, Kiet wolfing, Binh nibbling. Kiet admonished Binh for birdlike eating habits, then finished the roll Binh couldn't. He complemented the meal with pickled eggs and an orange soda. The privation of a night in a jail cell had made him ravenous.

The radio spoke the moment they walked into the COC. Tiger Six told Tiger One of Game's departure, that he had been fortifying his Golden Tiger with jiggers of black-market whiskey, the Jim Beam brand.

Next to report was Tiger Four. Four's transmission was a choppy mix of language and feedback howls. Binh finally solved the reception problem. Tiger Four, in an effort to be a casual spy, was leaning against an iron lamppost. Binh grumbled to Kiet that Four and the lamppost had become an antenna possibly capable of providing crystal-clear re-

126

ception to Melbourne, Australia, but not across town. He instructed Four to shift a meter in *any* direction.

Four said that Game was presently vectoring to the Core, that his mission at Checkpoint Delta had been rebuffed.

"Where is Tiger Four posted?"

"Interesting, Superintendent. Nha asked into the Soviet Embassy and they said no."

Interesting. Kiet thought of Ivan and Sasha.

Soon, Tiger Five, the operative at the Hickorn Continental, announced the arrival of Game, hospitality on the *terrasse* with Lard, and a sojourn upstairs.

Kiet did not have to ask who Lard was.

In twenty minutes, per Tiger Five, Game and Motor Two were exiting Checkpoint Echo and the Core, westbound on Avenue John F. Kennedy, unsteadily, at an unsafe rate of speed. Binh alerted Tiger Two.

"He sounds really drunk. He must've been drinking with Freddie Pogue too. He's headed for the bridge," Binh said. "He'll turn northbound on Ma San Boulevard and be there in five minutes. Let's go!"

Kiet and Binh hurried outside. Kiet jogged to the Citroen.

"No!" Binh cried. He hurdled a door of Fop Tia's red Fiat convertible and scuttled behind the wheel. "This is a much faster car, Superintendent."

Kiet groaned and got in with him. The automobile was reluctant to start. Binh cursed Italians and their engineering. Kiet smelled raw gasoline. It finally kicked over, although backfiring unhealthily.

Binh accelerated, burning rubber. Tiger Two called for Tiger One. Binh braked hard. Kiet's fingers imprinted the dashboard pad.

"Game is approaching," Tiger Two yelled through heavy static.

"Interdiction," Binh yelled back. "We'll be at Checkpoint Alpha in five minutes."

127

The pop of gunfire was unmistakable.

"Tiger One, over."

"He saw us. He U-turned. We fired in the air," Tiger Two screamed. "He didn't stop. We fired at him and missed. All Tigers, Game is on the loose."

"Where to?" Binh asked nobody in particular. "Where the hell is he going?"

There was an explosion. It came from the riverfront area, but south of the bridge. It was an echoing clap of thunder in a cloudless sky.

"God, what the hell was that?"

"Possibly a pocket of gas in the sewers," Kiet said, though not believing. An accidental calamity occurring in this blight of criminality did not seem ordained. He thought: bomb.

Binh shook his walkie-talkie in frustration, as if trying to dislodge a fragment of information. Kiet got out of the Fiat and stretched. Binh followed. He did not stretch. He paced. He radioed his Tigers. None had Game.

"I feel helpless, Superintendent. We can't close in on him if we don't know where to go. He's not showing at our checkpoints. Where else would he go?"

Kiet shrugged.

They heard a motorcycle engine. The harsh popping grew louder. Dung Nha drove into headquarters' courtyard. He dismounted the cycle, made a nominal and inebriated effort at lowering the kickstand, then allowed it to clatter onto the pavement.

Nha raised his hands.

Binh stared at Kiet in disbelief. Kit said. "I think he is asking us to arrest him. Shall we?"

Binh frisked Dung Nha, handcuffed him, and took a small card from his shirt pocket. Kiet knew it to be a Miranda Card, an instrument of legality carried universally by American law-enforcement officers.

"You have the right to remain silent," Captain Binh began.

128

18

Kiet and binh interrogated the deceased hero, Captain Dung Nha. It was agreed beforehand that Minister of Defense Cuong Van and his men would remain in the background. Capital punishment had been stricken from the Luongan criminal code years ago, but a military court martial could still result in the death penalty. Binh and Van's counterparts felt that Nha would speak more freely to civilians than to defense personnel, the fear of a ticket to a firing squad mitigated.

They interrogated Nha by candlelight. The explosion, presumably, had caused the power failure. Hickorn Metro's electrical grid was a French legacy, an overtaxed spider's web of lines, transformers, and corrosion. An outage in one corner of town might disable service in the opposite, a random quiltwork of blackouts in between.

To Kiet's relief, Nha was eager to talk despite the Miranda recitation. Binh's infatuation with the Miranda was puzzling in light of the contempt for it expressed by many of his District of Columbia mentors. Binh seemed to embrace the ritual as an imperfect advancement of civilization.

Kiet did not understand, but he respected Binh's misguided passion and avoided confrontations on the subject. He condoned Miranda, accepted it as a minor impediment, a temporary obstacle to the truth.

Dung Nha had no illusions about rights of silence and court-appointed defense attorneys. He lived in Luong, not Washington, D.C. He had never been in such serious trouble.

"I came to you for sanctuary, for protection," he told

Kiet. "I saw them firing at me from the Foh Ten Bridge and I knew I'd been led into a trap baited with my family. Do I have sanctuary?"

"Yes. If you have further appointments today, you may consider them canceled," Kiet said. "You and your former commander, Marsad Ref, please, what sort of mischief are you up to?"

"Ref was livid when the counterfeit zin began circulating. If anybody was to profit, it should be him. And us."

"Who is *us*?"

"Ref and the officers who joined him in Foh Ten. He owns Foh Ten, you know, but that isn't anything. It's an initial point to real money. We put out feelers in Hickorn. We have our people but we went into town ourselves, even Ref. You can get in and out if you do it right. We eventually traced the counterfeiting to this Yankee, Wheeler. We were too late. The Yankee was dead. We found the printing machine and took it."

"You also took the body of the late Roland Buzz Wheeler and removed evidence of the murder," Kiet said.

"We had to," Nha said. "If we were unluckily captured, I'd be denying a murder."

Dung Nha had sobered rapidly. His thoughts were organized, his speech unslurred. He reeked, though, of perspiration and motorbike fumes. His breath was powerful, like a cart load of spoiled fruit. "Where, please?"

"The river." Nha made chewing motions with his fingers.

"Of course," Kiet said, trying not to think about carnivorous fish. "The American fifty-dollar bills were yours, then?"

Dung Nha nodded. "They looked good, just like genuine Yankee money."

"What was your arrangement with the Soviets?"

The question surprised him. He looked at Kiet and then Binh.

Binh said, smiling, "A structured surveillance system. We had you clocked all the way, sport."

130

"The Russkis are endlessly trying to embarrass the Yankees. They're just as greedy too. I sold them counterfeit Yankee fifties. They can make money trading them on the black market and blame the Yankees for printing them."

"You weren't permitted to enter their embassy today," Kiet said.

Nha sneered. "The greedy bastards, they said the bills were inferior. It was their fault for trying to trade too much, too fast. These Communists, they have no grasp of business."

"Freddie Pogue has an excellent grasp of business," Kiet said.

"You saw me there too," Nha said, stating it as an answered question. "Pogue sells imported liquors. He is a conduit into Hickorn's cafés and bars."

"And Ref aims to control those establishments?"

"He does," Nha said.

"And opium too?"

Nha fluttered a hand. "Colonel Ref is patient. Opium is harder but it will come. The traffickers will be murderous opponents. Liquor first, opium later."

"I doubt if Pogue would accept counterfeit money of any denomination in payment."

"You're right, he won't," Nha said. "We have hard currencies too."

"Converted from zin you extorted from the poor of Foh Ten," Binh said angrily.

Nha did not emote. "That is primarily why we had to trace the counterfeit zin and, uh, adjust the trade in some form. The Yankee Wheeler, the bastard was devaluing our revenue."

"You and Pogue, please?"

"We agreed to pay a decreased wholesale price for his goods. In exchange, we will have monopolies, Pogue as an importer, us as retailers. His life will be leisurely. He can leave his briefcase in his room and live on the *terrasse* if he chooses."

131

"How can Pogue promise a monopoly on products he does not monopolize?" Kiet asked. "He probably sells a higher volume than any one of his peers, but that is no monopoly. The Continental is swollen with western peddlers."

Kiet's remark appealed to Nha's racism. He laughed and said, "Our bargain includes names of Pogue's business enemies and their primary customers."

"Ref's gang will persuade his competitors to relocate?"

Nha's laughter heightened in tone, a shrill cackle that pained Kiet's ears. "They can sell bandages in Cambodia. Viet soldiers guarantee no shortage of buyers."

"Extortion," Kiet said.

Nha winked at him. "That isn't a polite word."

"And with guns and bullets and explosives supplied by Pogue, Ref can readily accomplish the impolite. He can be Hickorn's—"

Kiet glanced at Binh.

"Godfather."

"Godfather. Yes," Kiet said. "A grenade rolled under a pedicab carrying a western liquor salesman would doubtlessly inspire colleagues to pursue the Cambodian bandage market."

"No, no. No guns and grenades."

"Former army officers, Luongan heroes, and you're not interested in munitions?"

Nha winked again. "We'll persuade—that's your word— we'll persuade by shoving the Yankees and Aussies and Jap and Frog salesmen around, beating them up if they don't cooperate, but no guns and grenades. Ref is finished with politics. His ambitions are crime and money. You can persuade a white man by kicking him in his fat butt, you know."

Nha's disclaimer was too absolute to be the truth. "You have not discussed weapons with Freddie Pogue?"

Nha spread his arms and gaped innocently. "No, no. Never. Only liquor and money."

132

The interrogation was degenerating into a friendly conversation. Kiet attributed Nha's evasive congeniality in portion to Binh's Miranda reading, the nonexistent rights a subconscious opiate. He paused, browsing through his mental arsenal of threats when a uniformed officer came in and gave Binh a note.

"The explosion, Superintendent. A bomb at Ou Vang's."

"Casualties?"

"Fortunately not, but damage is substantial. The blast wiped out a wall the junction box was on, knocking out power."

"A bomb," Kiet said, staring at Dung Nha.

"Not us."

"You are no longer a member of *us*, Nha."

"I know. I came to you to prevent soldiers from shooting me. I cannot return to Foh Ten now or ever. Colonel Ref would not believe I said nothing to you. He would have me tortured until I confessed, then kill me."

Kiet knew Marsad Ref too well; Dung Nha was not exaggerating. "Bomb," Kiet repeated.

"I'm sorry, but I told you everything. I paid for my sanctuary with absolute truthfulness, Superintendent Kiet."

Addressing him by name was a glaze on the lie, Kiet thought. A bonding of two honorable men. He continued staring.

"You must protect my family too," Nha said, avoiding Kiet's eyes by picking at his fingernails. "I've cooperated to the fullest."

Kiet was anxious to visit the bomb scene. Dung Nha could wait. "We intended to, but what are we to do with you?"

"You could install my family and me in a villa," Nha said in helpful eagerness. "By doing so you'd cut in half the manpower required to guard us if we were housed separately."

"Thank you for your advice," Kiet said. "Army troops

are seeing to your family's security. Captain Binh, where did I sleep last night?"

"Number Four, Superintendent."

"Splendid. I trust my room is still available."

Binh smiled. "It certainly is."

The Kingdom of Luong is not an industrialized nation. Factories worthy of the definition are concentrated in Hickorn. They manufacture cigarettes, beer, detergent powder, furniture, and cement. Altogether they employ thirteen thousand people.

One street east of Ma San Boulevard, at Avenue Leonid Brezhnev and Mu Luong is Ou Vang Bicycle Works. This is an area of warehouses and small plants, Hickorn's quasi-industrial district. Ou Vang Bicycle Works is two stories tall and occupies half a city block. Only the Golden Tiger Brewery across the street and Emerald Queen Cigarettes next to it are larger.

A United Nations survey once reported that the bicycle is the primary form of nonpedestrian transportation for seventy-three of every one hundred urban Luongans. Ou Vang Bicycle Works is the Schwinn of Luong. Tires, wheels, handlegrips, chains, and derailleurs are imported from France. Ou Vang assembles them to frames they build and paint. The workmanship is very good; Ou Vang bicycles hold their own against Hickorn potholes.

Kiet and Binh interviewed Ou Vang, the owner. They were at the scene of the blast, a rear corner of the brazing shop. There was a hole the size of a manhole cover in the masonry wall. Outside, Metro technicians were carefully repairing damaged power lines and connections. High voltage crackled like grease in a pan. Kiet's nostrils were assaulted by a blend of gunpowder and ozone.

"A spark touched off acetylene," Ou Vang said. "My men were having tea. Someone must have forgotten to shut off a valve on a tank."

134

The frowns of uniformed officers standing by told Kiet that this was an incorrect conclusion. "I was pleased to hear that nobody was injured."

"The best of luck, Kiet," Ou Vang said. "The brazing shop was vacant."

Ou Vang was the first son of the late founder of the same name. He was about forty but he looked older, his face lined by responsibilities and an obsessive trait termed by Binh as *workaholic*. Kiet knew Vang as honest and courageous, not the frightened liar he seemed to be at the moment.

"Odd," Kiet said, scanning the shop. "No damage to machinery or the bicycle frames you are fabricating except for chunks of the wall that were blown inward behaving as shrapnel."

"Acetylene is an extremely explosive gas, Kiet."

"Yes. I agree, but I wonder why the wall wasn't blasted *outward*."

Ou Vang shook his head. "Acetylene is unpredictable. Accidental explosions and fires aren't uncommon when you weld and braze."

"Accidental?"

"Accidental," Ou Vang said firmly. "One of your patrolmen attributed it to a bomb. That's ridiculous. He scared my men. If the rumor spreads, they'll be afraid to resume work."

"We can rule out a bomb? You have no enemies?"

"None. You had to investigate but there is nothing further that concerns you, Kiet. My employees were careless and the blame is mine. I'll lecture them and be more conscientious about monitoring safety procedures. It won't happen again, I assure you."

Ou Vang was so intimidated by something or someone that he would swear the sky was green. Kiet entered a final plea. "You can talk to me in confidence, Mr. Vang. I will help you."

135

"Thank you, no. The police can't prevent accidents."

Kiet and Binh excused themselves and explored the narrow alley behind Ou Vang Bicycle Works. On it, under the hole, was cement dust.

Kiet sniffed. "Gunpowder."

"*Plastique*, I think," Binh said. "American-made C-4, I believe. Its odor is a little sweeter than powder or dynamite. A safecracking ring in Washington used it. We never caught them, but I was a member of a detective team that investigated a burglary in a beautiful Georgetown home. The lid of the wall safe was embedded in a fireplace. The stuff has a mean kick."

Kiet scuffed a toe in the dust. This was a rare moment in which Binh's District of Columbia expertise was welcomed. "*Plastique* is normally contained in what, please?"

"Plastic explosives can be modeled like clay, Superintendent. The wall is porous. The *plastique* could be pressed into it and stick. Insert a tiny detonator and timer and get the hell away. Mercury fulminate is the usual choice. A minute or two later, boom!"

"Would remnants of the timer survive?"

"Yeah, but they've been rocketed halfway to Laos," Binh said knowingly.

"Ambassador Smithson's Vietcong sappers in 1960s Saigon enjoyed playing with *plastique*," Kiet said, thinking out loud.

"Ril Thoi and the Rouge have shown no such inclination, Superintendent."

"A passing thought. Marsad Ref is a likelier candidate."

"Dung Nha stonewalled when you zeroed in on bang-bang. I've been figuring protection racket from Square One."

Kiet blinked at this flurry of slang. "Protection?"

"The Mafia sells protection to merchants and other business owners," Binh explained. "If you don't pay them, they harm you."

136

"You pay them to protect you from what they will do to you if you don't pay them?"

"Exactly."

"This Mafia and the godfathers you refer to, they sound like they're in the same family."

"They *are* a family, Superintendent."

Kiet was tired of being pummeled by semantics. "Ou Vang can afford to pay better than most. Does this make sense? Ref extorted him. Vang refused. Ref warned him, detonating the bomb when Vang's people were out of range."

"If Vang doesn't pay, the next bomb will kill," Binh said.

"He will pay now. Ref has stolen his courage," Kiet said, wandering about in quest of physical evidence.

"Clean," Binh said discouragingly. "A professional job. There isn't much hope of finding clues."

"Of course," Kiet said. His travels brought him to the building on the other side of the alley, a rice warehouse. "But what is this?"

"What's what?"

"Cracking in the stucco, some old, some new."

"Concussion from the explosion."

"The new cracks have larger chips, like beads in a necklace string." With his pocketknife, Kiet gouged out a shard of glass, then another, then another.

He placed them in Binh's hand as if they were gemstones.

"Opaque," Binh said, squinting. "Different colors. A design painted on the glass maybe."

"Is *plastique* sufficiently pliable to be pushed through a bottle neck?"

Binh nodded yes.

"The pressure of pushing would not cause a premature detonation?"

"No. You need a spark."

"So do we," Kiet said. "And I think we have it."

Bamsan Kiet opened the front door of his villa and saw

137

smoke. Captain Binh nagged him endlessly about residential security, about adhering to basic procedures like locking his doors. Kiet could never remember. He regretted his laxity.

Kiet did not carry a gun. He backpedaled, intending to summon reinforcements in dealing with the arsonists or cigarette-smoking burglars.

A feminine voice called his name. Kiet reentered. The smoke was not smoke; it was steam. Joyce Wilson was standing in his living room, draped in a towel.

"You didn't come home last night," she said.

"You didn't get onto an airplane with Morajini and the Kanpuri. They are in Calcutta, enlightening the masses without you."

"I apologize for all the steam," she said. "I stayed awake last night waiting for you. I fell asleep in the shower an hour or two ago."

"You fell asleep standing up?"

"I shower in the lotus position."

"Of course. Answer my question, please."

"You didn't ask one. You said I hadn't gone to India."

Kiet groaned. "Why were you not on the airliner?"

"May we first obey a higher precedence?" Joyce lifted her arms. Gravity claimed her towel.

Kiet stared.

"Déjà vu," Joyce said.

Kiet followed her into the bedroom.

138

19

A SHEET COVERED them from neck to ankle. The ceiling fan rippled the sheet but accomplished little else, its paddles moving too lazily to influence heat and humidity. Kiet's cat was curled between the two perspiring human beings, half asleep and purring. If the animal had made a moral judgment, it had gone unnoticed.

Joyce and Kiet didn't speak immediately afterward. They absentmindedly studied their toes, wiggling them as if bored children manipulating hand puppets.

Kiet finally asked, "I don't think I can say this again without sounding callous, which I don't mean to be, but why are you not in Calcutta?"

"A spiritual obligation," Joyce said.

Kiet sighed and fluffed the sheet, which was sticking to him.

"Our gossamer master has channeled us to you—"

"I know, I know."

"I was walking to the ramp of the Air India plane when I was given a sign."

"A sign?"

"An observation that connected me to my omniscient oversoul. A *sign*, Kiet, an inarguable *sign*."

She had rolled over and was holding him, though not lasciviously. For that he was thankful. "Explain, please."

"A minute earlier I was in the terminal. A minute later I would have been on the plane. I wouldn't have seen what I saw. The timing was—was astral."

"Yes?"

"Dung Nha. I saw that captain in your photo who's supposed to be dead."

"Dung Nha," Kiet said, sitting up. "At the airport yesterday?"

"I was at the ramp. I don't know why I turned my head suddenly to the right."

"Silica?"

Joyce looked up at him and laughed. "You've been talking to Morajini. Silica is an off-the-wall theory of his very own. Fahwandi has never—"

"You are certain you saw Dung Nha?" Kiet interrupted.

"An old, four-engine, propeller plane was unloading beside the Air India jet. It had numbers on it but no name. I guess it was a cargo plane of some kind. Dung Nha and several other men in blue uniforms were supervising the unloading. The plane had a rear hatch and pallets full of cardboard cases were being rolled out. A forklift loaded them onto a flatbed truck."

"Blue uniforms?"

"You know, robin's egg blue. Kind of grungy. Epaulets with gold stripes and navy blue caps. They'd look sharp if they were washed and pressed."

"Customs," Kiet said, thinking that Marsad Ref wasn't merely bribing Customs, he *owned* the benighted agency. "Then?"

"The truck drove into a hangar next to the terminal. The other blue uniforms went into the terminal. Dung Nha followed the truck on foot. I told Morajini I couldn't go with him and the Kanpuri."

"Did he object?"

"No. He bowed to me in sadness and boarded the airplane. He knew."

"He knew?"

"That I had been redispatched. The higher the plane of enlightenment, the fewer words required for meaningful communication."

140

"Of course. But tell me, is redispatching similar to deprogramming?"

"They are diametrically opposed, Kiet."

"Splendid. Then?"

"I went back into the terminal and took the side exit nearest the hangar. I thought it was odd right off the bat that the doors were nearly closed. Every other hangar was wide open to catch a breeze. They were cracked just enough for somebody to get through.

"Dung Nha was in there by himself. He lifted a lid of one of the cardboard boxes real delicately, like he didn't want to bend a staple, like he planned to reseal it. He removed a bottle. It was one of those commemorative whiskey bottles."

"Excuse me?"

"Oh. I keep forgetting where I am. The distilleries bring out special bottles in limited editions for special occasions. You see them a lot at Christmas. Some celebrate events, some just celebrate people. Celebrities. They become collectors' items. For instance, the Seattle World's Fair of 1962. My father has one shaped like the Space Needle. He says it's worth hundreds of dollars now. Right after Elvis died, he was honored. They're worth *thousands* today."

"Elvis Presley," Kiet said knowingly.

"Uh huh. The bottle in that case was Janet Ann Selkirk. The tight metallic gowns she wears on the show, I'd know them anywhere." She sat up and made an hourglass gesture, then cupped her hands inches in front of her breasts and wrinkled her face.

Her envy puzzled Kiet. Compared to Luongan women, Joyce's slightly sagging lemons were mammoth. The Selkirk individual must be bovine, he thought. "Who, please, is Janet Ann Selkirk?"

"The reigning bitch goddess of nighttime soaps. Oops, here I go again. Okay, a soap is a soap opera. A soap opera is a serial shown weekly on TV, a, uh, continuing drama about wealthy and nasty people. I joined the Kanpuri and I still couldn't stop watching it. I couldn't!"

"Why do the characters have to be nasty?" Kiet asked.

"Well, if they weren't, you wouldn't tune in every week, would you?"

Kiet nodded no.

"Anyway, there are good people in conflict with the nasties who commit incest, adultery, murder and every crime in between. The good people maintain kind of a holding action against the baddies. Amanda Hustingcross is the worst, the most evil. Janet Ann Selkirk plays Amanda on *Monterey Bay*. Amanda goes through two husbands a season and who knows how many lovers. She sometimes kills them or has them killed. Monterey Bay is John Steinbeck country, Cannery Row and so forth. The early episodes borrowed from Steinbeck, but that escaped most regular viewers. They didn't know who Steinbeck was. Soap junkies are not avid readers."

Intellectual self-deprecation added to breast envy. Kiet did not care to stroll further in this psychological maze. "The nice people aren't scripted solid victories?"

"The ratings would slide."

"Dung Nha inspected a likeness of Janet Ann Selkirk," Kiet said, hoping to advance her story. "Did he open the bottle?"

"Yes. He stuck a finger into it and rubbed his finger and thumb together. He capped the bottle, put it back into the case, and reattached the staple."

"Were there markings on the case?"

"Canned condensed milk. A name brand. Come to think of it, the only one. The other cartons were marked liquid drain cleaner. Another name brand."

"Did Nha take the case?"

"Not then. He went out front to the terminal lot. He walked up to a taxi and talked for a minute to a man in the back seat."

"Can you describe the man?"

142

"He was heavyset and he had a red face."

"Luongan?"

"No. A white man. The taxi left and Nha got on a motorbike that was parked by the terminal. He rode into the hangar. When he came out the phony case of canned milk was strapped behind his seat. He drove to the highway. That's the last I saw of him."

"You are a wonderful detective, Joyce."

"I obeyed my spiritual obligation, Fahwandi."

Joyce kissed him on the cheek, lay down, and instantly fell asleep. She turned on her side, legs drawn up, a perfect nestling position.

Kiet wanted desperately to join her. After the strenuous activity of moments past and jail the night before, his body craved rest. He could not, though. His mind would not permit sleep, not as long as it was overstimulated by the red-faced, heavyset white man.

Kiet slipped into the bathroom and took a cold shower. To awaken his body through frigid abuse was his plan, and Joyce had depleted the hot water, anyway. He steered the Citroen through light evening traffic, to the Hickorn Continental Hotel.

Yes, Mr. Pogue was in his room, the desk clerk said. Kiet held out his hand and politely asked for a passkey. The clerk nervously informed Kiet that Mr. Pogue had given orders that he was not to be disturbed. Kiet asked once more, again politely, and snapped his fingers. The clerk had recognized Hickorn's superintendent of police and correctly interpreted the finger-snapping gesture. He complied without comment.

Kiet trudged the stairs, thinking fondly of elevators. Pogue's room was on the third floor. Kiet turned the key and entered darkness. His eyes adjusted to the naked, snoring mound on the bed.

It was an abnormally early bedtime for an entrepreneur

143

such as Freddie Pogue, but Kiet was able to see the reasons. The half-empty whiskey bottle on the nightstand. The woman beside Pogue, who was also naked. She was crouched now, legs tucked under her, a silent scream on her face.

Kiet flicked on the light and said, "I am not an intruder, not in the usual sense."

The woman relaxed. She knew Kiet. Every Hickorn prostitute knew every Hickorn police officer by sight. The woman was actually a girl, barely into puberty.

"You may put on your clothes," Kiet said, feeling a familiar mix of anger and sadness, the despair of yet another childhood lost to the allure of money.

The girl shrugged, hopped to the floor, and slipped on her only article of clothing, a tight slit dress in a style known as Suzy Wong. She crawled over Pogue, took an American five-dollar bill from the nightstand, whispered an even good-bye to Kiet, and walked out of the room. The exit was accomplished matter-of-factly, without shame or modesty. Kiet was reminded of the hypergalloping inflation plague; before counterfeiting had shriveled the zin, the standard price was ten U.S. dollars.

Pogue was stirring, scratching his scalp. "Chief! You. What the bloody hell?"

Kiet began searching the room. He found nothing in the nightstand but a complimentary French language bible. Pogue was messy. In a corner was a pile of dirty clothing. Kiet sorted through it with a foot.

By then Pogue was sitting upright, though none too steadily. "Chief, you goddamn bloody better have a search warrant."

"I keep search warrants in the glove compartment of my car, Freddie. Luongan law grants the superintendent of police that authority. If you insist, I will fill one out later and give you a copy."

"What're you looking for, mate? Tell me and I'll help you find it."

144

Mate? Pogue was evidently Australian tonight. Kiet dumped the contents of a briefcase on the bed. Papers only, the majority bearing the letterheads of western liquor wholesalers and restaurant supply manufacturers. "Get dressed, please. You are less attractive naked than you can possibly know."

Pogue retrieved a pair of boxer shorts from the laundry heap, pulled them on, and rose with difficulty. "Goddamn fracking police state is what Luong is." Kiet moved to the closet and Pogue's hang-up clothes. He removed the shirts and pants and jackets one by one, checked the pockets, and discarded them. Suitcases underneath were empty.

Pogue placed a hand on Kiet's shoulder. "Chief, the girl, she's sashaying her little buns back to the *terrasse*. I could send for her again and make meself scarce. Dicey little thing and hot as a three-dollar pistol. Dip your wick in that and you'd bloody well better hang on for dear life. Ride'm cowboy!"

Kiet spun around and slapped Pogue hard in the face. Pogue staggered on his heels and held his cheek. "Goddamn coppers. You got your nerve getting your nose jerked out of joint. These pissy-ass little backwaters like Hickorn, every cabbie in town has a thirteen-year-old virgin for sale. Virgins, Chief, every bloody one of them. Where do you get off playing daddy to every teenaged slut—"

Kiet hit Pogue with his fist. The peddler yelped, lurched backward, and fell spread-eagled on the bed. Kiet flexed his hand. The soft meat larded on Pogue's face cushioned the blow, but the punch had come from Kiet's toes. His knuckles stung from contact with bone.

"Police brutality is what it is," Pogue said, moaning. "I'm going to the embassy and file me a complaint. I'll have your ass in a sling, mate."

"Of late, I have been particularly unpopular at superpower embassies," Kiet said. "Which one, please? And, by the way, where is your passport?"

"I need to go to a hospital."

Kiet looked at him. Pogue's upper lip was puffing and the blood was a trickle. The damage was minimal, however, a reminder to Kiet that he was growing old. "Your passport, please."

"In there," Pogue said, pointing to the closet floor.

"This?" Kiet said, picking up a Webster's New Collegiate Dictionary.

"The maids won't bother a book. They'll suck a shilling off the rug with their nostrils, but you can't hustle a book on the street, can you?"

Kiet opened the dictionary. An inch-deep section of center pages had been hollowed out. He found a passport and a wallet. The wallet was thick with currency. Kiet counted the money. The Luongan zin amounted to—what had it degraded to today?—at maximum sixty American dollars. The remainder was U.S. greenbacks, four thousand dollars worth of twenties, fifties, and hundreds.

"Chief, look, you lost your temper. It happens to anyone. I'm a man who forgives easily. Can I treat us to a short slurp?"

"Yes."

Pogue sank into a chair by the nightstand and poured three fingers of whiskey into water glasses. He clinked his glass against Kiet's. Information logically followed conciliation; Kiet reciprocated the clink, his emotions as restrained as Pogue's.

"Chief, what are you suspecting me of? I'm an honest businessman with his nose to the wheel, eking a cruddy living. I ain't a pauper, but I'm not dancing on Easy Street either."

"The four thousand dollars in your wallet or a large percentage thereof, that strikes me as a deposit, a down payment, a reward for a successful sample."

Pogue licked his damaged upper lip and shook his head. "You pack a wallop, mate. I'd hate to tangle with you on midnight cobblestones."

146

Kiet knew Pogue was patronizing him. Since the flattery was being ladled on his manhood, he did not necessarily object. He said, "Marsad Ref."

Pogue looked off and stroked his chin. "Ref? The chap in Foh Ten, the renegade colonel?"

Kiet did not answer.

"Me and this bloke Ref, uh uh. If somebody's been telling stories on me, Chief, you been listening to fiction."

"Dung Nha."

"Who?"

Kiet sighed. "Dung Nha. He came here today. The two of you went to your room, this room."

"Him? Right. I remember. Ambitious little guy with a heap of moxie," Pogue said. "Him and me, well, Nha has his eye on liquor distributing, and him and me, we been talking. You can't have too many locals on your team, Chief. Competition's a killer."

"A bomb exploded at the Ou Vang Bicycle Works."

"I heard," Pogue said, shaking his head in disgust. "Them fracking Commie Rouges, they got no respect for humanity."

"Janet Ann Selkirk, who stars as the reigning bitch on *Monterey Bay*."

"Riddles. She's big on the telly in the States, ain't she?"

"Commemorative Janet Ann Selkirk bottles containing *plastique*."

"Fiction, Chief. Make that science fiction."

Kiet handed Pogue his wallet and the money. He pocketed the passport and stood.

"Hey—"

"Excuse me."

"You snagged me clearance papers."

"Is there a problem? Are you departing Luong soon?"

"Day after tomorrow. I have obli—"

"The Penang trade show."

"Bloody impressive memory, Chief. Tell you what, we

147

have us a swap. You give me the passport, I give you the wallet. We both close our eyes and count to ten. We open our peepers and you give me the wallet. My memory will've gone blank. I won't remember what was in the thing."

"Are you bribing me, Freddie?"

"Ugly terminology, mate. Acknowledgment and rewarding of mutual respect and harmony is how I regard it."

"Harmony," Kiet said. "A discussion of Marsad Ref would be harmonious."

"You got me at a disadvantage, mate."

"Nine Hundred Avenue Alexandre Loubet," Kiet said.

"Your hoosegow. I know the spot. You hauling me there?"

"As my young adjutant would say, I lack probable cause."

"So gimme the passport, will you please."

"Consider it misplaced," Kiet said. "And do have a nice evening."

20

INVIGORATED BY TEN hours sleep in his own bed, Bamsan Kiet reported to headquarters at midmorning, eager to lay a trap for Ref, Pogue, et al. Joyce had prepared a satisfying but bland breakfast of fried unpolished rice and vegetables, stating proudly that the dish possessed purifying qualities. Kiet recalled it as the preferred food of the 1960s and 1970s hippies. Neither they nor she seemed aware that, except for the absence of hot peppers, it had been a Luongan staple for centuries. He did not ruin her triumph.

Kiet called Captain Binh into his office. He placed Pogue's passport and a bottle of *Rhum Luong* he had brought from home on his desk, then described Kanpurin Sharla's eyewitness account and the confrontation with Pogue.

"You struck him, Superintendent?" said the astounded Binh. "That is so unlike you."

"Twice, regretfully," Kiet said, gauging Binh's reaction. "I lost composure."

Binh approved with reservations. "I'm sure I would have done the same. The man is a pig, but in Washington you would have been suspended and the mayor would be called on the carpet to answer questions on the TV news."

"We briefly discussed the concept of police brutality. This venue is unlucky for Mr. Pogue."

"Why didn't you arrest him?"

Kiet tapped the passport. "In a manner I did. Freddie is a prisoner of Luong."

Binh nodded. "And free to continue his *plastique* business under our surveillance."

149

Kiet shook his head. "Indirect surveillance, possibly. Pogue is too clever to tail."

Binh asked his next question by picking up the bottle. *Rhum Luong* was made in Hickorn. It was Luong's only distilled liquor, a dark rum not noted for smoothness. If flavor hadn't discouraged prospective exporters its cloudiness had. "Notice, please, that the seal is intact. I stock it for unwelcome guests, to shorten their visits."

"Dung Nha?" Binh asked, smiling.

"How is he getting along?"

Binh fluttered a palm. "Rocky. No delirium tremens yet, but he's getting there."

"Let's invite him in for a chat," Kiet said. "A chat and a drink before we release him."

"Release him, Superintendent?"

"For lack of evidence. As far as I am concerned, he is free to go."

Binh's smile expanded to a grin. "Ah. Free of his sanctuary. Him on his Honda, free as a bird."

"Dependent upon the speed of his feet and his wits. The motorbike is police property."

Binh was already out the door. He brought Dung Nha in. Kiet gestured to a chair. Nha sat, hands clasped tightly together. The shaking he sought to control broadcasted to his arms.

"How was your night?" Kiet asked.

"I couldn't sleep," Nha said. "You have maniacs in your jail who yammer endlessly."

"I know," Kiet said. He poured *Rhum Luong* into a cup and offered it to Nha. "Here. Steady yourself."

Dung Nha swallowed the contents in two gulps. Kiet shivered and refilled the cup, but held it on the desk. "Have you anything to add to yesterday's conversation, Captain?"

"I told you everything."

"All right, I believe you. Captain Binh, do you believe him?"

150

"I know an honest man when I see one, Superintendent."

"Splendid. Have a last drink with us, a—what is that expression, Captain Binh?"

"One for the road."

Nha drank more moderately, sipping, eyeing the police officers suspiciously. "You have a villa for us?"

"You and your family? Not exactly. Your family will remain where they are, guarded of course."

"Me?"

"You, sir, have been adjudicated to be a public nuisance. Your jail sentence has been served. We will escort you to the Foh Ten Bridge and release you."

"I have not been tried in a court of law," Nha cried.

"Public nuisance is a misdemeanor charge, Captain Nha. Luongan law grants magistrate authority in such offenses to senior police officers."

"Please. Marsad Ref will torture and kill me," Nha pleaded.

"No. You have told us nothing we did not know. Persuade—my word—persuade him of your loyalty. Ref is a reasonable man."

"He isn't a reasonable man, Superintendent Kiet. He will torture and kill me. He hates my drinking. No matter what I say, he'll believe I got drunk and compromised him."

"I cannot detain you any longer on a misdemeanor," Kiet said. "I need a felony. Captain Binh?"

"Conspiracy," Binh suggested. "Conspiracy would be good."

"What conspiracy?"

"Conspiracy in extortion, conspiracy in committing property damage with explosives, conspiracy in the attack against the Ou Vang Bicycle Works," Kiet said.

Nha looked at Binh. "You said I had the right to remain silent. Don't I have the right to remain silent?"

Binh looked at Kiet, sighed, then looked at Nha. "Not really."

151

"Silent or not, I'm innocent of these conspiracies. I can't help you."

"Is there gasoline in the Citroen?" Kiet asked Binh.

"A full tank," Binh said.

Kiet took handcuffs from a drawer and tossed them to Binh. Binh assisted Nha to his feet with a hard jerk on his shirt collar and snapped the cuffs on his wrists.

"Come," Kiet said. "We shall prove to you that you are too cynical about your colonel."

Nha protested throughout the trip, saying, "Ref isn't reasonable. He doesn't think like normal people. If something goes wrong, he automatically assumes that somebody betrayed him. I've been in your custody for twenty-four hours. He'll assume the worst."

Kiet and Binh ignored him. They had let him bring the *Rhum Luong*. There was just ample clearance in the handcuff chain for Nha to cup it between his hands. Nha raised the bottle frequently. The foul liquor gradually took some of the edge from his voice. They stopped on Ma San Boulevard, two hundred meters from the bridge. Kiet said, "A splendid day for a walk, and the exercise won't hurt me. I'll accompany you to your freedom."

"To my murder," Nha said morosely. "Promenade me. Show me off. Sign my death warrant for sure."

Binh got out from behind the wheel and opened Nha's door. "For good measure," Nha went on, "you'll probably hug me at the bridge, like you love me for telling you every secret."

"As repugnant as it is to both of us," Kiet said, appreciative of the idea. "I will walk you onto the bridge itself, stuff money into your shirt pocket, and plant a wet kiss on your lips."

"No! Get in the car. Go somewhere, anywhere but this. I'll talk to you!"

Binh gunned the engine in an enthusiasm not shared by the Citroen. It lurched, spun its tires, and died. He re-

152

started and proceeded northward on Ma San Boulevard.

"Goddamnit!" Nha screamed. "There might be snipers waiting for me on the other side of the bridge. Didn't you think of that?"

Paranoia, Kiet thought. But, then, *Rhum Luong* was known to seep into the brain's psychological alcoves. He twirled a finger. Binh u-turned, cutting off a bus that skidded sideways and bleated its horn in that peculiar order.

"I changed my mind," Nha said. "Take me to my family. I won't talk if you don't."

Kiet's eyelids were clenched, trapping an afterimage of the careening bus. "Yes," he told Binh. "Do it. No rush, though. No hurry."

"How many troops are at her home?" Nha asked.

"A company at the very least," Kiet said, exaggerating. "If Ref wants you that badly, he'll die in a suicide assault. Your information, please."

"After I'm taken to my family."

Kiet groaned, glanced at Binh, and stamped the floorboard. Binh understood. He braked to a skidding stop and shut off the ignition. They were beside a barber shop. Hair was being cut with hand clippers, faces shaven with straight razors. Kiet saw a barber bending over a customer with tweezers; the ancient Luongan custom of male depilatory treatment was dying slowly.

"Talk to us *now*," Kiet said.

"No."

Binh had also noticed the barber shop. "Superintendent, Nha is shaggy. Should we buy him a haircut and a shave before we dump him on the bridge? If we clean him up, nobody can accuse us of mistreating prisoners."

"Splendid idea," Kiet said. "An example of how generous we are toward favorite prisoners, those who cooperate."

"I didn't set off the bomb at Ou Vang but one of our boys did," Dung Nha blurted.

"Vang would not pay?"

"He said we were punks. If we tried to push his men around, they'd work us over with hammers and wrenches."

"Captain, you previously told us that you extorted exclusively with muscle."

"Muscle persuades—your word—the little businessmen. The good money comes from selling protection to the wealthy, the Ou Vangs. They have to be taught respect. Bombs teach respect."

"A single case of canned condensed milk will not teach a great amount of respect," Kiet said. "Not for a man with Ref's ambitions."

"Colonel Ref and the Yankee Pogue are meeting tomorrow."

"*Plastique?*"

"Yes. Grenades and machine guns too. A supply that will last us for years."

"Where and when is the meeting?"

"I don't know. The airport, I think. I made preliminary arrangements. I was the go-between, but neither Pogue nor Ref told me any details."

"You paid thousands for the Janet Ann Selkirk bottles."

"Three thousand Yankee dollars," Nha said. "I delivered it to Pogue when you saw me at the hotel."

"A bag man," Binh said.

"How much is Ref paying for the entire shipment?"

"Particulars on the meeting place and price went back and forth in sealed envelopes."

"Considerable, I expect," Kiet said. "Extorting Foh Ten paupers and the average Hickorn businessman, it cannot be too lucrative. Due to the current inflation, less so by the day."

"In a year, Marsad Ref will be swimming in money," Nha said.

Binh laughed. "That does him no good now. If Freddie Pogue takes plastic, I'm the Duchess of Windsor."

Kiet closed his eyes. "Translation, please."

154

"Plastic. You know, credit cards. A figure of speech."

"American Express?" Kiet asked, dimly comprehending.

"Right. Pogue won't accept a promise or even a signed note. Cash on the barrelhead. That's how he does business, period."

Kiet addressed Nha. "Excellent point. Sponging a few zin from whores and sandwich-cart vendors strikes me as—"

Binh finished the sentence. "Nickel dime, penny ante."

"Colonel Ref understands that problem. He hinted to me that he is going to try to barter," Nha said.

"He figures to barter what?"

"I don't know. Ref doesn't divulge important decisions to anybody."

"Is the ordnance already in Hickorn?" Kiet asked.

Nha hesitated. "I don't believe it is. If the rendezvous is at the airport, they may be making the swap there, right after the shipment comes in."

"In a hangar, on the ramp at an arriving airplane, where?"

"Superintendent, I've told you everything I know. Allow me to go to my family. I beg you."

Kiet turned around and faced Dung Nha. "If you are withholding the tiniest scrap of evidence, our agreement is annulled. We will march you across the bridge."

One-third of the *Rhum Luong* remained. Nha was slack, slumped in the seat, the bottle held loosely between his legs. His eyes were the color of flawed rubies. This former army captain, a deceased hero of the Kingdom, reminded Kiet of an animal on his back, paws upward in a demonstration of innocuousness.

"I'm not lying or concealing, Superintendent. I'm not anxious to die."

Kiet decided that they had extracted every drop of juice from the man. He instructed Binh to chauffeur Nha to his wife's quarters. They released him to guards and drove to headquarters, exchanging thoughts enroute.

"Do you believe him, Superintendent?"

155

"Believe what?"

"That Pogue and Ref have a rendezvous at the airport tomorrow."

"I believe that they are meeting tomorrow," Kiet said. "Somewhere. Airport was an afterthought. A specific location sounds more authentic. He knew they were meeting, but I don't think he knows where. He was adding artificial value to his information."

"So we didn't think we were being shortchanged and boot his raggedy ass across the Foh Ten Bridge?"

"Exactly. Nha is reckless. Ref used him as a Hickorn liaison. If someone was recognized in town, better that it be him than Ref. Nha is also a drunk. Ref is not stupid. He would not entrust this transaction to a reckless drunk."

"I can't begin to guess what Ref has to barter," Binh said. "Obviously he's in a cash-flow pinch. That scumbag Pogue, no way in hell is he going to accept an IOU."

"An IOU?"

"I Owe You," Binh said, spacing the words.

Kiet suppressed a groan. Slang defined by itself was doubly irritating. "Explain, please."

"A promissory note."

"Yes," Kiet said. "Concentrate on commodities. What generally flows into Foh Ten and what generally flows out?"

"Well, zilch goes out. Nothing's produced there. What goes in? Foh Ten's economy is based on thievery. Whatever they can steal, haul in, and sell."

"Bulk," Kiet said. "We must think bulk. Ref's commodity cannot be tiny. Gemstones, opium, gold? No. They are preferable to cash these days. If Ref had them, he would therefore not be cash-flow-pinched. He could sell them, pay Pogue foreign currency, and avoid this dilemma he appears to have."

"Bulk," Binh repeated. "Maybe, maybe not. The solution is to follow Pogue."

"Again, no. The man is too slick."

156

"Ref?"

"Presuming that he would personally bring the commodity out?"

"He wouldn't," Binh conceded. "Should we focus on the other end, the *plastique*?"

"The *plastique* is already in Hickorn," Kiet said. "Freddie Pogue places duty above drinking and whoring. I could not have surprised him drunk with the little girl last night if his merchandise was in transit."

"I'm confused, Superintendent. We can't tail Pogue, and you say we have no chance at interdicting Ref."

"I will speak to Cuong Van," Kiet said. "I will ask him to post new sentries near the bridge and on adjacent streets, fresh spies in civilian clothes. As many as Cuong can provide."

"And what are they to do?"

"Trail any person entering Hickorn with cargo they cannot conceal in their clothing."

"Our structured surveillance system."

"Walkie-talkies," Kiet said. "Tigers, a COC, everything."

"I like it," Binh said. "I like it."

21

AN AMAZING VARIETY and quantity of goods poured into Foh Ten. Over their walkie-talkies, Binh's Tigers reported a stream of appliances, furniture, clothing, produce, and live pigs and chickens. The bulk items were not necessarily contraband, but Foh Ten possessed no public markets. Its residents were cash-poor and its economy was centered on larceny and crude barter.

By noon, Kiet had listened to observations of thirty-seven possible felonies. Hardly anything noticeable had moved in the opposite direction. He recalled science articles in the overseas edition of *Time* magazine, stories of black holes, astronomical phenomena with gravity so powerful that they sucked in everything close, including light rays. This was Foh Ten: Hickorn's black hole of loot.

At 12:07, a Tiger radioed that a taxicab transporting a nun and her baggage had just crossed the bridge into Hickorn, proceeding southbound on Ma San Boulevard.

"Tiger One to Tiger Two," Binh said. "Big taxi or little taxi?"

"Big taxi, Tiger One. Buick Roadmaster."

Kiet looked at Binh. The "little taxis," blue-and-creme Renaults and English Fords of 1960s vintage, dominated Hickorn's cab fleet. A "big taxi" was an American-made, tailfinned monstrosity with a wraparound windshield and slabs of pitted chrome. None had been manufactured later than 1958. The few still driveable served as downtown shuttles and airport limousines. Operators gouged high fares from westerners, who perceived them as two-ton vaults, protection against Hickorn's lethal traffic.

158

Kiet's question was unspoken. Binh presented it to Tiger Two. "Subject vehicle previously monitored within surveillance timeframe? Over."

"Negative, Tiger One."

"Ask about the baggage, please," Kiet said. "Ordinary luggage would fit in the trunk. A cathedral would fit in the trunk of a Roadmaster."

"Tiger Two, request elaboration on formentioned personal belongings."

"Tiger One, secured by rope on roof rack, cubical, approximately one-point-five meters to a side, contents concealed by cardboard."

Ref's long-term *plastique*, Kiet thought. A thousand pounds of death. If it accidentally detonated, Hickorn would have a flat skyline. No, no—wrong! Ref is the buyer; the ordnance *must* be at the Roadmaster's destination. "Does your secondary Tiger know the nun?" Binh asked.

"Negative, Tiger One. She was in the backseat and there were sun reflections on the glass. Black-and-white habit. Hooded. Plain, harsh, ugly features."

"Marsad Ref incognito, Superintendent?"

Kiet began to speak, but didn't. Tiger Two had described every Luongan nun Kiet knew. Binh was Roman Catholic. Though not a zealot, the young adjutant's faith had been pounded into bedrock at parochial schools. A quip from an agnostic, a superior or not, that Buddhist monks were likewise unappealing would not heal the bruise. Besides, the question had merit.

"Ask your Tigers to advise us on the progress of the Buick Roadmaster," Kiet said.

Binh was happy to. Tiger Seven saw it turn from Ma San Boulevard onto Avenue Leonid Brezhnev, then swing southward on Mu Luong. Binh consulted his blackboard. Tiger Ten was posted two blocks south on Mu Luong, at Avenue Alexandre Loubet. Tiger Ten should have a sighting, but he didn't.

Binh called Tiger Thirteen, farther south on Ma San Boulevard. Negative. Tiger Eight, north on Ma San, midway between Loubet and the bridge. Negative. To the east, Tigers on Mu Pakse and Avenue Charles de Gaulle. Negative.

"Vanished, Superintendent," Binh said. "Disappeared."

Kiet pondered the black hole articles. Light beams, yes. Entire solar systems too. But no force in the universe could gobble an antique Buick Roadmaster taxicab and its alleged nun passenger.

"Come," Kiet said, getting up.

"We can't desert the COC," Binh protested. "The structured surveillance system will fall apart."

"Bring your radio with you," Kiet said. "A mobile COC, like that wondrous District of Columbia van."

"These radios are low-powered. A car's metal top causes too much static."

"An open-roofed vehicle then," Kiet suggested reluctantly. "Fop Tia's sporty convertible."

Binh smiled. "Let's go for it."

Binh thankfully drove sanely, negotiating corners on all four tires. Kiet marked on a map locations of the Tigers last contacted. The sector inside those Tigers consisted of fourteen city blocks. He eliminated all but the northwesterly six. With the exception of the Soviet Embassy, none of the buildings situated on the rest had garages. If the Buick had entered the Bolshevik compound, the day belonged to the criminals anyhow.

Kiet obliterated that unthinkable prospect from his mind and directed Binh to cruise the northwesterly six, crisscrossing. Their compressed sector was the neighborhood of the Ou Vang Bicycle Works, Hickorn's humble industrial district.

"No Roadmaster," Kiet said when they had traveled each street twice.

160

"I suggest we bring in troops to interview everybody on the streets and go door-to-door, Superintendent."

Kiet shook his head. "Too many doors, too little time."

"I am not criticizing, but it seems to me that Freddie Pogue is the key. He could have led us to—"

"I thank you for not criticizing me, Captain," Kiet snapped. "Nobody is too slick to be—oh, forget it."

Binh's lips were locked in a pout. Face had been lost. Worse, Binh's non-criticism was deserved. Concentration on Foh Ten and Marsad Ref was chancy, far riskier than primary attention to a man whose starting position was known. Would it have been so difficult to establish surveillance on a Caucasian peddler with a liking for alcohol and thirteen-year-old virgin prostitutes? This miscalculation might cost Kiet more than lost face, it might cost him his job.

"The plants and warehouses have overhead doors for their trucks," Binh said, ending an uncomfortable silence. "Lift it. Zip, in goes the Buick. Roll it back down. Fifteen seconds, max. Somebody sees a big taxi, blinks, and before anything registers it's gone."

Binh had given Kiet an idea that was less pure inspiration than an opportunity to discard bad choices.

"Workers, Captain, the workers within these plants and warehouses. Are they not also witnesses?"

"Yeah. Well, sure. What are you driving at?"

An opportunity to create a truce too, Kiet thought. But only if the idea is Binh's. "I am wondering about accomplices, Captain, workers who are providing Ref and Pogue a private place to do their business."

"No, Superintendent. I don't doubt for a minute that guys working around here have been recruited into Ref's Mafia, but it can't be private if they're an audience. Take the brewery. Hundreds work there. Privacy is the key word. Remember what Dung Nha said? Ref plays it awfully close to the vest. Ref's driver is really one man more than he'd

161

prefer. He wouldn't be along if Ref didn't need him for his nun-in-the-taxicab scam."

"Agreed," Kiet said, fighting the urge to prompt. "Of course you're right."

"Wait a second," Binh said, slowing the car.

"Yes?"

"Some of these buildings, especially the warehouses, they look vacant. I recommend we narrow down our search to vacant-looking warehouses with overhead doors."

Kiet slapped his forehead. "I should have arrived at the same conclusion. I am a stupid old man."

Binh patted Kiet's arm. "No, no, no, Superintendent. You aren't! We're a great team because of our interaction. If I miss something, you pick up on it, and vice versa."

Kiet smiled. The truce was an authentic peace. "Further recommendations, please."

"You've got my juices pumping now," Binh said, snapping fingers. "Hold it. The rice warehouse on the alley behind Ou Vang's?"

Kiet consulted his map. "It is one of the three or four that qualify."

"We passed it a couple of minutes ago. I saw a light on the upper level."

"Occupied?"

"Maybe, maybe not," Binh said. "The bomb at Ou Vang's made a helluva racket and imbedded glass fragments in the outside wall. I'll bet it shook the rafters, but nobody came out to investigate."

"True," Kiet said. "Did you see a light on then?"

"No. Did you?"

"No."

"Well," Binh said, "people leave lights on at night to discourage burglars, but seldom during the day. Metro charges an arm and a leg for electricity."

Hickorn Metro's rates were exorbitant, but their billing agents were not yet threatening nonpayers with dismem-

162

berment. "Therefore, the warehouse is customarily empty, but today it isn't?"

"Exactly, Superintendent."

Binh circled the block and went slowly past the warehouse. It had two tiers. A pair of roll-up garage doors fronted the single level. Painted-over windows and a pedestrian door on the two-story portion were shielded by a sliding iron grille and a padlock. Two windows on the second floor, overlooking the lower roof, were painted over with filth. Slashes of bright yellow showed through streaks in the grime. The building was pre-Independence and unmarked.

"Ideal architecture for rice storage," Kiet said.

"Right. They unload sacks in the low end and stack them in the high."

"Speculators," Kiet said.

Binh nodded. "Yeah. They hoard in a depressed market and sell when rice prices jump. The inflation that's ruining us, I guarantee it's bursting at the seams."

"Who owns it?"

"Three guesses, Superintendent, and the first two don't count. Fop Tia and his partners."

Time did not permit deliberation of the mysterious first and second guesses. Whoever they were, Kiet was baffled by their positioning ahead of the correct candidates. "Please stop at the Esso," he said.

The Esso gasoline station was on a corner, fifty meters from the warehouse. Kiet gave Binh his map and told him to radio his Tigers, no tricky phraseology and codes please, no time for it. Order them to notify Cuong Van and to establish a perimeter around the six blocks marked, bringing as many reinforcements as they can muster, he added.

"We'll be letting the cat out of the bag," Binh protested.

"Are you afraid that we are chasing the wrong party?"

Binh shrugged. "We can't be one hundred percent sure."

"Foh Ten, a nun, and a big taxi," Kiet said. "A strange brew. And if that building holds tons of explosives, we will

163

need every available soldier to evacuate the area. Our department lacks the manpower."

"What if we're wrong, Superintendent?"

"Then I will be walking a beat in Foh Ten, but logic is on our side." Kiet cupped his hands. "Imagine something else going wrong, Captain. Imagine a crater the size of National Stadium."

Binh swallowed. He started talking on the radio, talking fast. Kiet borrowed a ladder from an Esso attendant. He and Binh lugged it to the rice warehouse and propped it against the lower wall. Kiet removed his sandals and started climbing. Luckily the roof was tile, not tin. If they were careful, they would not be overheard.

"Superintendent, shouldn't I be the—"

"Come. Join me, please."

"I wish you'd carry, Superintendent."

Carry as in carry a gun, Kiet knew. He disliked firing high-caliber pistols because of the recoil, disliked even more the feel and appearance on his person. American plainclothesmen concealed them under their suit coats, but they didn't work in Hickorn's jacketless climate. Once, shortly after promotion to superintendent, Kiet had tried on a shoulder holster and saw in a mirror an older man with leather straps pressing into flesh beneath a shortsleeved white shirt. No amount of nagging by Binh altered his conception of a well-dressed bandit chieftain.

Kiet looked down. "May we postpone this continuing debate? Our mission is voyeurism, not heroism."

"Well, still," Binh mumbled, following Kiet upward.

They approached the upper-level windows on their toes. Binh took the street side, Kiet the rear. Both were unlocked, cracked about six inches for ventilation. Binh put a finger to his, very slowly doubling the gap. Kiet heard voices.

Kiet eased himself prone. The tile was hot. His bare feet were hotter. He wiggled burning toes, thinking how unlike toe-wiggling on a sizzling roof above criminals and explosives was to toe-wiggling in bed with Joyce.

He too widened his window. Directly below was the big taxi, the Buick Roadmaster, its driver seated on a fender, arms folded, a pistol handle protruding from a pants pocket. The driver was intently watching his passenger, the nun, whose hood was down, and the third individual in the warehouse. The Roadmaster's cargo remained lashed to its roof, but the cardboard had been removed. It was Roland Wheeler's magical photocopier.

The nun had a shaved head and was smoking a cigarette. The nun's face was leathery, skin stretched over sunken cheekbones like drum membranes. The nun was, of course, Marsad Ref.

Ten feet from Ref, standing in front of a hill of fifty-kilo rice bags was Freddie Pogue. Next to Pogue was a pyramid of cartons. Kit counted roughly thirty. The logos and brand names were foreign, printed in English: Tide, Salem, Kotex, NAPA Auto Parts, Charmin, Del Monte, Campbell's Soup, Vat 69. Kiet speculated that Pogue had imported them piecemeal.

Laid out at Pogue's feet, as if samples, was a semicircle of whiskey bottles, glandular representations of Janet Ann Selkirk. Pogue was also holding a Selkirk decanter with a cylindrical device attached to the cap. A wire ran from the device to a switch. Pogue's thumb was poised above it.

"Detonator," Binh whispered.

Kiet shushed him and they listened.

"Seventeen thousand American new for your copier, but what can I do with the bloody thing, print bad counterfeit?" Pogue said, smirking.

"It's modern," Ref said. "Sell it."

Pogue said. "Fence it for a goddamn fracking ten percent, I will. It ain't worth a farthing to me, mate. You say you don't have my asking price in cash. I'm a good fellow, so I stick me neck out a mile when you tell me you got something pricey to trade and you try to pawn off this fracking machine."

"Accept it and the cash we have. We'll pay you install-ments," Ref said.

Pogue laughed and shook his head. "You slopes are all alike. You think the world owes you a bloody living. Cough up the root of all evil, mate, or begone."

"A am an honorable man, Mr. Pogue," Ref said slowly and evenly. "Why do you mock and insult me?"

"Don't give me no guano about losing face, colonel. You came here to ram the shaft up me arse, you did."

Marsad Ref drew from his nun's habit a long-barreled revolver and pointed it at Freddie Pogue. "This slopehead is taking the *plastique*."

Pogue touched the detonator switch with his thumb. "Not while I got insurance you're not."

Ref aimed his revolver and cocked the hammer. "Sui-cide in the line of duty is woven into Asian cultures, not yours. You aren't the type. Mate."

Ref fired. Pogue's head snapped backward. He slammed against the rice bags. Kiet winced, knowing that Pogue was dead before he slid to the floor.

Binh had already drawn his .45 automatic. "Freeze, Ref," he yelled. "You're under arrest."

Ref spun around, waving the revolver like a wand. Kiet saw the driver jump off the Buick's fender, pistol in hand. He shouted to Binh.

Binh fired twice. The driver dropped his weapon, clutched the top of his head, and fell to his knees. Ref fired at Binh. The shot blew off his left shoulder board. Binh squeezed his trigger again. There was a click.

Kiet saw Ref grin and measure his target. Kiet had the walkie-talkie. He flung it into the warehouse. Ref jerked and fired at the clattering noise. Binh, meanwhile, attempted to eject the dud round. "Jammed," he screamed, digging at the breech.

Kiet fisted his window pane. The glass few out intact, stouter than decades-old putty. Ref and his revolver framed Kiet in the rectangle, a portrait artist and his subject.

"Kiet," Ref said simply, mild surprise registering on his face.

Kiet did not return the greeting. He flattened on the roof tile as if a diver bellyflopping into a swimming pool. He gripped the windowless sash, which prevented a slide into the alley. The grip wasn't entirely fortunate.

Binh had cleared the dud round and was shooting. Marsad Ref was shooting. Kiet would later learn that while Ref was emptying his revolver at him, Captain Binh was emptying his .45 automatic at Ref, inserting a second magazine when the first was spent. A Binh bullet pierced Ref's aorta, five millimeters from the heart. Another Binh bullet severed Ref's carotid artery. Others pierced rice bags and gouged chips in the warehouse floor. Ref's obsession with killing Bamsan Kiet had made Ref the human equivalent of a carnival shooting-gallery target.

Kiet knew none of this until later because a Ref bullet had split the dry, age-weakened wood of the window sash at the point of Kiet's grip, had entered his palm, and had considerately exited between metacarpal bones.

Kiet's ears were ringing. He vaguely remembered troops on the scene, attracted by the gunfire, Cuong Van himself scrambling up the ladder. This was before he had seen the hole in his hand. Made squeamish by *any* blood and gore, Bamsan Kiet had fainted at the sight of his own.

22

HIS ROYAL HIGHNESS, Prince Novisad Pakse, racked nine billiards balls in a diamond configuration, chalked his cue ball, and broke the balls with a powerful shot that belied his age and frail demeanor. Colored balls exploded every which way, colliding with table cushions and one another.

"Nine-ball, Superintendent," Prince Pakse said, brushing lint from a jacket sleeve. "I have been invited to a nine-ball tournament next week in Honolulu. I initially declined, but since you've disposed of some major problems, I can attend with my mind at ease."

"Thank you, Your Highness."

Kiet was a guest in the Royal Billiards Room, a grand chamber into which Kiet's villa would fit. His Royal Highness wore a black tuxedo, the uniform of billiards tournaments. He wore it during serious practice sessions to acclimate himself to a competition environment. Those who underestimated Luong's ruler derided him in such dress as an emaciated penguin. They did not repeat the insult to Prince Pakse's face, nor to Bamsan Kiet's.

Pakse offered Kiet his cue. "Would your injury permit you to play, Bosha? The rules are simple. Sink the nine balls in numerical order."

Kiet flushed with pleasure at Pakse's use of his childhood diminutive. He flexed his hand. "I can try, Your Highness. It feels almost normal."

"May I see your wound? I've been concerned. Our climate encourages every infection known to man."

Kiet lifted the dressing. The punctures on both sides of

168

his palm were nearly healed.

"I understand you lost consciousness due to blood loss."

"Yes, Your Highness." Kiet felt his face burn.

Prince Pakse smiled. "Please don't take offense, anybody, but I cannot avoid thinking of stigmata. As you know, I am Roman Catholic. Captain Binh, you are too, are you not?"

Binh and Joyce Wilson were also guests in the Royal Palace. They stood at a deferential distance, in awe, silent as fixtures.

"Yeah—well, yes, Your Highness."

Pakse winked at Binh. "Disregard my blasphemy, if you will. Your superintendent is brave and magnificently efficient, but hardly divine, is he? Lad, you have my gratitude for your fine shooting, for ridding Luong of that monster, Ref. The table is yours, Bosha."

Billiards was not Kiet's game. He grazed the one ball, aiming for a corner pocket. It banked off two cushions and stopped at the center of the table.

Prince Pakse chalked his cue and studied the balls intently, as if he were playing a kinetic form of chess. He asked, "Bosha, are you confident that Marsad Ref and Fop Tia weren't in alliance?"

"I am, Your Highness. Ref was as bothered by the counterfeiting and resulting inflation as we. He pinpointed the source just hours after we did."

"Ref's men didn't kill the American, Wheeler?"

"No. Thugs hired by Tia, I believe."

Pakse struck the one ball. Click. It fell into a side pocket.

"Will you ever apprehend the murderers?"

"Perhaps someday. We arrest one on another charge and he talks, hoping to be our friend. Or words exchanged during a drunken bar dispute are relayed to us."

"Ah, drunkenness," Pakse said. "Our Captain Nha?"

"He is with his family, under heavy guard," Kiet said. "Cuong Van has not yet decided what to do with him."

169

Click. The two ball traveled the length of the green felt and vanished into a corner pocket. "Must Hickorn continue to fear Ref's gang?"

Kiet shook his head. "Without their leader and their explosives, no. Not on a destructive scale. Ou Vang and the other wealthy businessmen they intended to extort have regained their courage."

Click. Click. The three ball was resting on a cushion by a side pocket. Pakse banked it into the opposite pocket. The cue ball then backspinned and struck the four ball, moving it toward a corner pocket. "Bosha, critics will inevitably complain that your handling of our former mayor was inappropriate."

Kiet cleared his throat. "It, uh, I admit, yes."

"Summary justice?"

"Yes."

"In lieu of no justice?"

"Yes. He has many contacts and arrangements, Your Highness."

"And a cancerous bureaucracy. I agree entirely. Tia was becoming a worry. If he had been reelected, I'd strongly considered offering him an ambassadorship to be rid of him. Your contribution of his booty to Totisa Bu and the Royal Treasury pleased me enormously. Forgive my devil's advocacy." Click. The four ball was an easy victim. "But permit me a bit more. The rice warehouse belonged to Tia and his partners. If he and Ref weren't in league, how did Ref gain access to the warehouse?"

"We have been interviewing Tia's partners, Your Highness. We have no written admissions thus far, but it appears that they were coerced by Ref."

Click. Pakse's cue ball kissed the five ball, which dropped into a side pocket. "Regardless of methods, Bosha, our sad, little zin is the beneficiary. I'm informed that only seven hundred of them will buy an exalted American dollar. The Soviets and that oily new ambassador, Shiherazade, how do you perceive their role?"

"As opportunists, Your Highness. They were intrigued by the chaos, but realized that it was unmanageable and bowed out before they were embarrassed."

Click. Six ball in a corner, click, seven ball in a side. Pakse leaned his cue on the table and said to Joyce, "You are a beautiful young lady and Superintendent Kiet tells me that you are the best amateur detective he has ever known. He could not have solved the case so expeditiously without your assistance. I am going to ask you two questions, neither of which are meant to be degrading. What is it your religion believes in? Why do you conceal your body in jungle fighter's colors and crop your lovely red hair in a crew cut?"

"Second question first," Joyce said. "My core Fahwandi dresses us to glorify sea, sky, and earth. My surrogate Fahwandi desires my hair to grow out. First question second. A higher enlightened plane."

Prince Pakse squinted, puzzled. "Your terminology is new to me. Your faith doesn't intimidate its disciples with sulfur and damnation?"

Joyce smiled serenely. "No, Your Highness. We teach only elevation of consciousness."

Click. Eight ball in a corner. "Impressive, young lady, but I should advise you that no religion has thrived without an afterlife doctrine. Eternal glory for the good, hellfire for the wayward. I've been informed you're leaving Luong today."

Kiet and Joyce exchanged longing glances. Throughout the night they had exchanged cliches of both cultures, of the plight of star-crossed lovers, of Kipling's assertion. *East is East, West is West . . .*

"Kiet is driving me to the airport, Your Highness. I'm rejoining my people in Calcutta."

"Bosha, how did you know Freddie Pogue was bluffing with his detonator? Why didn't you and your adjutant leap off that roof and run for your lives?"

"Marsad Ref was not bluffed, Your Highness. I trusted his judgment."

171

"The foul communing with the foul?"

"Yes," Kiet said.

Pakse sank the nine ball, ending the game. "Absolute, total, unequivocal trust, Bosha?"

Kiet's legs weakened. He took a deep breath. "No, Your Highness. No."